ALFALFA

Ag TT 84-1-1281

VSESOIUZNAIA ORDENA LENINA AKADEMIIA
SEL'SKOKHOZIAISTVENNYKH NAUK IMENI V.I. LENINA
Vsesoiuznaia Ordena Lenina i Ordena Druzhby Narodov
Nauchno-Issledovatel'skii Institut Rastenievodstva
Imeni N.I. Vavilova

V.I. LENIN ALL-UNION ORDER OF LENIN ACADEMY OF
AGRICULTURAL SCIENCES
N.I. Vavilov All-Union Order of Lenin and Order of People's Friendship
Scientific Research Institute of Plant Industry

ALFALFA

[*Lyutserna*]

A.I. Ivanov

Edited by

D.D. Brezhnev
Academician VASKhNIL

Translated from Russian

Amerind Publishing Co. Pvt. Ltd., New Delhi
1988

Kolos Publishers
Moscow, 1980

Translated and published under an agreement for the United States
Department of Agriculture, Washington, D.C., by
Amerind Publishing Co. Pvt. Ltd., 66 Janpath, New Delhi 110 001

Translator : Dr. A.K. Dhote
General Editor : Dr. V.S. Kothekar

Printed at Prem Printing Press, Lucknow, India

This book discusses the evolution, introduction, and breeding of alfalfa. A scheme of evolution for species of different ploidy levels is proposed for the first time for the genus *Medicago* subgenus *Falcago*. Based on many years of field studies and an analysis of published data, centers of localization of important breeding characters have been pinpointed, and biotopes and centers of introgressive hybridization identified in the Central Asian gene center. The breeding and biology of the initial material are detailed since such material holds great promise for different directions in breeding.

Contents

Foreword

Among perennial fodder grasses the most familiar and widespread in world agriculture is alfalfa. It is cultivated in more than 80 countries and in every continent of the globe in an area exceeding 35,000,000 hectares, in varying natural and economic zones and varying ecological conditions—from the temperate taiga belt to the tropics. The maximum area under alfalfa is found in the steppe and subtropical belts, but the optimal conditions for the growth and development of this crop are to be found in the irrigated lands of the arid subtropics, in the so-called grape belt.

High productivity, highly nutritive green mass, record protein yield from a unit area, good hay yields without massive doses of chemical fertilizers, and other properties of alfalfa have all contributed to an increase in the area of its cultivation. In fact, the increment in crop areas, given the introduction of alfalfa into new regions in recent years, would be far higher but for the constant seed deficit in the Soviet Union as well as abroad.

In the Soviet Union the crop area of alfalfa is 5,100,000 hectares. The main areas under crop are concentrated in the forest-steppe, steppe, and subtropical zones. In recent years the area under alfalfa has steadily moved into new regions—the Baltic republics, Belorussia, the Nonchernozem zone of the RSFSR, Yakutia, and even regions in the Far North. In the southern part of our country, in regions under irrigation, alfalfa is capable of yielding up to 1,000 quintals of green mass per hectare in seven to eight cuttings, while in the temperate belt of the north the yield is 100 to 120 quintals per hectare in two cuttings.

The most important factor in expansion of cropped areas and increment in yield potential of alfalfa is the development of high-yielding varieties and hybrids suitable for growing in different natural and economic zones of the Soviet Union and reflecting the nature of exploitation of the crop in natural and artificial phytocenoses. Success of plant breeding is greatly determined by: a) correct selection of initial material for wholesome characters; b) application of appropriate methods; c) utilization of the rich breeding, genetic, and botanical diversity of the crop from the unique world collection of the All-Union Institute of Plant Industry

(VIR); and d) proper understanding of the history, origin, evolution, and taxonomy of alfalfa. All these aspects have been more or less appraised by A.I. Ivanov, the pre-eminent specialist in the Department of Fodder Crops of the All-Union Institute of Plant Industry (VIR).

Based on new data pertaining to the history and distribution of this crop, its taxonomy, cytology, genetics, immunochemistry, breeding, and other disciplines, the author has proposed a fundamentally new scheme of evolution of the genus *Medicago* L., giving due consideration to ploidy levels of its species, their area of distribution, crossability, morphology of vegetative organs, biological characters, identity of idiograms of pachytene chromosomes, and so forth. Reflecting the phylogenetic links between individual species, this scheme offers a general idea of the origin of the subgenus *Falcago* of the genus *Medicago* L., reveals the genetic nature of the emergence of individual species, and traces the course of many centuries of introgressive hybridization between species in the two most important gene centers of the genus—Asia Minor and Central Asia.

The subgenus *Falcago* of the genus *Medicago* has been assessed for the first time in terms of foci of localization of important breeding characters of alfalfa (microcenters). I.A. Ivanov has also presented the data compiled in Phase I of the field studies undertaken by the VIR (1969 to 1978) in Kazakh SSR on mobilization and conservation of plant resources, and identification of biotopes of promising perennial species of alfalfa and centers of their introgressive hybridization.

Many years of study of the world collection of alfalfa under different ecological conditions (steppe, desert, taiga zone, alpine areas, irrigation, dry farming) and in the laboratory (refrigerator and photoperiod chambers, etc.), enabled the author to identify rich initial material that holds great promise for different directions in breeding. Numerous correlations have been established between morphological, major economically important characters and biological properties of alfalfa plants of different species and varieties, indicating that selection through indirect indices can be highly effective.

D.D. Brezhnev,
Academician of the V.I. Lenin
Academy of Agricultural Sciences
(VASKhNIL)

Introduction

Alfalfa is cultivated in all agricultural zones throughout the world. In the northern hemisphere it is found beyond the Polar Circle (Scandinavian countries, up to 69° N) and in the southern hemisphere is extensively cultivated in Oceania (New Zealand, 45° S) and South America (Argentina and Chile, 55° S). Because of high yields, good fodder qualities, and agronomic importance alfalfa is popularly known as the "queen" of fodder crops. Soviet and foreign agriculturalists agree that it is the basic perennial fodder crop throughout the world.

The largest cropped areas under alfalfa are found in the USA (11.14 million hectares), Argentina (7.5 million hectares), and the Soviet Union (5.1 million hectares). Alfalfa is cultivated under irrigated and natural rainfall conditions. Under irrigated conditions, with eight to ten hay cuttings, this fodder crop is capable of yielding 800 to 1,000 quintals/hectare of green mass and 10 to 14 quintals/hectare of seed, but may yield up to 20 quintals with artificial breeding of pollinators. It is characterized by high resistance to cold and drought, and good response to irrigation and large doses of chemical fertilizers.

The green mass of alfalfa is characterized by a high protein content, well balanced with respect to amino acids. It is enriched with vitally important vitamins (A, B, C, D, E, H, K, P, PP) and various micro-elements essential for the normal growth and development of all species of cattle and birds. The fodder from alfalfa—fresh grass, hay, silage, and grass meal—is relished by all types of animals, and its digestibility as high as 70 to 80%.

The practical value of alfalfa is not restricted to its fodder qualities alone. It also performs other important economic and biological functions: it enriches the soil with nitrogen, is a good predecessor for many agricultural crops, cleanses the soil of pathogens of cotton wilt, serves as a desalinator crop in the case of secondary salinization of the soil, is a good green-manure and nectar-producing crop, and reduces the devastating effect of water and wind erosion by binding the soil. The well-developed root system of alfalfa in the second to third year of growth produces 80 to 120 quintals per hectare of root mass and stubble in the arable layer of soil, which is equivalent to the application of 40 to 60 tons of farmyard manure in terms of nitrogen content, phosphorus, potash, and other elements. Cultivation of alfalfa in crop-rotation fields not only improves soil fertility, but also increases the yield of subsequent crops.

Further expansion of areas under alfalfa and its cultivation in new regions would yield an increase in production of highly nutritive fodder, facilitate reclamation of eroded and undulating lands, and augment the productivity of natural haylands and pastures.

In a critical analysis of the problems invloved in the study of alfalfa (in addition to agronomic problems which are solved variously in different countries depending on specific conditions and the nature of crop use), two major aspects are distinguishable.

The first aspect—botanic-geographic—is concerned with problems of origin, distribution, evolution, introduction, and taxonomy of alfalfa. Significant contributions to the study of these problems have been made by Soviet scientists (A.A. Grossgeim, E.N. Sinskaya, A.I. Belov, I.T. Vasil'chenko, P.A. Lubenets, M.V. Kul'tiasov, O.Kh. Khasanov, and others), primarily because of the fact that three of the classical centers of origin of alfalfa are situated in the territory of the Soviet Union, namely, the Asia Minor, Central Asian, and Euro-Siberian centers; all three are primary centers for different species of the genus *Medicago*.

The second aspect is marked by an in-depth study of cytological, genetic, and breeding factors, spearheaded by scientists in North America. In Europe scientists in Hungary, France, and Italy are aligned with the Canadian-American school of approach to the study of alfalfa. Genetic breeding research in the USA and Canada is attributable to the fact that these countries lack valuable natural populations of alfalfa and have based their work on the initial material introduced from the Old World. Significant contributions to the solution of genetic and breeding problems based on the evolution of individual species and determination of theoretical bases for alfalfa breeding have been made by K. Lesins, J.L. Bolton, C.B. Gillies, D.H. Heinrichs, J.P. Simon, E.H. Stanford, Z. Staszewski, P. Rotili, G.L. Stebbins, H.L. Carnahan, P. Guy, C.H. Hanson, N.E. Hansen, W.M. Clement, R.W. Cleveland, E.T. Bingham, K.H. Evans, G. Demarly, T.P. Palmer, I. Bócsa, and others.

In recent years interest in alfalfa has considerably increased in every continent throughout the world and the area under this crop has expanded. Great success has been achieved in the field of breeding but yet the demand for new, high-yielding varieties has not been met due to the intensification of agriculture. It is well known that the success of breeding is greatly determined by the correctness of selection of the initial material, implementation of promising methods, and an understanding of the rich genetic, breeding, and botanical diversity of this crop as found in the gene centers of N.I. Vavilov, which constitute a unique world collection of alfalfa housed in the All-Union Institute of Plant Industry (VIR). Effective use of the specific and varietal diversity of alfalfa for breeding purposes depends on the level of study, consideration of biological and economic parameters, and a knowledge of the problems of the history, origin, evolution, and taxonomy of the crop.

The author is deeply grateful to the scientists and research scholars of the VIR, VNIIZKh, Aral Experimental Station of the VIR, Shortandin Branch Station, and other institutions for their assistance in this study.

CHAPTER I

Evolution and Taxonomy of Perennial Species of Alfalfa

HISTORY AND DISTRIBUTION OF ALFALFA

Name of the crop. One of the indirect indexes of antiquity of cultivation of a given crop is the number of names by which it has been known (Khoroshailov, 1959*; Ivanov, 1969). Even today alfalfa is known by different names in different countries and continents.

Ancient Greeks called alfalfa *medicai* and ancient Romans called it *medica*. According to Piper (1935) and Klinkowski (1931, 1933), in the rural areas of Italy alfalfa is still called *erba medica*. In Spain it is known as *mielga* or *melga*. However, this crop is generally known as *alfalfa* or *lucerne*. The first name is linked with the advancement of this crop through northern Africa, and the second through southern Europe.

According to Piper, the ancient Iranian name of the crop could not be retained. The Arabs changed the original Iranian words after finding the following names: *to fesfisat—isfast—elkasab—alfasafat—alfalfa*. From northern Africa, under the name alfalfa, lucerne traveled to Spain and then, via the ocean, all countries of the New World.

Bolton, Goplen and Baenziger (1972) mention that in the Babylonian texts written in 700 B.C. alfalfa is mentioned under the Assyrian name *aspasti*, which when translated into Persian becomes *aspoasti*, meaning horse fodder. The word *aspasti* has undergone many changes during its centuries-old history but its final version has now been confirmed, i.e., alfalfa.

In Kashmir (India) alfalfa was known by the name *Ashwa-Bal*, which in English means horse power. In China it was called *mu-su*. In Arabic, in addition to derivatives from the word "alfalfa", it was known by two other names—*ratba* (green alfalfa) and *quatt* (dry alfalfa, hay).

There are many folk names for alfalfa: violet grass, helix grass, red

*Several sources cited in the text are not referenced in the bibliography—General Editor.

clover, median grass, wild clover, sinyushnik, Chilean clover, burgundy clover, amurka, and so on.

The present name of the crop—lucerne (in various versions—luzern, luserne, lucern)—is contemporary in origin. Bolton (1962) writes that it was first used in 1587.

In my opinion, a more reliable explanation of the origin of the word "lucerne" is given by De Candolle (1825, 1919), who writes that the ancient Spanish word *eruye* was changed by the Catalans to *useradas, userdas, lizerne.* In southern France the Spanish word acquired a new phonation—*laouzerde*—which was later shortened to *lauserne, luzerno* (glowworm), *luzerna* (lamp). This name became accepted for the crop in all countries of Europe, including the eastern part of Spain, as well as in South Africa and Oceania.

The name of the genus *Medicago,* according to most researchers, originated from the word *medica.* Alfalfa was called *Herba medica* (midi grass) in ancient Greece and Italy. The crop was so named because in the fifth century B.C., at the time of the Greek-Persian war, it was brought to Europe from the Midian Kingdom (western Iran). The word "medicago" was first used as a taxonomic unit by J.P. Tournefort while devising the taxonomy of alfalfa half a century before the adoption of binomial nomenclature as developed by Carolus Linnaeus.

Hendry (1923) holds a somewhat different opinion, considering that the name *medic—medica—medicago* originated not from the word "Midia" (ancient Iranian state), but from the word "Median" (Mesopotamian), the name of the province in which alfalfa crops were first discovered by Greek warriors.

Primary centers of cultivation. The history of cultivation of alfalfa dates back to antiquity, when the composite cultivated species *M. sativa* L. was brought under cultivation. According to Bolton, it was this unique species in the world which drew the attention of man long before the written word.

According to Bolton (1962) the cultivation of alfalfa began not 2,500 to 3,000 years ago, as suggested by Vasil'chenko (1948), Popov (1950), Zykov (1967), and Khasanov (1972), nor even 4,000 to 5,000 years ago, as proposed by Sinskaya (1950) and Tarkovskii (1972), but 6,000 to 6,500 years ago. Research by other authors (E.N. Sinskaya, M. Uryson, L. Liki, R. Liki, D. Kirkbride, and others) has convinced me that the origin of alfalfa as a cultivated crop could have taken place even 1,000 to 1,500 years earlier than suggested by J. Bolton, i.e., 7,000 to 8,000 years ago.

De Candolle (1825) considers India the primary center of cultivation of alfalfa. Belov (1931) and Ovchinnikov (1934) give this honor to the region of western Persia (Iran). Sinskaya (1950) maintains that the Armenian highland should be considered the native place of cultivated alfalfa, where irrigated farming was well developed in the neolithic age, especially in the kingdom of Urartu and Khetta. Some scientists (Shain, 1948; Vasil'chenko, 1948; Khasanov, 1971) express a common viewpoint: In their opinion the primary center of origin of alfalfa as a cultivated crop is the territory of the republics of Central Asia. Konstantinov (1932) mentions Central Asia as the most probable region. According to Zhukovskii (1971) alfalfa as a cultivated plant began its triumphal journey from Mongolia through the oasis of Central Asia and Asia Minor and farther to the Mediterranean. Grossgeim (1919) gives the honor to the Caucasus and Trans-Caucasus. Tarkovskii (1964), in addition to the foregoing, also mentions western China, while Bolton (1962) votes for Asia Minor and Central Asia, and Kul'tiasov (1967) writes that the cultivation of alfalfa is linked with the hilly regions of south-eastern Kazakhstan and the southern regions of Siberia.

It is obvious from the above account that researchers have not reached a unanimous conclusion regarding the primary center of cultivated alfalfa.

It is my opinion that alfalfa came under cultivation not through one, but several independent channels at different historical times. *M. sativa* could have been brought under cultivation not in just one place, say Trans-Caucasus (more accurately, the territory of the Armenian highland which includes Trans-Caucasus and adjacent regions of contemporary Turkey and Iran), but in several civilizations. One such (in addition to those just mentioned) could have been southern Turkestan. From the first center alfalfa did not spread notably after it reached Mesopotamia.[1] From the second center it triumphantly marched through all the ancient civilizations of the Old World, including the Mediterranean, China, and India.

Ancient distribution. According to the Canadian researchers Bolton, Goplen, and Baenziger (1972) the oldest record of the cultivation of alfalfa is an archaeological inscription discovered at the time of excavations in Turkey in the region Corum-Alacahöyük dating back to 1400 to 1200 B.C. Citing the report of the Ministry of Agriculture of Turkey, the authors confirm that this inscription states that in ancient times (3,300 years ago) alfalfa was the main fodder crop, well known in the Old World, and used to prepare feeds for all species of domestic animals.

Citing Willer, Bolton (1962) reports that in less ancient literature alfalfa is also mentioned. Here he refers to the Babylonian texts dating back

[1]In Mesopotamia, under high agronomic conditions of irrigated farming, a highly cultivated alfalfa emerged, which I.T. Vasil'chenko has identified as an independent species, *M. mesopotamica* Vass. More details about the formation of this alfalfa will be given in the next chapters.

to 700 B.C. Klinkowski (1933) has noted a much later period for the first mention of alfalfa, i.e., 625 to 561 B.C.

Both Wing and Klinkowski are convinced that the "useful grass" mentioned in the Daniel bible is actually alfalfa. Bolton doubts the correctness of the Klinkowski and Wing assumption, but agrees with Klinkowski when he cites Aristophanes (440–380 B.C.) and Aristotle (384–322 B.C.). According to Bolton, references about the cultivation of alfalfa available in the works of these thinkers are the oldest and most reliable. Furthermore, there is also a reference to alfalfa in the period 300 B.C. in the works of Theophrastus. Thereafter, Bolton states, there are no references to this crop in the ancient world up to the time of the Roman empire.

Based on an analysis of the history of the Middle East and the Mediterranean, with no mention of primary literary sources, Hendry (1923) states that the cultivation of alfalfa began much earlier in Asia Minor. He asserts that Semirian traders from Mesopotamia even in 7000 to 4000 B.C. conducted a lucrative exchange of goods in the eastern Mediterranean where marine trade flourished at the time. Among the wide range of goods plants resembling alfalfa were in great demand. Furthermore, the plains of Mesopotamia (Iraq) were the traditional meeting place for the ancient peoples of Asia, Africa, and the regions of Europe bordering them. Hence the "triumphal march" of alfalfa through conquered lands of this primary center of civilization dates back to antiquity, to the pre-Christian era, and follows the path of historical civilization from east to west.

According to Theophrastus, as cited by the Canadian researchers, alfalfa was brought to Greece from Midia in the fourth century B.C. at the time of the Persian invasion of Ellada through the Balkan Peninsula.

The history of the ancient Greek and Roman empires provides a basis for assuming that among the particularly valuable items acquired by the Romans through their heritage of Greek civilization in the second century B.C. was alfalfa. According to the literature available, this crop, new in Europe, spread rapidly in Italy and the countries bordering the Roman empire.

Many thinkers in that historical period have written about the use of alfalfa in the agriculture of the Roman empire. According to Pliny alfalfa came to Italy from Greece and had been brought to Greece by the Persians during the war of 492 to 490 B.C.

According to Stewart (1926) there were as many as 50 well-known Greek books in the Roman empire which contained information pertaining to agriculture and mention the use of alfalfa. Unfortunately these ancient sources have not survived to the present day. In his opinion alfalfa was brought to Itlay in 200 B.C.

The works of ancient thinkers also mention the multifaceted uses to which alfalfa could be put. Varon, for example, noticed that alfalfa attracted honeybees. He proposed that the seed be sown at the rate of 34 pounds per acre (38 kg/ha; the seeds were sown without preliminary scarification), which does not differ significantly from modern recommendations for the Mediterranean zone. Pliny recommended the application of chalk or lime to an alfalfa crop before flowering and sowing in well-drained soil.

Calumella mentioned that alfalfa increases the fertility of the soil, and also warned his readers that excessive feeding of animals with alfalfa could cause hyperemia. He states that once sown, alfalfa will continue to grow for a period of ten years; in one season it will yield four and sometimes even six cuttings; lean cattle of any breed fatten on alfalfa; one ingerum (a unit of area) provides fodder for three horses for an entire year; and the yield of alfalfa can reach 12 tons per acre.

The works of Calumella and other thinkers show that the Romans knew this crop well; the Greeks and Persians had been familiar with alfalfa long before it came into Roman hands. Yet the extensive knowledge exhibited by the Romans about this plant prompted Ahlgren (1949) to consider them the "father of agronomy of alfalfa".

From the boundaries of the Roman empire, which included contemporary northern Africa, Spain, France, the Balkans, and the Lower Danube, alfalfa spread to other areas of the European continent where (except in the oasis of northern Africa) it remained wild and was not cultivated.

The cultivation of alfalfa in the east, according to Hendry (1923), can be traced to the Chinese emperor Wu who, in 126 B.C., organized an expedition under the guidance of general Can Kien in the region of modern Turkmenia for the purpose of exchanging short-statured Chinese horses for tall Turkmenian horses. On acquiring the new breed of horses, the general also took some local seeds of alfalfa because the Turkmenian horse required high quality fodder. Not long after Can Kien's return to China alfalfa appeared in the imperial gardens and from there spread throughout the northern provinces of the country.

An analysis of the foregoing historical facts makes the following conclusion possible. In the wake of agriculture the spread of alfalfa from ancient Iran (including the region of Soviet Turkmenia) and Asia Minor took place through two channels: a) westward through Greece, Italy, Spain, North America, and countries of the European continent and the New World; and b) eastward through India and China.

Migration of alfalfa through countries and continents in the Christian era. Calumella reports that in the first century A.D., right up to the fall of the Roman empire (395–410 A.D.), Roman colonists cultivated alfalfa in Andalusia (southern Spain), the central part of Switzerland, and southern France. However, alfalfa did not receive particular recognition in Europe after the fall of the Roman empire. The German tribes did not grow alfalfa after destroying the ancient civilization, but mainly cultivated rye and barley.

Hendry believes that the reintroduction of alfalfa took place in the eighth century from northern Africa to Spain and northward toward the Atlantic through Gibralter upto Pireneev. The spread of the Arabic name for lucerne, i.e., alfalfa, in Spain and, after crossing the ocean, in the New World, together with the Roman word "medica," confirms this assumption.

The reintroduction of alfalfa throughout Europe, according to Klinkowski, originated from Spain. He believes that alfalfa came to France in 1550, to Belgium and Holland in 1565, to Austria and Germany in 1750, Sweden in 1770, and Russia in the eighteenth century. In the same century alfalfa was introduced into the New World and Oceania. The arrival of alfalfa in America, in the words of Bolton, Goplen, and Baenziger, marked a new era of "rapid expansion" whereby it became the "queen" of fodder crops. The distribution of alfalfa in the various countries and continents of the world is presented in Table 1.

The introduction of alfalfa in the Americas is generally linked with the colonization of the mainland by the industrious Portuguese and Spaniards, which began in the sixteenth century. From Peru, alfalfa came to Chile and Argentina and in 1775 was brought to Uruguay.

Early missionaries introduced alfalfa from Mexico into the southern states of the USA—Texas, Arizona, New Mexico, California. Stewart (1926) confirms that in 1836 alfalfa was known in many regions of southwest USA. However, according to Hendry, introduction of the "Chilean clover," as alfalfa was then called, into California USA from Chile during the "gold rush," played a great role in the spread of this crop in the southern states. By the end of the nineteenth century alfalfa of Spanish origin (Chilean) was well known in the states of Utah, Kansas, Colorado, Montana, Iowa, Missouri, and Ohio. In the eastern part of the continent, due to poor winter hardiness, prevalence of acidic soils, or dry climate, Chilean alfalfa was not a success.

According to other sources (Scofield, 1908) almost simultaneous with the Spaniards and Portuguese, New England colonists brought alfalfa to the eastern coast of North America. In 1736, i.e., 100 years before the introduction of "Chilean clover" in California, alfalfa was recorded in the state of Georgia, in 1739 in North Carolina, and in 1791 in New York. However, it became established only on calcareous soils in New York state. Hence 150 years later, about 1899, reports Bolton, the area

Table 1. Distribution of alfalfa in countries and continents

Initial state, region	Century, year	Region of migration		Reference
		Part of world	State, region	
1	2	3	4	5
Armenian highlands	VII-VI, 1000 B.C.	Asia	Mesopotamia	Ivanov, 1977
Mesopotamia	VII-VI, 1000 B.C.	Europe, Asia, Africa	Mediterranean	Ivanov, 1976
Southern Turkestan	VI-V, 1000 B.C.	Asia	Middle East, Central Asia	Ivanov, 1977
Mesopotamia (Iraq)	7000-4000 B.C.	Europe, Africa, Asia	Mediterranean	Hendry, 1923
Urartu, Khetta	XIII-VI B.C.	Europe, Africa, Asia	Assyria, Babylonia, Asia Minor, Trans-Caucasus, Persia	Sinskaya, 1969
Southern regions of Central Asia (Sogdiana, Baktria, Parikania, and other states of southern Turkestan)	II-I, 1000 B.C.	Europe, Africa, Asia	Asia Minor, Caucasus, Persia, China, India	Vasil'chenko, 1948; Shain, 1948; Popov, 1950; Khasanov, 1971; and others
Mongolia	1000 B.C.-IV B.C.	Asia, Europe, Africa	Central and northern Asia, Assyria, Khaldeya, Persia, Arabia, Roman Empire, other Mediterranean countries	Zhukovskii, 1971

Persian Kingdom	Europe, Asia, Africa	Egypt, Babylonia, Arabia, Eurasia, Central Asia	VI–V B.C.	Ovchinnikov, 1937; Bolton et al, 1972
Midia (Eurasia, Iran, southern Turkestan)	Europe, Asia	Greece, India	VI–V B.C.	De Candolle, 1883; Stewart, 1926; Klinkowski, 1933; Ahlgren, 1949; and others citing many sources of ancient Greek and Roman historians
Southern Turkestan	Europe	Greece	V B.C.	Shain, 1948
Central, northern, and eastern Asia	Europe, Africa	Greece, Roman empire, northern Africa	2500–2000 years ago	Tarkovskii, 1974
Greece	Europe, Africa	Roman Empire, northern Africa	II B.C.	Klinkowski, 1933; Bolton, Goplen and Baenziger, 1972 citing ancient thinkers
Roman empire	Europe, Africa	Northern Africa, the Balkans, Spain, France, Switzerland, and other states of southern Europe comprising Roman Empire	I–IV B.C.	Ivanov, 1976
Southern Turkestan	Asia	India, China	126 B.C.	Hendry, 1923
Northern Africa	Europe	Spain (reintroduced)	VIII	Hendry, 1923

(Contd.)

Table 1 (*Contd.*)

1	2	3	4	5
Spain	1550, 1565, 1570–1573	Europe	France, Italy, Belgium, the Netherlands, Switzerland, Rhine province	Klinkowski, 1933; Vasil'chenko, 1948; Bolton, 1962; and others
Spain	1650–1750, 1770 XVIII	Europe	Austria, Germany, Switzerland, Russia (European part)	
Spain	Early XVI, XVI	America	Mexico, Peru, the USA, Canada	Stewart, 1926; Scofield, 1908
Peru	XVI–XVII, 1775	America	Chile, Argentina, Uruguay	Stewart, 1926; Klinkowski, 1933
Mexico	XVII	America	USA (south)	Bolton, 1972
Chile	1736	America	USA (south)	Stewart, 1926
France	XVIII	Australia	Australia	Daday, 1961–1963
France	1850	Africa	South Africa	Rogers, 1967; Bolton, 1962
Germany, France	XVIII–XIX	Europe	Russia	Batyrenko, 1916; Lubenets and Plotnikov, 1950; and others
France	1850	Oceania	New Zealand	Bolton, Goplen, and Baenziger, 1972
USA, Argentina	XIX	Oceania	New Zealand	Palmer, 1967
Soviet Union	1931–1933	Asia	Mongolia	Ivanov, 1969
USA	1954–1955	Australia	Australia	Daday, 1965–1968

under this crop east of the Mississippi River comprised only 1.0% of the reclaimed land. The rapid expansion of area under alfalfa in the eastern part of North America is associated with the introduction in 1857 by the German emigrant, W. Grimm, of the old Franconian hybrid population of alfalfa, namely, Grimm from Germany; other types (Baltic and Kossak from Europe, Ladak from Asia)[2] brought valuable germ plasm to the continent, which was successfully used in breeding programs.

Alfalfa entered South Africa quite late and, moreover, not from the northern part of the region where it was known in the pre-Christian era, but from France where it was called lucerne, and not alfalfa as in northern Africa. In 1850 this crop was multiplied in Cape Colony in ostrich farms. Initially Provence alfalfa was a great success here; later, writes Bolton (1962), the Chinese alfalfa from Tibet was introduced and was highly valued for its winter hardiness.

Alfalfa reached Australia at the end of the eighteenth century from France. In 1806 (Rogers, 1967) alfalfa was officially approved by the Chief Royal Governor for cultivation as a fodder crop. However, the area under alfalfa increased slowly in this continent. In 1883 it occupied only 2,000 acres (810 ha) and was mainly cultivated in the province of New South Wales on alluvial soils of the valleys of the Hunter and Peel Rivers. Hence the first national population of alfalfa was named "Hunter River". By 1920 the area under this variety had increased to 100,000 acres (40,500 ha). In spite of the complex genotype of the local variety, Hunter River (V. Rogers believes that the varieties Provence, Smooth Peruvian, Arabian, and American Common contribute to its origin), Daday characterizes it as a variety of Mediterranean origin.[3]

Later alfalfa from Peru (variety Hairy Peruvian) was introduced in the continent courtesy of the USA, but in 1954–1955 while launching a breeding program the National Academy (CSIRO) included other improved varieties well known in the countries of the Orient and brought to Australia from the USA: African (local variety of Egypt introduced in the USA in 1924), Du Puits (improved variety of France introduced in the USA in

[2]The variety Baltic was evolved from a population of unknown European origin and named after the place of its cultivation in the state of South Dakota. The population Kossak (Kazak) was introduced in the USA by Professor Khansen from Russia. The seeds were given to Khansen by V.R. Vil'yams, who had collected them from a plant growing in the southeastern part of the European part of the USSR. The population Ladak was introduced in the USA from Kashmir (India).

[3]I concur with Daday because populations from France (Provence and others) constitute the base of this variety. The variety Arabian (and may be the African from Egypt) is also of Mediterranean origin. The Peruvian alfalfa and variety American Common have a common Chilean origin and through Chile are closely related to the alfalfas of he Mediterranean gene center.

1946), Caliverde (a USA variety resistant to diseases and developed using the Turkestan alfalfa from the Soviet Union), Rambler (a rhizomatous variety of Canada developed using the wild yellow alfalfa from the Soviet Union), and Indian (a local variety of India introduced in the USA).

The first national improved variety of alfalfa, Cancreep (Canberra Creeping—alfalfa obtained from Canberra), was developed over a period of 14 years and released for cultivation in 1968; it was intended for cultivation in the meadows and pastures of Australia. Multiplication of this new variety has been very slow; in 1974, i.e., six years after its introduction, the cultivated area did not exceed 10 ha.

According to the Canadian researchers (Bolton, Goplen and Baenziger, 1972), alfalfa entered New Zealand in 1850 and, moreover, not from Australia but from Europe. Palmer (1960, 1967) asserts it was introduced from South America, in particular from Argentina.

The main varieties of New Zealand—Marlborough and Wairau—were developed on South Island. The variety Marlborough is the product of selection from the ancient Australian population, Hunter River, and the French variety, Provence. The presence of variegated and yellow-flowered plants in the variety Marlborough as well as its winter dormancy provided a basis for Palmer to suggest that Marlborough contains the germ plasm of variety Grimm.

Returning to Table 1 let us mention that in Mesopotamia cultivation is not possible without irrigation (Vasil'chenko, 1949). Hence this region cannot be considered a primary center of cultivation of alfalfa since the plant does not grow there except in fields (Sinskaya, 1950). Thus in the interfluve of the Tigris and Euphrates Rivers cultivated alfalfa was introduced from the neighboring Anatoli-Turkestan region.

In the pre-Christian era cultivated alfalfa from Mongolia, then a backward country inhabited by nomadic tribes not engaged in agriculture, could not penetrate into the oasis of the ancient civilization of Eurasia and the Mediterranean, despite Zhukovskii's (1971) assertion to the contrary, because the most reliable period for the beginning of agriculture in Mongolia is the seventh to eighth centuries, and the period of maximum development of agriculture the thirteenth to fourteenth and sixteenth centuries. Furthermore cultivated alfalfa could not have been grown in the severe climate of Mongolia since there it does not overwinter. From the entire genus *Medicago,* subgenus *Falcago,* only one wild species, *M. falcata* L., grows in this country, which entered there from neighboring Siberia and Altai, while *M. varia* Mart. is grown as a cultivated crop only on a negligible scale.

It is evident from the scheme of migration of cultivated alfalfa through countries and continents (Figure 1) that its distribution in the pre-Chris-

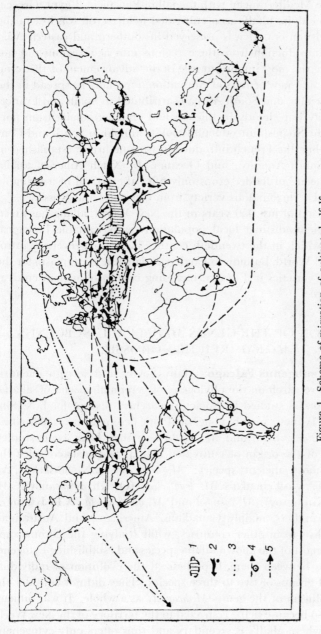

Figure 1. Scheme of migration of cultivated alfalfa through countries and continents.

1—primary center of cultivation; 2—migration in pre-Christian era; 3—migration from Phoenicia through the Mediterranean; 4—routes of primary use of gene pool of cultivated alfalfa in Christian era; 5—important reintroductions.

tian era was restricted to regions of the Mediterranean Sea, and south and east Asia. In the Mediterranean with the fall of Phoenicia, Egypt, Greece, and the Roman empire alfalfa as a cultivated fodder crop was lost in the wake of the Christian era. It was preserved in southern and eastern Asia, but its further introduction from these regions into new regions did not occur. Therefore the most important role in the advancement of this crop through ancient and new centers of cultivation, especially its spread in the New World, Oceania, and South Africa is attributed to Spain and France, which secondarily but already in this era had obtained alfalfa from northern Africa. The Spanish introduction took firm hold in South and Central America, while the French introduction became firmly established in West Europe, South America, and Oceania. In North America alfalfa became the "queen" of fodder crops only after the arrival of a valuable winterhardy and a rhizomatous variety from Germany and Russia.

Within a period of just 350 years in the New World, alfalfa has given rise to independent, distinct local populations with valuable biological characteristics, which in the twentieth century have been reversely introduced in the Old World, but now as carriers of valuable germ plasm for the improvement of varieties in Eurasia, including centers of ancient cultivation of this crop.

EVOLUTION OF THE GENUS *MEDICAGO* L. SUBGENUS *FALCAGO* (REICHB.) GROSSH.

Phylogeny of subgenus Falcago. Many Soviet and foreign scientists have conducted research on the phylogeny of perennial species of alfalfa. The range of species studied by Soviet researchers (except for E.N. Sinskaya and A.I. Ivanov) mainly concerned four perennial taxa: *M. sativa, M. falcata, M. tianschanica,* and *M. trautvetteri*; they have been studied in the context of the origin of cultivated alfalfa. Scientists consider the following the most ancient species: *M. hemicycla* (E.N. Sinskaya), *M. tianschanica* (I.T. Vasil'chenko), *M. trautvetteri* (O. Kh. Khasanov), *M. falcata* (M.V. Kul'tiasov), *M. coerulea* and *M. quasifalcata* (A.I. Ivanov).

Foreign researchers, mainly Canadians, Americans, and Australians, but also specialists from other countries, while studying the chromosome morphology of most of the known alfalfa species and establishing cytogenetic relationships between them, hypothesized the evolution of individual species or small groups of two to three species. They did not consider the problem of evolution of the genus *Medicago* L. as a whole. It was difficult for them to do so because being restricted to the territory of the New World and Oceania, where alfalfa is secondary and thus offers only cytogenetic data, they had no opportunity to observe the variability of species under natural conditions, especially in primary centers of origin and formation, which are situated in the territory of the Soviet Union and adjacent countries.

To date no researcher has compiled the phylogenetic scheme of the subgenus *Falcago* (Reichb.) Grossh. of the genus *Medicago*, reflecting the phylogeny of most of the perennial species, distinguished by ploidy level, which have evolved as independent taxa at different levels of the process of evolution. Sinskaya has combined closely related species into independent groups and labeled them "species complex". The taxa included in one complex must be similar in morphology, occur in coincident or adjacent geographic areas, and be readily crossed with one another. On the basis of interaction between species of one circle and independent alfalfa species of another circle, researchers have established phyletic links between different groups of species, which have been classified as phylogenetic links of the second or third order (Figure 2).

According to Sinskaya, in addition to *M. hemicycla* Grossh., *M. coerulea* Less. and *M. trautvetteri* Sumn. are also related to ancient closely related species (circle of species of the first order). These species have the same ploidy level ($2n = 16$) and are readily crossed with each other. Phylogenetically they line up as follows: *M. hemicycla*—*M. coerulea*—*M. trautvetteri*.

The second circle (complex—according to E.H. Stanford and C.R. Gunn) is formed by the tetraploid ($2n = 32$) species *M. sativa* L. and *M. falcata* L., which are being used for cultivation and also readily cross with each other; they are morphologically similar to a great extent, come from adjacent geographic areas of distribution, and in hilly regions are often

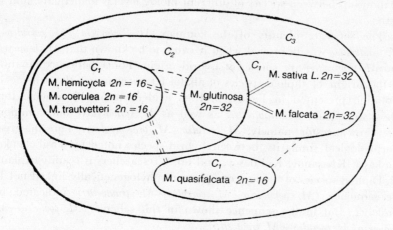

Figure 2. Scheme of evolution of perennial species of alfalfa (from Sinskaya, 1950).

found growing side by side. The tetraploid Caucasian species *M. glutinosa* Bieb. is considered by Sinskaya an intermediate species between the diploid *M. hemicycla* and the tetraploid *M. sativa* and *M. falcata*. American and Canadian geneticists do not share the viewpoint of Sinskaya. They consider *M. glutinosa* more closely aligned with the tetraploid group of species and have combined *M. sativa*, *M. falcata*, and *M. glutinosa* in a single complex: *M. sativa—M. falcata—M. glutinosa*.

These two complexes: 1) *M. hemicycla—M. coerulea—M. trautvetteri* and 2) *M. sativa—M. falcata—M. glutinosa*, according to Sinskaya, form a circle of species of the second order through *M. glutinosa*, and with the addition of another diploid species of the Caucasian gene center, *M. quasifalcata* Sinsk., characterized by some isolation, form a circle of species of the third order. Other species of the subgenus *Falcago* are not considered in the scheme proposed by Sinskaya.

Today, in the context of new data on the history and distribution of this crop, taxonomy, cytology, genetics, breeding, and other disciplines, the scheme of origin of alfalfa suggested by E.N. Sinskaya needs to be reexamined since it does not incorporate a common system characterizing the relationship of species on the basis of variability of important genetic and morphological characters (number of chromosomes, geographic area, color of corolla, shape of pod, morphology of chromosomes, etc.); species are not correctly placed in the evolutionary chain; the initial originator is not correctly defined and species of the subgenus *Falcago* are not adequately covered; the evolutionary role of allo- and autoploidy in the process of species formation is not explained or its interpretation not convincing; heterogeneous species are combined in a common complex; the interrelationship between species of different ploidy level is inadequate, and so forth.

The separate identity of the complex *M. hemicycla—M. coerulea—M. trautvetteri* was disproved when it came to be known that *M. hemicycla* and *M. trautvetteri* are species of hybrid origin. For a better explanation of the origin of diploid species of alfalfa let us examine the scheme of evolution presented in Figure 3. It is evident from this scheme that *M. hemicycla* and *M. trautvetteri* as well as *M. sativa* have one common, very close ancestor, namely, *M. coerulea* (*M. praecoerulea*). Thus the great morphological similarity between hybrid species noted by Vasil'chenko, Sinskaya, Khasanov, Kul'tiasov, and other researchers is readily explained. Diploid species of the first complex are phylogenetically linked not in the sequence (*M. hemicycla—M. coerulea—M. trautvetteri*) indicated by Sinskaya, but in the sequence shown in this scheme (*M. coerulea—M. hemicycla, M. coerulea—M. trautvetteri*).

Definite parallelism in diploid hybrid species is also observed in the

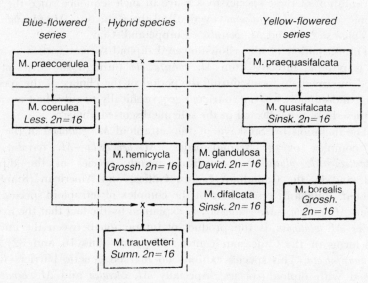

Figure 3. Phylogenetic scheme of promising diploid alfalfa species used in cultivation.

yellow-flowered parent *M. quasifalcata* (*M. praequasifalcata*), the initial species for *M. hemicycla*, which is externally similar to *M. difalcata*, the initial species for *M. trautvetteri*.

According to the scheme given here (Figure 3), the evolution of the yellow-flowered series began with the ancient form of *M. quasifalcata*, the endemic mesophytic species of the Caucasian gene center. This is also reported by Sinskaya (1950) and Lubenets (1972). The latter author also indicates the hybrid nature of *M. hemicycla* from *M. coerulea* and *M. quasifalcata*. The South Kazakhstan alfalfa (*M. difalcata* Sinsk.) is the most xeromorphic ancestor of the ancient mesophytic species *M. glandulosa* David and occupies an intermediate position, while *M. borealis* Grossh. is a more hydrophilous modification of the crescentoid alfalfa.

The geographic areas of the diploid yellow-flowered species represent a common chain with links found from south to north in the following sequence, with the aridity of the climate also indicated: *M. quasifalcata* (mesophyte, hilly valleys of the Caucasus and riverine floodplains of northern Trans-Caucasus)—*M. difalcata* (xerophyte, arid belt) and *M. glandulosa* (moderate xerophyte, steppe zone)—*M. borealis* (hydrophyte, northern geographic area of crop, forest belt).[4] It is possible that

[4]The division of alfalfa species (in comparing species with each other and the genus as a whole) into mesophytes, xerophytes, and hydrophytes is conditional because alfalfa per se is susceptible to drought, especially soil drought.

the evolution of these species took place in such sequence since the geographic area of *M. difalcata* covers all of the Caucasus, *M. glandulosa*—the Volga steppe, and *M. borealis*—Europe and Asia.

The formation of all yellow-flowered diploid species with a straight pod is possible directly from *M. quasifalcata* through the series of so-called intermediate forms during the period of the climax of the species, which undoubtedly was not restricted geographically to only the Caucasus. All these links are reflected in the scheme discussed above.

The inclusion by Sinskaya of the tetraploid *M. glutinosa* in the species complex of the second order (*M. hemicycla*—*M. coerulea*—*M. trautvetteri*—*M. glutinosa*), comprising mainly species of the diploid level, and by the Canadian (Lesins, Gillies) and American (Stanford, Clement, Bingham) researchers in the complex of tetraploid species (*M. sativa*—*M. falcata*—*M. glutinosa*), is explained by the fact that the hybrid species *M. glutinosa* is the product of interaction between the ancient wild forms of the Caucasian center—*M. sativa* (2n= 16 and 32) and *M. quasifalcata*. This species exhibits no marked genetic barriers when crossed with diploid species, especially *M. coerulea* and *M. hemicycla,* which indicates their phylogenetic affinity. The Canadian geneticist Lesins (1961) has, as it were, confirmed this opinion when he writes that exceptions are found when crosses at different ploidy levels are highly successful.

Genetic data does not refute this conclusion. Both the hybrid species of the Caucasian region—*M. glutinosa* and *M. hemicycla*—have in fact close phylogenetic roots. Sinskaya (1950) has already demonstrated the affinity of these species.

Lesins and Gillies (1972) report that in spite of its isolation, *M. quasifalcata* is capable of crossing well with closely related species of different ploidy levels. In their experiments the diploid *M. quasifalcata* crossed with the tetraploid *M. glandulosa* produced fertile tetraploid hybrids.

According to Ivanov, hybridization between diploid and tetraploid species, especially between *M. quasifalcata* (2n= 16) and *M. praesativa* (2n= 32), and according to Lubenets, between *M. quasifalcata* (2n= 16) and *M. sativa* L. subsp. *caucasica* (Vass.) Lub. (2n= 32) was a very important evolutionary process. Interploid crossing ensured not only the transmission of germ plasm in the formation of new groups, forms, populations, ecotypes, species etc., but also ensured diversity of chromosomal restructuring, which eventually led to autopolyploidy, i.e., the development of the contemporary *M. sativa* and *M. falcata*. Hence polyploidy does not always create a total barrier of isolation between diploid and tetraploid forms of alfalfa.

M. glutinosa crosses freely with representatives of the second complex,

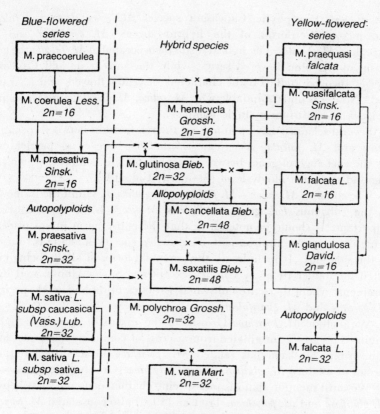

Figure 4. Phylogenetic scheme of species of perennial alfalfa of the Caucasian gene center.

namely, the tetraploid species *M. sativa* and *M. falcata*. This has been confirmed by the experimental data of several researchers. Here let me cite just the work of Evans and co-authors (1966) who obtained 52 to 60% hybrids by crossing *M. sativa* with *M. glutinosa* and *M. falcata* with *M. glutinosa*.

The phylogenetic scheme of cultivated and promising perennial species of alfalfa of the Caucasian gene center is presented in Figure 4.

Today the origin of the young species *M. varia* from *M. sativa* and *M. falcata* has been universally recognized. The evolution of the species has been convincingly proved by geneticists and plant breeders and thus all earlier doubts have been laid to rest.

The origin of *M. falcata* is linked with the diploid species of the Caucasian gene center. The diploid *M. falcata* is found throughout the geographic area of its tetraploid homologue. It is a transitional form between the ancient mesophytic Caucasian species *M. quasifalcata* and *falcata*-like mesophytic forms of the hybrid species *M. hemicycla* and the tetraploid *M. falcata*. The hybrid forms incorporated in *M. falcata* the germ plasm of the blue-flowered series, while the ancient diploid Caucasian species incorporated in it the characters of yellow flowers and a straight pod. Now it is understandable why *M. sativa, M. falcata,* and *M. glutinosa* genetically constitute a single complex.

Several scientists have pointed out the relationship between species *M. sativa* and *M. falcata*. American researchers believe no barrier exists for the exchange of genes between members of this complex, which have one and the same ploidy level (Stanford et al., 1972).

The complex *M. sativa—M. falcata—M. glutinosa,* within the framework of the subgenus *Falcago* of the genus *Medicago* is agronomically very important. It should be noted here that the entire germ plasm presently being used for the improvement of cultivated species of alfalfa is restricted to this complex. It includes all the perennial forms of alfalfa being cultivated for fodder in every country except the Soviet Union, and in all continents where there are cultivated varieties of diploid wild species of *M. borealis* and *M. quasifalcata*.

We include *M. polychroa* Grossh. in the group of species of hybrid origin. This species originated from a cross of common alfalfa of Caucasian origin. Sinskaya has related *M. polychroa* to a varicolored subspecies of alfalfa—*M. glutinosa* subsp. *polychroa* (Grossh.) Sinsk.

We must mention that distinct specific characters do not exist between *M. glutinosa* and *M. polychroa*. Troitskii (1938) also considered *M. polychroa* a species of hybrid origin from *M. glutinosa* and *M. eusativa* [*M. sativa* L. subsp. *caucasica* (Vass.) Lub.].

The hexaploid alfalfas *M. cancellata* Bieb. and *M. saxatilis* Bieb. are allopolyploids. The same conclusion was drawn by Lesins and Lesins (1960) while studying the chromosome morphology of several alfalfa species. It is assumed that the first species was developed through hybridization of the *falcata*-like forms of *M. glutinosa* and *M. quasifalcata*. It is evident from the foregoing scheme (see Figure 4) that the initial parental species are related to each other in origin and despite different ploidy levels crossing occurs quite satisfactorily between them (Sinskaya, 1950).

The second hexaploid species is phylogenetically closer to the first. It was developed through hybridization of the yellow-flowered form *M. glutinosa* with *M. glandulosa*. Stanford (1972) noticed the close homology of karyotypes of the hexaploid *M. saxatilis* and the tetraploid *M. sativa*— the species related to *M. glutinosa*. This once again confirmed the hybrid origin of hexaploid species and their link with the blue-flowered series in spite of the fact that these species are distinguished by a yellow corolla.

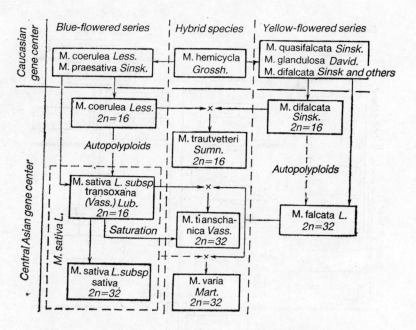

Figure 5. Phylogenetic scheme of species of perennial alfalfa of the
Central Asian gene center.

Both the hexaploid species are distributed within the geographic range of
the initial parental species. Bingham and Binek (1969) think that the
hexaploids found quite often among tetraploids under natural conditions
are the result of the union of n and $2n$ gametes.

The phylogenetic scheme of cultivated and promising perennial alfalfa
species of the Central Asian gene center is depicted in Figure 5. From the
viewpoint of phylogeny of the genus this gene center as a whole is secondary,
with diploid and tetraploid species occurring less often and hexaploid
species absent altogether. In the given scheme attention is directed to
the relationships between hybrid species and the yellow-flowered series.
The origin of all the alfalfa species presented in this scheme has already
been discussed.

The general scheme of evolution of the subgenus *Falcago* of the genus
Medicago is depicted in Figure 6 (presented here for the first time). The
basis for its compilation were many years of research on alfalfa in collection nurseries and natural phytocenoses, including centers of active introgression adjacent to the Central Asian gene center, as well as critical
evaluation of the data presented in numerous publications by other
scientists. All the species in the scheme have been arranged in a definite

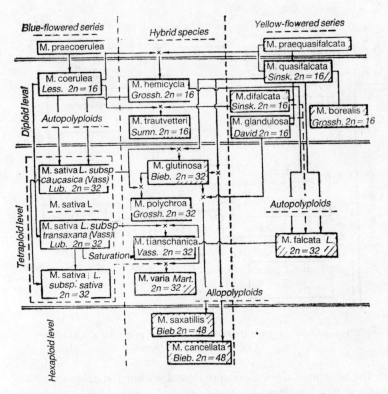

Figure 6. Phylogenetic scheme of alfalfa species important for
cultivation and their derivatives.

system based on the ploidy level, color of corolla, geographic range of
distribution, crossability, morphology of pachytene chromosomes, etc.

The scheme is drawn with due consideration to the phylogenetic relationships between individual species and provides a general idea of the
origin of the entire subgenus *Falcago* of the genus *Medicago*. It reveals the
genetic nature of individual species and also shows the course of centuries
of introgressive hybridization between species in two important gene
centers of the genus—Caucasian and Central Asian.

Additionally, the scheme shows that some hybrid species have closely
related ancestors (*M. hemicycla* and *M. trautvetteri*, *M. glutinosa* and *M.
polychroa*, *M. tianschanica* and *M. varia*, *M. cancellata* and *M. saxatilis*).
Some species of hybrid origin (*M. hemicycla*, *M. tianschanica*, *M. trautvetteri*)
were not recognized as such until just recently.

Based on the cytogenetic studies conducted by Lesins and Lesins (1960,
1961, 1962, 1963, 1963a, 1964, 1965, 1966), Gillies (1968, 1970, 1970a,

1971), Bingham (1968, 1968a, 1969, 1971), Clement (1963, 1968), Clement and Stanford (1966), and other researchers, with due consideration for the above-mentioned scheme, one is aware of closely related parallels between some species, indicating a close genetic and morphological relationship. Such parallels are seen in the case of *M. quasifalcata* and *M. difalcata*, *M. quasifalcata* and *M. glandulosa*, *M. quasifalcata* and *M. borealis*, *M. tianschanica* and *M. sativa*, *M. glutinosa* and *M. polychroa*, *M. sativa* and *M. falcata*, and *M. tianschanica* and *M. varia*.

It has been pointed out above that under natural conditions it is difficult to distinguish *M. glutinosa* and *M. polychroa*, *M. tianschanica* and *M. sativa*, *M. difalcata* and *M. glandulosa*, *M. coerulea* and *M. agropyretorum*, and so forth.

Close morphological similarity between aerial parts is an important criterion in the homology of karyotypes, even if an incompatibility barrier has arisen during the course of evolution (Figure 7). Canadian and American geneticists have come to this same conclusion. This means that some taxa identified by the authors as species, especially in the young Central Asian gene center, are in fact not independent species but rather introgres-

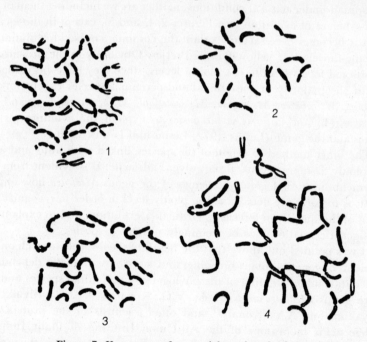

Figure 7. Karyotypes of perennial species of alfalfa.
1—*M. falcata* (2n=32); 2—*M. coerulea* (2n=16); 3—*M. sativa* (2n=32); 4—*M. varia* (2n=32).

sive hybrids (*M. ochroleuca* Kult., *M. lavrenkoi* Vass., *M. kultiassovii* Vass., *M. alaschanica* Vass., *M. schischkinii* Sumn., *M. alatavica* Vass., and others) or taxa of infraspecific rank [*M. tianschanica* Vass., *M. polychroa* Grossh., *M. tibetana* (Alef.) Vass., *M. agropyretorum* Vass., and others].

In this way the general course of evolution of the genus *Medicago* proceeded from diploid ancestors to tetraploid and hexaploid species, through polyploidy and hybridization. The origin of alfalfa species occurred in two ways: without change in the chromosome set or by doubling the chromosome number. An example of the first type is the phylogenetic scheme of the diploid species of alfalfa. In this case one sees gradual variability with multiple intermediate forms in the transitional zone. When the process of origin of the species occurs through chromosomal doubling, transitional forms are very few or absent altogether. In such cases, at the borders of merging geographic areas of species with a different chromosome number, a physiological barrier is created that prevents the crossing and "escape" of the species.

In the classification of P.A. Lubenets (which we are using as a springboard) transitional forms are not described even though they are quite widespread under natural conditions; neither are we including them in the basic schemes of evolution (see Figures 2, 4, and 5), except in those cases when it becomes necessary to explain the common course of evolution of the blue-flowered or yellow-flowered series. Obviously in the presence of transitional forms of different ploidy levels, since they have been identified in the majority of the annual and perennial species except for *M. glutinosa*, *M. arborea*, *M. rugosa*, *M. scutellata*, *M. dzhawakhetica*, and *M. schischkinii*, by and large it is far easier to explain the evolution of the species and the genus (Lesins, 1972; Lesins and Lesins, 1960).

The other method of origin of the species, linked with auto and allopolyploidy, is more recent, progressive, and facile. It is evident from the aforementioned phylogenetic schemes of the genus *Medicago* how important it is to correctly determine the ploidy level in order to recognize the origin of the species, to forecast their further evolution, and to explain the phylogenetic relationships of seemingly unrelated species.

It was pointed out above that the depth of theoretical research on the problems of genetics, plant breeding, and taxonomy of alfalfa depends on an accurate understanding of the phylogeny of individual species and the entire genus *Medicago* as a whole. V.G. Konarev, I.P. Gavrilyuk, I.F. Shayakhmetov, A.V. Konarev, and other scientists in the protein and nucleic acids laboratory of the All-Union Institute of Plant Industry (VIR), working with the genus *Triticum*, have proven that given the present level of development of the biological sciences it would be inappropriate to establish phylogenetic relationships between plant species without in-depth biochemical research. Moreover, the immunochemical method of analysis of reserve proteins in seeds has been proved a reliable method of verification of the phylogeny and taxonomy of legumes.

With due consideration for these requirements and extensive morphological and genetic data, I have proposed a new phylogenetic scheme of important alfalfa species and their derivatives. According to this scheme the species of alfalfa are divided into two evolutionary series: yellow-flowered and blue-flowered. The interaction of these basic species, which led to the origin of hybrid forms, is shown. The diploid, tetraploid, and hexaploid species are given. The protein and nucleic acids laboratory of the All-Union Institute of Plant Industry (VIR) analyzed 14 perennial species, including all the groups of this scheme, as well as nine annual species. Research was conducted by the method of double immunodiffusion and continuous rocket immunoelectrophoresis. Serums of species of the blue-flowered series *M. coerulea* (diploid) and *M. sativa* (tetraploid) and the species *M. falcata* (tetraploid) representing the yellow-flowered series were used in the analysis.

The proteins were extracted from fatless flour by 1 N solution of NaCl in a phosphate buffer (pH 7.0) in cold. Immune serums were obtained by intramuscular immunization of rabbits. Injections were repeated three times with an interval of one week between each. Reimmunization was done one month later. Each rabbit received a total of 100 mg of protein.

Double diffusion was conducted in 1.5% agar on a neutral citrate buffer (pH 8.6). In addition to the traditional double diffusion method, the modern immunochemical method of continuous rocket immunoelectrophoresis was used. The principle of the method is based on the division of protein mixture in gel with serum under an electric field. The advantage of this method is that it enables one to better differentiate individual antigens and to establish their quantitative proportions. The continuous rocket immunoelectrophoresis method was implemented in 1.0% agar on a neutral citrate buffer (pH 8.6) at a voltage of 6V/cm for two hours.

In the preliminary stage of the work we determined the antigen composition of the serums obtained. It was found that with the detection of one protein by the double diffusion method of three serums, one and the same component appeared from each serum in different intensities. Maximum redistribution in the intensity of resolution of individual components was recorded for the serums of *M. falcata* and *M. sativa*. However, antibodies for each antigen were present in all the serums. In continuous rocket immunoelectrophoresis of the serum of *M. sativa* four components were identified. The first component in electrophoretic mobility (closest to anode) was resolved with equal intensity by all the serums; the second component was more intensely resolved by the serums of *M. falcata* and *M. coerulea,* but the third and fourth components were well differentiated by the serums of *M. sativa* and *M. coerulea*. Some redistribution of the content of individual components was observed even in the analysis of serums of perennial species of alfalfa.

A more diverse picture was seen in the case of annual species: Apart from redistribution of the individual components they exhibited certain differences in degree of immunochemical identity. For example, the species *M. platicarpos* and *M. orbicularis*, as well as the species *M. cancellata* and *M. tribuloides*, which are close to each other, have been identified from the common series.

Thus immunochemical analysis, revealing the similarity of constituent proteins in seeds of species of the genus *Medicago*, reaffirmed that readily crossable species of the genus *Medicago* have a basically similar protein spectrum. Similar uniformity of protein characters, which reflect the genetic structure of the species, could have emerged as a result of the interaction of genes during the early stages of evolution. Annual species of alfalfa, whose active evolution is not yet complete, have been found to be more distinctive in the immunochemistry of the proteins in their seeds.

It was found that among the perennial species of the subgenus *Falcago*, especially at the diploid level, in terms of constituent proteins the blue, hemicyclic, and South Kazakhstan alfalfa—the ancient diploid species included by me in different evolutionary series of the genus *Medicago* L.— are not identical to the polyploid species. They differ markedly from the tetraploid series in the absence of an entire group of constituent proteins. This indicates the phylogenetic distance and different quality of these species and hence emphasizes their separate identity. At the tetraploid level, due to weakening of the incompatibility barrier and for other reasons, distinct phylogenetic distance between wild alfalfa species, barring a few exceptions, is almost never observed, while such species of alfalfa as the common alfalfa, yellow alfalfa, glandular alfalfa, and varicolored alfalfa are almost identical in protein constituents (Figure 8). The immunochemical similarity of the proteins of these species indicates their close phylogenetic relationships, which should not be ignored when tracing the evolution and taxonomy of these species. It was also found that some hybrid species are likewise identical in protein contents (*M. varia, M. tianschanica, M. polychroa*).

In general it may be stated that immunochemical analysis of the proteins of seeds of perennial alfalfa species has confirmed the identification of the species used in the scheme. Obviously, future and deeper studies of the evolution of the genus *Medicago* will inevitably lead to valuable additions and changes in the given scheme. Considering the specificity of this crop (cross-polinated entomophilous plant) and the difficulty of establi-

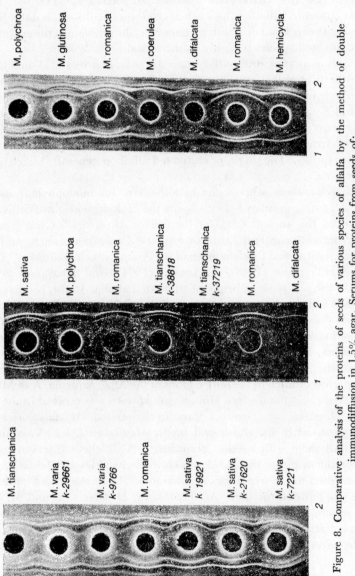

Figure 8. Comparative analysis of the proteins of seeds of various species of alfalfa by the method of double immunodiffusion in 1.5% agar. Serums for proteins from seeds of: 1—*M. sativa*; 2—*M. romanica*.

shing the authenticity of some species, it is very important to conduct cyto-chemical analysis on genetically pure initial material.

Origin of the cultivated species M. sativa L.[5] The fact that common cultivated alfalfa is an ancient crop whose cultivation dates back thousands of years is not disputable. However, the problem of the evolution of the cultivated species is highly controversial.

According to numerous publications *M. sativa* L. grows wild on a large area in the subtropical and temperate regions of Eurasia, which includes the Mediterranean, Middle and Near East, the Caucasus, Central (south-west) and South Asia. The maximum gene concentration of *M. sativa* in their most diverse combination is confined to the foothills and hilly valleys of Armenia, eastern Anatolia, Iran, Afghanistan, Central Asia and Kashmir (India). The origin of cultivated alfalfa is generally linked with these regions.

Most researchers support the hypothesis of the monophyletic evolution of *M. sativa*. Sinskaya (1948) favors the diphyletic origin of cultivated alfalfa from the ancient forms of the species *M. hemicycla* Grossh. of the series Praecocissimae and Europaeae of the Caucasian branch, and the series Euasiaticae and Euafghanicae of the Asian branch. Bordakov (1929, 1934), Vasil'chenko (1948), Tarkovskii (1964), and Khasanov (1971) recognize the polyphyletic origin of cultivated alfalfa. In this context Bordakov has indicated three centers of origin of *M. sativa*: Pamir-Iranian, southeast Asia Minor, and Mesopotamia. Tarkovskii proposes that the cultivated species began to evolve concomitantly in four centers: Central Asia, China, Iran, and India.

Vasil'chenko (1948) names four ancient centers of origin of the culti-vated species confined to the hilly regions of the Alps, Armenia, Asia Minor, Central Asia and the western Himalayas. *M. varia* was evolved in the first center, *M. grandiflora* (Grossh.) Vass. in the second, *M. tianschanica* and *M. agropyretorum* in the third, and finally *M. tibetana* (Alef.) Vass. in the fourth. All these wild species, according to Vasil'chenko, served as the basis for the origin of the composite cultivated species, *M. sativa* L.

According to the hypothesis of Khasanov, the phylogeny of cultivated alfalfa was built on the use of *M. tianschanica*, *M. transoxana*, and *M. traut-vetteri* which, according to his conviction, are closer to the most ancient cultivated alfalfas, namely, Khiva, Turkestan, and Semirechensk.

The wide range of variability of morphological and biological charac-

---

[5]*M. sativa* L. refers to the composite cultivated species as described by numerous authors until the publication of the classification by Lubenets (1972), who excluded from cultivated species all hybrid varieties and populations with a blue variegated corolla, relating them to another separate cultivated species of hybrid origin, *M. varia* Mart.

ters and properties of *M. sativa,* polymorphism of pods and polychromism of corolla, and exceptional diversity of ancient populations and improved varieties formed or developed at different places in the geographic area of cultivated species, also attest to the very complex phylogeny of *M. sativa* and hence unanimity of opinion has not been reached.

For many years researchers of various countries called *M. sativa* a composite species by distinguishing within the taxon not only types, ecotypes, groups, varietal types, races, and subspecies, but even several independent species; this indicates that the genotype of the cultivated species is in fact complex and in all probability the origin of *M. sativa* is closely linked with the wild alfalfas of the ancient Mediterranean.

In my opinion the primary center of the genus *Medicago,* including the ancestors of the cultivated species *M. sativa,* is the Caucasus and southern Trans-Caucasus (northwestern part of Iran and northeastern part of Turkey). From here the genus spread to all the countries and continents of the world. In this region, even today, the maximum number of alfalfa species at all known ploidy levels have been found. We shall later describe in detail the gene centers of *Medicago.* Here let us mention only that young tetraploid species of alfalfa are concentrated in the hilly belt of the central region, some of which are of hybrid origin, for example *M. tianschanica, M. trautvetteri, M. varia,* and their stabilization process not yet completed (*M. varia*), or completed at the diploid level (*M. trautvetteri*), or even transiting to the tetraploid level.

From the Caucasian-Asia Minor gene center cultivated alfalfa was introduced into Mesopotamia where, under conditions of irrigation, a local population developed with a high degree of structural refinement, that has been indentified by Vasil'chenko as an independent species, *M. mesopotamica.*

The Mesopotamian alfalfa, according to Sinskaya, was distinguished from the Syrian and Yemen alfalfas by the fact that the last two are very similar to the wild hilly forms due to poor agronomic conditions. I believe the reason for this lies not so much in poor agronomy, although there is no denying the latter, but in the diversity of genotypes. The origin of the Syrian and Yemen alfalfas was highly affected by ancient populations of the phylogenetically much younger and less conservative Turkestan branch. This is attested to by their lower response to irrigation, constitution of the bush, growth rhythm, morphological characters, and biological properties inherent in some Turkestan populations and hilly wild species of the Central Asian center.

But the Mesopotamian alfalfa is more conservative in color of corolla. It is distinguished by a high degree of uniformity because it was isolated from wild species over a span of many centuries; hence its heredity became concentrated in a direction suitable for man and fixed cultural characters appeared in each generation.

Many centuries of isolation of the initial populations of alfalfa brought to Mesopotamia at the dawn of agriculture insuring only intraspecific (more often intrapopulation) crossings, absence of wild species similar to the ancient cultivated form in rate of growth and development, total absence of forms of alfalfa capable of growing faster under conditions of irrigation and intensive farming, or segregation into progenies with a high growth rate when crossed with the initial population, led to a situation wherein the Mesopotamian alfalfa developed as a crop exhibiting such characters as early maturation, multiple cuttings, rich foliage, erect bush, soft stems, etc. and became an expression of the cultivated branch of *M. sativa* with an ultracultural constitution for conditions of intensive agriculture.

In the phylogenetically much younger populations of the Turkestan branch, whose evolution took place in the vicinity of the readily intercrossable wild species, the characters of wild alfalfas appear quite distinct. The following conditions facilitated this phenomenon: presence of great diversity of wild material of the tetraploid series similar to cultivated populations in terms of growth rate and development, low level of agronomy, absence of prolonged anthropogenic barriers or reliable isolation, severe climatic conditions, especially during winter, introduction of fewer cultural forms from other countries of the ancient eastern region, absence of genetic barriers (diploid species) preventing crossing of the highly polymorphic, phylogenetically young tetraploid species, and so forth.

It is thought that the introduction of alfalfa for cultivation began not with one species, but with the acquisition by man of several wild species of different ploidy levels growing in ancient centers but nevertheless with highly organized agriculture.

In spite of the fact that polyploidy is not an absolute barrier to the intercrossing of diploid species, especially those that have very few or no transitional forms ($2n = 16$ and 32), the formation of the cultivated branch of *M. sativa* was most modest. During spontaneous hybridization, very rare under natural conditions, in species with different chromosome numbers ($2n = 16$ and $2n = 32$) the ploidy level of genotypes was raised to tetraploid (Sinskaya and Maleeva, 1959). Stanford, Clement and Bingham (1972) report that in crosses of diploids with tetraploids under artificial conditions generally 5 to 15 hybrid progenies are obtained per 1,000 crossings.

It is not difficult to visualize that under natural conditions the output of hybrids would be far less.

The evolutionary role of diploid species (to say nothing of the tetra-

ploid species of the Central Asian gene center) in the origin of the cultivated *M. sativa* was in fact considerable, but appeared earlier when the
diploid wild *M. sativa* had evolved, but not at the time of the universal
formation of tetraploid forms of *M. sativa*, the progenitors of the cultivated
forms of this species.

Under cultivated conditions such as intensive farming on irrigated
lands not a single diploid species of alfalfa could compete with tetraploid
M. sativa in growth rate; a few individual hybrids retained in the plant
stand could not change (without being changed themselves) the rapid
species formation process (or affect it significantly) taking place within
the ancient populations of the cultivated species, and inexorably bringing
them closer to the modern cultivated forms.

Another aspect is the crossing between tetraploid species. Here the
isolation barrier is completely absent. No doubt tetraploid species were
involved in the origin of *M. sativa*, especially in the Central Asian gene
center, but this participation did not relate to the formation of the
species, but rather its fragmentation leading to the contemporary polymorphic level. The actual origin of the species took place earlier, at the
diploid level.

In this context the scheme of evolution of cultivated alfalfa proposed
by Vasil'chenko is noteworthy, according to which all initial wild species
interrelated with each other are tetraploids (Figure 9). The scheme of
Vasil'chenko reflects the second stage of origin of this species from its wild
ancestors. The author correctly presents the common course of evolution
of the genus—from ancient diploid species to much younger tetraploids;
the shortcoming of this scheme is the separateness of all the species, as
though no phylogenetic relationships exist between them.

While examining the proposed evolutionary scheme of *M. sativa* one
cannot hold that this species originated from *M. varia* since it has now become known that the latter is a hybrid of *M. sativa* and *M. falcata*. Neither
could *M. sativa* have originated from *M. tianschanica* since the latter is a
derivative species from the ancient forms of *M. sativa*. Phylogenetically
it is a hybrid species backcrossed by the cultivated alfalfa and, according
to the opinion of Belov (1965), Zhukovskii (1971) and Ivanov (1974), this
taxon is not at all an independent species, but represents a Central Asian
branch of the wild *M. sativa*. As for the other two species—*M. grandiflora*
and *M. tibetana*, which according to Vasil'chenko participated in the formation of the primary gene pool of the cultivated alfalfa, these taxa, according to Lubenets (1972) and other researchers, are also not independent
species, but synonyms of the cultivated species: the first—the wild Caucasian subspecies *M. sativa* L. subsp. *caucasica*, and the second—the wild
Asian subspecies *M. sativa* L. subsp. *transoxana*. From these subspecies deve-

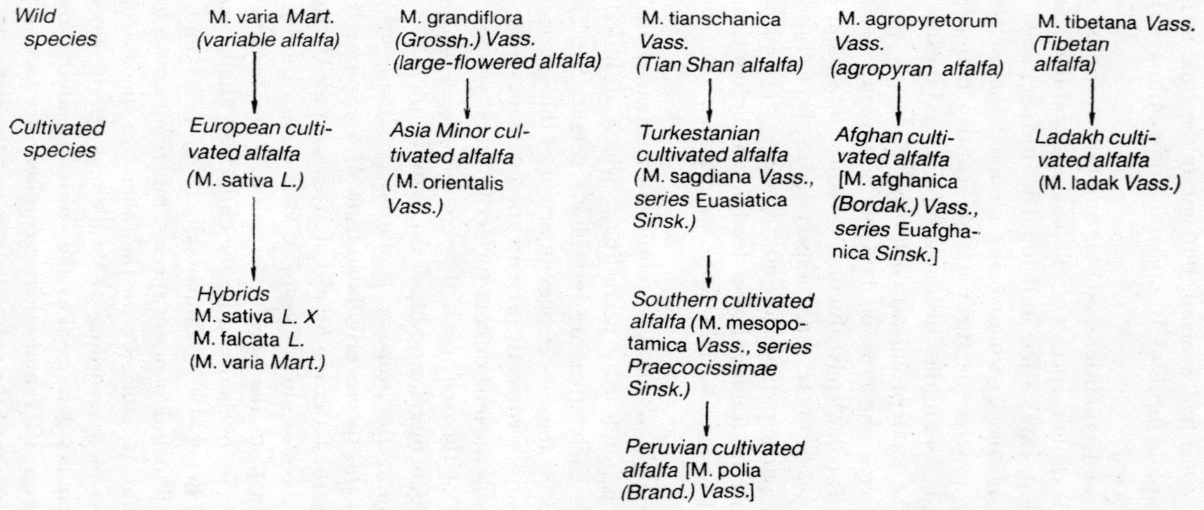

Figure 9. Scheme of evolution of cultivated species of alfalfa according to I.T. Vasil'chenko (1948).

Wild species

Cultivated species

M. varia Mart. (variable alfalfa)

European cultivated alfalfa (M. sativa L.)

Hybrids M. sativa L. × M. falcata L. (M. varia Mart.)

M. grandiflora (Grossh.) Vass. (large-flowered alfalfa)

Asia Minor cultivated alfalfa (M. orientalis Vass.)

M. tianschanica Vass. (Tian Shan alfalfa)

Turkestanian cultivated alfalfa (M. sagdiana Vass., series Euasiatica Sinsk.)

Southern cultivated alfalfa (M. mesopotamica Vass., series Praecocissimae Sinsk.)

Peruvian cultivated alfalfa [M. polia (Brand.) Vass.]

M. agropyretorum Vass. (agropyran alfalfa)

Afghan cultivated alfalfa [M. afghanica (Bordak.) Vass., series Euatghanica Sinsk.]

M. tibetana Vass. (Tibetan alfalfa)

Ladakh cultivated alfalfa (M. ladak Vass.)

loped a large number of cultivated taxa of lesser rank (some of them had been elevated by authors to the rank of independent species, but were related by Lubenets to the cultivated subspecies of common alfalfa, *M. sativa* L. subsp. *sativa*).

If we exclude from the scheme the independent hybrid species *M. varia* Mart., then the four remaining species are nothing but wild *M. sativa*. It was found that the cultivated *M. sativa* originated from the wild *M. sativa* growing in two gene centers: Caucasian (*M. grandiflora*) and Central Asian (*M. tianschanica, M. agropyretorum, M. tibetana*). Diversity of speciation of *M. sativa* is evident in the much younger Central Asian gene center; the phylogeny of the cultivated species, according to Vasil'chenko, is not polyphyletic but diphyletic from the ancient wild forms of the Caucasian and Central Asian gene centers and, more precisely, from two wild subspecies of *M. sativa* established in these centers.

Similar comments are applicable to the opinion of Khasanov who indicates that *M. sativa* originated from *M. transoxana, M. trautvetteri,* and *M. tianschanica*. We have already mentioned the involvement of Tian Shan alfalfa in the origin of cultivated species. The diploid species *M. trautvetteri* is not related to the group of multiple-cutting alfalfas. It has a long dormant period and is a hybrid of *M. coerulea* (2n = 16) and *M. difalcata* (2n = 16). This species is not easy to cross with tetraploids.

The participation of *M. agropyretorum* and *M. transoxana* in the origin of cultivated species, as suggested by Vasil'chenko and Khasanov, is fully justified. Both taxa are tetraploids. However, they are not independent species but probably close derivatives of the cultivated alfalfa. Lubenets considers them synonyms of the cultivated species, in particular that of the Asian subspecies of *M. sativa*.

Sinskaya's views on the origin of cultivated alfalfas are much closer to the truth. If we exclude from her scheme (Figure 10) the series Europaeae, giving rise to the steppe climatypes (west European, south European, and east European), belonging to *M. varia*, then this scheme better explains the concluding stage of the origin of cultivated species. The earlier genealogy of the species—from wild diploid ancestors to tetraploid forms of the early series—requires verification. The difficulty in explaining the early stages of evolution of the cultivated species relates to the fact that Sinskaya selected the ancient hybrid species *M. hemicycla* as the initial originator of this scheme.

In my opinion the phylogeny of *M. sativa* proceeded in the direction of strengthening cultural features: erectness, profuse foliation, soft stems, intense growth, enlarged leaf blade, enlargement and curling of pod, concentration of root system in arable soil layer, intensification of hydromorphism of plants, and so forth. Involvement of the hybrid species with

36

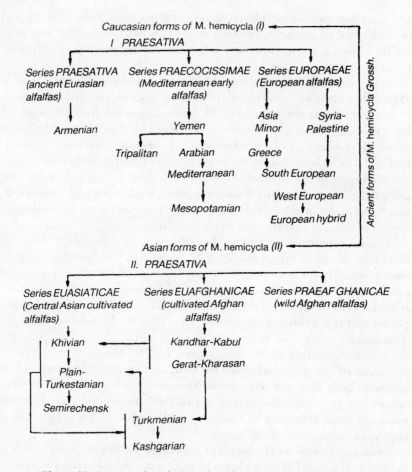

Figure 10. Scheme of evolution of cultivated alfalfas according to
E.N. Sinskaya (1950).

yellow flowers was imperative in the early stages of evolution of *M. sativa*.
This itself partly explains the polychroism of the corolla of the cultivated
species and change of shades in color of the corolla depending on method
of cultivation (irrigation, rainfed, or dry farming).[6] Variegated flowers
could have been introduced in the gene pool of the cultivated species by
M. hemicycla—a hybrid species closer to the ancient forms of *M. sativa, M.
tianschanica,* and *M. trautvetteri.*

[6]Research conducted by Vasil'chenko, Konstantinova, Sinskaya, Kul'tiasov, Wald-
ron, Klinkowski, and others has shown that the color of the corolla is not only a character
of hybrid origin, but also an ecological character.

The most ancient blue-flowered species of alfalfa is neither the hybrid *M. hemicycla,* as asserted by Sinskaya, nor the hybrid *M. tianschanica,* as asserted by Vasil'chenko and Khasanov, but *M. coerulea.* The genealogy of *M. sativa* begins from this very species, and the scheme is as follows: *M. praecoerulea*—*M. coerulea* (2n = 16), Caucasian and Asian forms—*M. prae-sativa* (2n = 16), Caucasian and Asian forms (autopolyploid)—*M. praesativa* (2n = 32), and further according to Sinskaya's scheme.

Numerous cytological and genetic researches conducted by the Canadian researchers Lesins, Gillies and Baenziger also prove that *M. hemicycla* is a hybrid species. In the opinion of these authors *M. sativa* could not have originated from *M. hemicycla.*

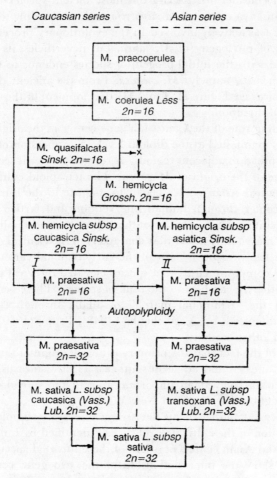

Figure 11. Phylogenetic scheme of *M. sativa* L.

The involvement of *M. hemicycla,* derived from the ancient forms of *M. coerulea* and *M. quasifalcata,* is quite likely in the formation of the diploid *M. praesativa.* Here one can agree with the evolution scheme of common alfalfa developed by Sinskaya, reflecting the general course of development of the cultivated species. The phylogeny of *M. sativa,* without division of species into series, climatypes, ecotypes, varietal types (as done by Sinskaya) is depicted in Figure 11.

To correlate Sinskaya's scheme and mine is not difficult since both depict diphyletic origin from the ancient forms of Eurasian and Central Asian centers and include the common ancient ancestors of alfalfa growing in the Caucasian gene center. The only difference in the two schemes is that while I consider *M. coerulea* the most ancient species of the genus *Medicago,* Sinskaya considers *M. hemicycla* such. According to my scheme, *M. hemicycla* was actively involved in the evolutionary process during the early stages of phylogeny of *M. sativa,* but nevertheless its origin is no doubt linked with the initial progenitor species endemic to Central Asia and the Caucasus, namely, *M. coerulea.* From the ancient diploid forms of *M. praesativa* (see Figure 11, I and II) development of the schemes proceeds in one direction.

The leading role of the Caucasian gene center in the origin of cultivated alfalfa is manifested at the diploid level when ancestors of the cultivated species spread to adjacent regions. A reverse process is seen at the concluding stage of the origin of *M. sativa*: The tetraploid cultivated alfalfa from the Central Asian center began to migrate to the Eurasian-Trans-Caucasian center through human intervention and farther to the Near East, the Mediterranean, Africa, southern Europe, and finally to the New World. We may boldly assert that characters of the Central Asian alfalfas are more or less present in most of the early regional varieties—populations of the composite cultivated species elevated by Vasil'chenko, Sinskaya, and other researchers to the rank of species. These very factors are linked with the "triumphal march" of alfalfa through countries and continents discussed by Vasil'chenko (1948), Popov (1950), Tarkovskii (1974), and other authors.

In spite of the fact that the primary center of origin of the genus *Medicago* is the Caucasus and adjacent southeast Trans-Caucasus, the Central Asian center has played an important role in the spread of cultivated alfalfa throughout the Old and New World.

The lower half of the scheme devised by Sinskaya is completely devoted to a description of the cultivated subspecies identified by Lubenets for the Caucasian and Asian centers of origin of the cultivated species; however, it does not show the interrelationship of the two gene centers, which exists in nature. In the scheme developed by Ivanov this interrelationship is shown. As for the phylogeny of the cultivated species at the level of groups of varietal types and varietal types, groups of ecotypes and ecotypes, it is well represented in the work of Lubenets (1972).

For the young Asian forms of *M. sativa* a much simpler path of phylogeny is also possible: directly from the doubling of chromosomes of *M. coerulea* through intermediate forms resembling *M. agropyretorum* to the lower ploidy populations of *M. sativa* L. subsp. *transoxana*. This viewpoint of mine is shared by Shcherbina and Perchik (1973).

The transition from diploid to tetraploid level is the most important link in the phylogenetic scheme of *M. sativa*. Authors vary in opinion about this problem. Armstrong (1954) considers the cultivated species an alloploid of related diploid species. The same opinion is held by U. Urat and D. Britten who observed nonhomologous synopsis of chromosomes in pachytene and translocation in tetraploid plants.

In the earlier works of American researchers, cited by Sinskaya and Maleeva (1959), the opinion was expressed that cultivated alfalfa is autopolyploid or allopolyploid. In much later works tetrasomic inheritance is constantly proved, which is characteristic of autopolyploids.

An important role in establishing relationships between alfalfa species is played by the morphological similarity of aerial organs. Botanists are fully aware that in the Central Asian region the alfalfa species—blue, prostrate, common, and Tian Shan—are morphologically similar.

The blue alfalfa belongs to the rapidly disappearing ancient species. Once upon a time its area of distribution was considerably wider than now. Advancement of the genus *Medicago* from the Caucasian gene center to Central Asia, Tibet, Pamir, Altai, Siberia, and other regions was associated with the eastward migration of the ancient diploid species—*M. coerulea*, *M. hemicycla* (in the Central Asian gene center *M. trautvetteri*, a species closer to it), *M. quasifalcata* (in the Central Asian center *M. difalcata*, a species closer to it) and *M. falcata*. In their new center tetraploid species evolved from the diploid species and considerably expanded their primary centers in due course of evolution.

Stebbins (1947) considers the cultivated species a segmental alloploid. He explains the evolution of the species as follows: Initially the cultivated alfalfa was autopolyploid, then after pollination by a small number of other species it became segmental allopolyploid, which is manifested in the nature of its inheritance, atypical for an allopolyploid, different chromosomal aberrations, and the weak polyploidy of the species. Sinskaya and Maleeva do not wholly endorse Stebbins' viewpoint, stating that *M. sativa* is either an autopolyploid or segmental alloploid.

Cleveland and Stanford (1959), emphasizing the low frequency of formation of quadrivalents in tetraploid alfalfa compared to induced (artificial) autotetraploids, conclude that *M. sativa* is in part a diploidized autotetraploid. Gillies (1970), due to the difficulty of comparison of some pairs of pachytene bivalents of a tetraploid plant, came to the conclusion that the tetraploid is a diploidized autoploid or segmental alloploid.

It is evident from this brief cytogenetic review of *M. sativa* that the data was subjectively interpreted by the researchers. They proved that *M. sativa* (and also *M. falcata* and even *M. varia*) is an alloploid, autopolyploid, segmental allopolyploid, diploidized autoploid, and finally, an autotetraploid. The highly polymorphic nature of all wild alfalfa species attests to the possibility of very diverse combinations of forms within the species. Nevertheless, most of the latest cytological data indicates that the cultivated alfalfa is functionally autotetraploid.

The most important proof of the autotetraploid nature of *M. sativa* is considered the complete synopsis of chromosomes, as observed in a large number of dihaploids, obtained from unrelated tetraploids. Autotetraploid origin of the cultivated alfalfa has been proved by the research of Ledingham, Julen, Grun, and other scientists, who have found quadrivalents during meiotic analysis of karyotypes of tetraploids. Experimental data obtained through phylogenetic studies of alfalfa testifies to the great evolutionary importance of autoploidy, an importance far greater than usually recognized.

TAXONOMY OF PERENNIAL SPECIES OF ALFALFA

In the pre-Linnaean period alfalfa was classified by Bauhin (1620), Morisson (1685), and Tournefort (1700). The work of Tournefort, in which 46 species are listed and the genus *Medicago* so named for the first time, had a great impact on C. Linnaeus, the founder of binomial nomenclature.

Carolus Linnaeus (Linné) (1753) described the genus on the basis of a typical specimen of *M. radiata* L., which was later transferred to the genus *Melissitus*. In Linné's classification a total of 21 species are mentioned and described, but the distinguishing characters barely differentiate. Some species of the genera *Trigonella, Trifolium,* and *Melilotus,* closely resembling alfalfa, were also included in his classification.

In the post-Linnaean period, right up to the present day, many researchers have struggled with the classification of this genus.

In classifying alfalfa most researchers have paid attention to the shape and degree of curling of the pod, color of corolla, and duration of plant life. Phylogenetic relationships between species, their ploidy level, and morphology of chromosomes were rarely taken into account. It is not feasible to analyze here all the systems proposed by various authors. Let us discuss instead the basic classifications that more comprehensively high-light the subgenus *Falcago*.

Serenge, Reichenbasch, Buasse, and Urban have proposed classifica-tions in which subgenera and sections are separated, thereby considerably perfecting the system. Particularly noteworthy is the classification of Urban in which the genus *Medicago* is subdivided into two subgenera and ten sections. The subgenus *Eumedicago* Urb. includes the following sections: membranous fruit—*Hymenocarpoides* Gris., hop-shaped—*Lupularia* Ser., crescentoid—*Falcago* Reichb., round—*Orbiculares* Urb., intertwisted—*Intertextes* Urb., and scutiform—*Scutellatae* Urb.; the subgenus *Cymatium* Urb. comprised four sections: spicate—*Rotatae* Boiss., compact spiral—*Pachyspirae* Urb., spiral fruited—*Euspirocarpae* Urb., and loose spiral—*Leptospirae* Urb.

The classifications of Taubert, Asherson, and Grebner are similar to the system proposed by Urban. All the classifications of the early period suffered from serious shortcomings, which have been appropriately pointed out by many researchers.

The most comprehensive classifications of the genus *Medicago* have been developed by Soviet botanists—Grossgeim, Vasil'chenko, Sinskaya, Lube-nets, and Khasanov.

Grossgeim divided the genus *Medicago* into four subgenera—*Lupularia* (Ser.) Grossh.*, *Falcago* (Reichb.) Grossh., *Orbicularia* Grossh., and *Spiro-carpos* (Ser.) Grossh., seven sections, and eight series, in which 36 species are included. In the subgenus *Falcago*, species of which are of greatest interest to agriculturalists, he included 18 perennial species: common (*M. sativa* L.), yellow (*M. falcata* L.), northern (*M. borealis* Grossh.), stony (*M. saxatilis* Bieb.), Tian Shan (*M. tianschanica* Sumn.), semitwisted (*M. hemicycla* Grossh.), blue (*M. coerulea* Less.), varicolored (*M. polychroa* Grossh.), glutinous (*M. glutinosa* Grossh.), greenish (*M. virescens* Grossh.), villous (*M. papillosa* Boiss.), Dzhavakheta (*M. dzhavakhetica* Bord.), marine (*M. marina* L.), Shishkin (*M. schischkini* Sumn.), scaly or rocky (*M. rupestris* Bieb.), checkered (*M. cancellata* Bieb.), and Rumanian (*M. romanica* Prod.).

It is important to note that Grossgeim, contrary to Vasil'chenko (1948), Sinskaya (1950), and Kul'tiasov (1967), considers common alfalfa a single indivisible species with numerous infraspecific taxa.

Sinskaya excluded the greenish alfalfa from the system of Grossgeim and related it to the Dagestan foothill ecotype, while Lubenets excluded

---

*Spelling of author names in taxonomic divisions often differs from spelling in the text and bibliography since the Israeli orthography has been followed in this translation—General Editor.

the Shishkin alfalfa, considering it an infraspecific taxon of the Tian Shan alfalfa. Observing the rule of priority of names of species, Lubenets points out that the Rumanian alfalfa in the classification of Grossgeim should more appropriately be called the glutinous alfalfa (*M. glutinosa* David.). All the remaining species identified by Grossgeim, according to Lubenets, are independent species with good distinguishing characters, and this very classification, considered the most successful, is extensively used by botanists, plant breeders, and agricultural practitioners.

According to Vasil'chenko (1949), the subgenus *Falcago* comprises 46 species, i.e., 28 species more than included in the classification by Grossgeim. Unfortunately many of these species lack a separate area of distribution and good distinguishing characters. Without considering the cultivated alfalfas from the subgenus *Falcago* included by Vasil'chenko, Lubenets (1972) excluded (treated as synonyms) 26 species of alfalfa: wheatgrass, Alatavian, Tibetan, Roborov, pale yellow, large-flowered, Caucasian, Tadzhik, smooth-podded, Hissarian, Kopet Dag, Kul'tiasov, Lavrenko, Komarov, Alashan, semithorny, Akhtinian, riverine, Beipin, Rodop, Gunib, Grossgeim, Tersko-Kuban, twisted, Rupin, and semi-bushy. In addition to Lubenets, the system of Vasil'chenko has been critically evaluated also by Zhukovskii (1965a, 1971), Sinskaya (1969), Khasanov (1971, 1972), Lesins and Gillies (1972), and others.

Sinskaya (1950) includes 18 perennial species in the flora of the Soviet Union, of which three are new and not covered in the system of Grossgeim: *M. tetrahemicycla* Sinsk. from Afghanistan, *M. quasifalcata* from the foot-hills of northern Caucasus, and *M. difalcata* from southern Kazakhstan. Lubenets does not recognize the first species as an independent taxon. According to Sinskaya, the crescentoid alfalfa and South Kazakhstan alfalfa are independent species.

Khasanov (1971) excludes six wild (identified by Vasil'chenko) species growing in Central Asia from specific taxa: *M. ochroleuca, M. lavrenkoi, M. rivularis, M. subdicycla, M. kopetdaghi,* and *M. tadzhikorum.* He considers all of them no more than subspecies of *M. tianschanica, M. transoxana, M. agropyretorum,* and *M. trautvetteri.* Khasanov also does not recognize *M. kultiassovii* Vass. as an independent species, relating it to the common alfalfa.

After compiling a genetic collection in the University of Alberta (Canada) comprising more than 2,000 specimens and studying the morphology of chromosomes, karyotypes, compatibility, and variability of characters of most of the specific taxa, Karl Lesins and his school (Lesins, Gillies et al.) raised doubts about the existence of several annual and perennial species of alfalfa. Lesins and Gillies (1972) point out that some researchers tend to treat infraspecific taxa or, simply, interspecific hybrids as independent species without considering the factor of variability. According to them the synonyms of *M. sativa* at diploid and tetraploid levels are: *M. coerulea* Less., *M. lavrenkoi* Vass., *M. agropyretorum* Vass., *M. asiatica* Sinsk., *M. jemanensis* Sinsk., *M. mesopotamica* Vass., *M. sogdiana* Vass., *M. transoxana* Vass., *M. kopetdaghi* Vass., and *M. tadzhikorum* Vass.; the synonyms of *M. falcata* L. are: *M. borealis* Grossh., *M. erecta* Kotov., *M. glandulosa* David., *M. quasifalcata* Sinsk., *M. romanica* Prod., *M. difalcata* Sinsk., and *M. tenderiensis* Opperm.; the synonyms of the interspecific hybrid species *M. varia* Mart. are: *M. grandiflora* Vass., *M. komarovii* Vass., *M. media* Pers., *M. ochroleuca* Kult., *M. tianschanica* Vass., and *M. trautvetteri* Sumn.; the existence of several annual alfalfa species is also doubted: *M. turbinata* Willd., *M. doliata* Carmign., *M. maculata* Sibth., *M. globosa* Urb., *M. marginata* Willd., *M. cuneata* Woods., *M. applanata* Willd., *M. gerardii* Waldst. and Kit., *M. depressa* Jord., *M. germana* Jord., *M. agrestis* Ten., and others.

There are several controversial points in the works of the Canadian researchers. For example, it is doubtful that *M. lavrenkoi* with small, 1.5 to 2.0 twists or sometimes falciform pods (a character indicating hybrid origin of the species) should be treated as a synonym of *M. sativa*. As derivatives of *M. falcata* the Canadians relate almost all yellow-flowered diploid species of hybrid origin with falciform and straight pods and a separate area of distribution. As synonyms of the interspecific hybrid *M. varia*, together with other species, they have also enlisted the large-flowered alfalfa, Komarov alfalfa, pale yellow alfalfa, Tian Shan alfalfa, and Trautvetter's alfalfa. As a matter of fact, all these species are interspecific hybrids, but evolved from more ancient species than did *M. varia*. Their origin is closely linked with the diploid and tetraploid wild species of the montane and foothill belt which we have described at length in earlier sections of this book. In contrast to the Canadian researchers Lubenets has related the Komarov alfalfa ($2n = 16$) to *M. trautvetteri*, and the pale yellow alfalfa ($2n = 32$) to *M. tianschanica*. Lubenets relates the large-flowered alfalfa to *M. sativa*, but Vasil'chenko relates it to the series of Tian Shan species. According to the color of corolla, the large-flowered alfalfa is without doubt related to the hybrid species and cannot be affiliated to *M. sativa*.

Inaccuracies in certain conclusions drawn by the Canadian cytogeneticists pertaining to the synonyms of *M. sativa*, *M. falcata*, and *M. varia*, can be explained by the fact that they worked under laboratory conditions and in experimental plots—far removed from the places of natural growth of the wild species—and have not seen the great diversity of forms concentrated in the primary centers of origin of this crop.

At present the most simple and easy-to-use classification of perennial species of alfalfa is the one proposed by Lubenets (1972). It has been accepted by plant breeders and agronomists.

Lubenets identifies 21 species in the subgenus *Falcago* (Reichb.) Grossh.

Diploid species (2n = 16)
Northern alfalfa—*M. borealis* Grossh.
Crescentoid alfalfa—*M. quasifalcata* Sinsk.
Glandular alfalfa—*M. glandulosa* David.
South Kazakhstan alfalfa—*M. difalcata* Sinsk.
Blue alfalfa—*M. coerulea* Less.
Semitwisted alfalfa—*M. hemicycla* Grossh.
Trautvetter's alfalfa—*M. trautvetteri* Sumn.
Downy alfalfa—*M. papillosa* Boiss.
Alpine alfalfa—*M. dzhavakhetica* Bordz.
Prostrate alfalfa—*M. prostrata* Jacq.
Dagestan alfalfa—*M. daghestanica* Rupr.
Rocky alfalfa—*M. rupestris* Bieb.
Marine alfalfa—*M. marina* L.

Tetraploid species (2n = 32)
Common alfalfa—*M. sativa* L.
Variable alfalfa—*M. varia* Mart.
Yellow alfalfa—*M. falcata* L.
Glutinous alfalfa—*M. glutinosa* Bieb.
Varicolored alfalfa—*M. polychroa* Grossh.
Tian Shan alfalfa—*M. tianschanica* Vass.

Hexaploid species (2n = 48)
Checkered alfalfa—*M. cancellata* Bieb.
Stony alfalfa—*M. saxatilis* Bieb.

Like Grossgeim, Lesins and Gillies, Lubenets also does not consider the cultivated alfalfa as a species complex with multiple independent species (according to Vasil'chenko—7, Kul'tiasov—9, Sinskaya—10), but a single species with several interspecific taxa. The division of cultivated alfalfa into several independent species, according to Lubenets, did not gain acceptance. Because of the assertion by Vasil'chenko about the independent status of the species *M. varia* Mart., overlooked by Grossgeim, Lubenets considerably restricted the scope of the species *M. sativa* L. by relating to it only the cultivated and wild blue-flowered populations. He related all the hybrid forms of *M. sativa* × *M. falcata* to *M. varia*.

GENE CENTERS OF ALFALFA ACCORDING TO THE THEORY OF N.I. VAVILOV AND SUBSEQUENT ADDITIONS

Distribution of species according to gene centers. N.I. Vavilov discovered eight geographic centers of origin of cultivated plants: Chinese, Indian (with Indo-Malayan region), Central Asian, Eurasian, Mediterranean, Abyssinian, Southern Mexican, and South American. P.M. Zhukovskii has added four new centers—three independent (Australian, Euro-Siberian, and North American) and one expanded, viz., African, which automatically included the small but very important Abyssinian center of N.I. Vavilov. The Indian center of N.I. Vavilov, which included the Indo-Malayan region (Malayan archipelago, the Philippines, Indochina), was later identified as a separate Indonesian-Indochinese center. Hence, at present 12 centers of origin of cultivated plants have been established. Their names and serial numbers are given below according to Zhukovskii (1968):

I—Sino-Japanese (N.I. Vavilov)
II—Indonesian-Indochinese (N.I. Vavilov)
III—Australian (P.M. Zhukovskii)
IV—Indian (N.I. Vavilov)
V—Central Asian (N.I. Vavilov)
VI—Eurasian (N.I. Vavilov)
VII—Mediterranean (N.I. Vavilov)
VIII—African (P.M. Zhukovskii)[7]
IX—European-Siberian (P.M. Zhukovskii)
X—Central American (N.I. Vavilov)
XI—South American (N.I. Vavilov)
XII—North American (P.M. Zhukovskii)

The richest natural gene reserve of alfalfa is located in the Soviet Union. Three centers of origin of *Medicago* L. are concentrated in our country: Central Asian, Eurasian, and European-Siberian (Table 2).

The Central Asian gene center is considered the primary center of origin of species such as *M. sativa* L. (highly polymorphic Euro-Asian species), *M. tianschanica* Vass., *M. difalcata* Sinsk., *M. trautvetteri* Sumn. (Central Asian species), and *M. coerulea* Less. (Caucasian-Central Asian species). Endemic to the center are the diploid species *M. coerulea* Less. from the northeastern region of the Caspian lowland, the tetraploid wild Asian subspecies

[7]According to N.I. Vavilov—Abyssinian center. P.M. Zhukovskii included the entire continent in this center and named it the African center, attributing to himself priority of discovery.

46

Table 2. Botanical diversity of perennial alfalfa species of VIR collection according to gene centers of N.I. Vavilov and P.M. Zhukovskii (as of January 1, 1978)

Species	Distribution of specimens per center of origin (P.M. Zhukovskii, 1968)												Total
	I	II	III	IV	V	VI	VII	VIII	IX	X	XI	XII	
	Diploid species (2n=16)												
M. daghestanica Rupr.	—	—	—	—	—	2	—	—	—	—	—	—	2
M. coerulea Less.	—	—	—	—	2	13	—	—	15	—	—	—	30
M. hemicycla Grossh.	—	—	—	—	—	18	—	—	—	—	—	—	18
M. difalcata Sinsk.	—	—	—	—	6	—	—	—	12	—	—	—	18
M. trautvetteri Sumn.	—	—	—	—	1	—	—	—	15	—	—	—	16
M. quasifalcata Sinsk.	—	—	—	—	—	33	—	—	—	—	—	—	33
M. glandulosa David.	—	—	—	—	—	3	—	—	—	—	—	—	3
M. borealis Grossh.	—	—	—	—	—	—	—	—	25	—	—	—	25
M. dzhavakhetica Bord.	—	—	—	—	—	3	—	—	—	—	—	—	3

	Tetraploid species (2n=32)												
M. sativa L.	38	5	12	12	503	301	100	3	433	12	36	141	1,596
M. falcata L.	1	—	—	—	10	14	1	—	148	—	—	3	177
M. polychroa Grossh.	—	—	—	—	—	18	—	—	—	—	—	—	18
M. glutinosa Bieb.	—	—	—	—	—	10	—	—	1	—	—	—	11
M. varia Mart.	—	—	—	—	1	—	—	—	135	—	—	52	188
M. tianschanica Vass.	—	—	—	—	11	—	—	—	—	—	—	—	11
	Hexaploid species (2n=48)												
M. cancellata Bieb.	—	—	—	—	—	1	—	—	—	—	—	—	1
M. saxatilis Bieb.	—	—	—	—	—	1	—	—	—	—	—	—	1
Total	39	5	12	12	534	417	101	3	784	12	36	196	2,151

Table 3. Botanical diversity of annual alfalfa species of VIR collection according to gene centers of N.I. Vavilov and P.M. Zhukovskii (as of January 1, 1978)

Species	Distribution of specimens per center of origin (P.M. Zhukovskii, 1968)												Total
	I	II	III	IV	V	VI	VII	VIII	IX	X	XI	XII	
M. lupulina L.	1	—	1	—	4	7	5	—	14	—	—	1	33
M. arabica (L.) Huds.	—	—	—	—	—	—	1	—	—	—	—	2	3
M. scutellata (L.) Mill.	—	—	1	—	2	—	—	—	3	—	—	—	6
M. orbicularis (L.) Bartalini	—	—	1	—	4	3	—	—	2	—	—	1	11
M. tuberculata Willd.	—	—	—	—	—	—	—	—	1	—	—	—	1
M. ciliaris Willd.	—	—	—	—	—	—	1	—	—	—	—	—	1
M. minima (L.) Bartalini	—	—	—	1	2	—	—	—	—	—	—	—	3
M. denticulata Willd.	3	—	1	—	3	4	2	—	2	—	—	2	17
M. rigidula (L.) All.	—	—	—	—	3	1	1	—	1	—	—	—	6
M. tribuloides Desr.	—	—	—	—	1	—	1	—	—	—	—	—	2
M. nigra Willd.	—	—	—	—	—	—	—	—	1	—	—	—	1
M. truncatula Gaerth.	—	—	6	—	—	—	—	—	—	—	—	—	6
M. laciniata L.	—	—	—	—	—	—	—	—	3	—	—	—	3
M. arborea L.	—	—	—	—	—	—	1	—	—	—	—	—	1
M. agrestis Ten. ex DC	—	—	—	—	2	—	—	—	—	—	—	—	2
M. litoralis Rohde	—	—	1	—	1	—	—	—	—	—	—	—	2
M. meyeri Grun.	—	—	—	—	2	—	—	—	—	—	—	—	2
M. sinskiae Ul.	—	—	—	—	1	—	—	—	—	—	—	—	1
M. murex Willd.	—	—	—	—	—	—	—	—	2	—	—	—	2
M. intertexta Mill.	—	—	—	—	2	—	—	—	2	—	—	—	4

									Total
M. reticulata Benth.	1	—	—	—	—	—	—	—	1
M. tornata Mill.	2	—	1	—	—	—	1	—	4
M. rotata Boiss.	—	—	—	—	—	1	—	—	1
M. terebellum Willd.	1	—	—	—	—	—	—	—	1
M. polymorpha L.	1	—	—	—	—	—	—	—	1
M. rugosa Desr. in Lam.	—	—	1	—	—	—	—	—	1
M. constricta Dur.	—	—	2	—	—	—	—	—	2
M. lanigera C. Winkl. and B. Fedtsch	—	—	2	—	—	—	—	—	2
M. globosa Presl.	—	—	2	—	—	—	—	—	2
Total, 29 sp.	17	4	34	1	14	13	33	6	122

M. sativa L. subsp. *transoxana* (Vass.) Lub., several regional ecotypes of *M. falcata* L. (Eurasian highly polymorphic species), and the Central Asian group of varietal types of cultivated subspecies *M. sativa* L.

Taking into consideration the earlier proposed scheme, this gene center is the primary one for the species *M. komarovii* Vass., *M. sogdiana* Vass., *M. ladak* Vass., *M. asiatica* Sinsk., *M. agropyretorum* Vass., *M. tadzikorum* Vass., *M. kopetdaghi* Vass., *M. rivularis* Vass., *M. alatavica* Vass., *M. schischkini* Sumn., *M. tetrahemicycla* Sinsk., *M. lavrenkoi* Vass., and *M. kultiassovii* Vass. In the new version of classification by Lubenets these species are not represented, even though some of them have distinct morphological characters and small separate geographic areas of distribution, and deserve to be identified as separate taxa of much smaller rank.

The Central Asian gene center is the primary and evidently one of the basic centers in the world of origin and evolution of annual alfalfas. Regarding the botanical-geographic diversity of annual species there are strong competitors such as the Mediterranean (VII) and Australian (III) gene centers as well as the Crimean region of the European-Siberian (IX) gene center (Table 3).

In the Central Asian gene center species were brought under cultivation from wild forms for the first time, which finally evolved into world-famous varietal types of cultivated alfalfa with valuable biological characteristics: plain Turkestan, Semirechensk, Khiva, Kashgar, Kandhar-Kabul, Gerat-Khorasan, and others. Local and improved varieties of this gene center are the carriers of germ plasm of such important characters as bushiness, heat resistance, responsiveness to irrigation and chemical fertilizers, resistance to salinity, and high protein content. The wild material of the Central Asian gene center is the world's potential source for drought-resistant species since populations grow here which are highly xerophytic: pubescent aerial organs, pigmentation of stem, high lodging, sometimes prostrate, or semi-erect bush, lanceolate, fewer leaves, slender but deeply penetrating root system, rhizomatous, etc. (Figures 12 and 13).

In the Central Asian gene center are found the endemic ecotypes of wild yellow alfalfa, which evolved in the hilly regions of Tien Shan, Altai, Dzhungarian-Alatau, and the desert-steppe belt of the northern Turan plain transitional province: Altai steppe, Altai foothills, Turgan floodplains, western Kazakhstan floodplains, Tien Shan foothills, Dzhungarian hilly, central Kazakhstan hummocky, northern Turan sandy, Zaisan floodplains, and eastern Tien Shan hilly region.

M. sativa L. subsp. *transoxana* (Vass.) Lub. is also found extensively in the Central Asian gene center, mostly in the plain belt, foothills, and lower chain of the mountains. In the upper belt of the hills where climatic conditions are more severe and the soil less fertile lies the region of localization

of *M. falcata* L. The entire intermediate belt of Tien Shan is occupied by
M. tianschanica Vass., the hybrid species whose phenotype, depending on

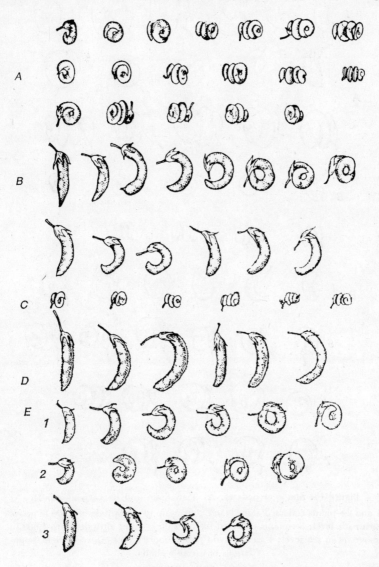

Figure 12. Shape of pods of : A) common, B) yellow, C) blue, D) South Kazakhstan, and E) Trautvetter's alfalfa.

1 and 2—wild populations growing in low-lying areas; 3—wild populations growing
in dry valleys.

Kazakh SSR, 1969–1977.

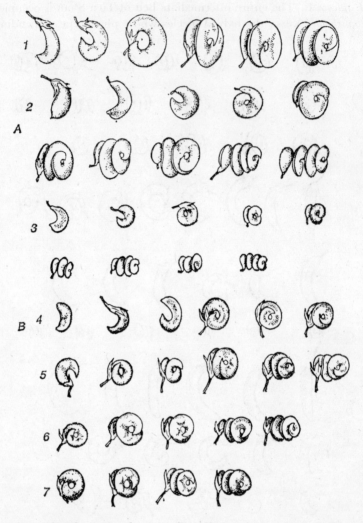

Figure 13. Shape of pods of: A) Tian Shan and B) variable alfalfa.
1 and 2—plants collected along water courses up to an altitude of 1,200 m above mean sea level; 3—plants collected in dry valleys at an altitude up to 1,600 m above mean sea level; 4 and 5—wild populations; 6 and 7—weedy field populations of variable alfalfa.
Kazakh SSR, 1969–1977.

growing conditions, manifests either in the direction of the blue-flowered parent (in which case the Tian Shan alfalfa is totally undistinguishable from the wild common alfalfa) or in the direction of the *falcata* type (dominance of characters of yellow-colored corolla and crescentoid pod). The main stock of genes of the interspecific hybrid is concentrated in the lower part of the slopes where *M. sativa* grows. This is facilitated to a great extent by the topography of the area which determines the direction of flow of genes, viz., altitude, wind, hydrological regime, and so forth.

M. tianschanica is a comparatively young, still unstabilized tetraploid taxon of hybrid origin, with some modicum of separate identity, which has been prematurely elevated to the rank of species.

Populations of the Tien Shan hilly interspecific hybrid, migrating downward and reaching the introgression belt located in the foothills, are actively involved in the recurring process of hybridization and back-crossing with the blue-flowered parent. The rich natural diversity of *sativa* forms of hybrid origin localized in the hilly valleys, lower chain of mountains, and foothills of Tien Shan accounts for the premature elevation to rank of species of many forms of hybrid origin, which do not have a separate distribution area and are barely distinguishable from one another.

The process of absorption of hybrid populations by one of the parental species, for which natural conditions are more favorable, is observed quite often in nature, especially if the initial species are in introgression (centers of introgression of alfalfa are discussed in greater detail later).

Compared with the first, hybrid forms are fewer in number, scattered in the hills, and due to the process of natural selection fix *falcata* characters in the progeny. The higher the altitude of their growing region and the more severe the conditions for growth, the greater the similarity of their phenotype to the yellow-flowered parent. Regularity of similar scattering of species is observed not only in the vertical belt, but also in extensive geographic regions. Rich botanical diversity of blue-flowered populations is evident in the much warmer western part of Tien Shan. Populations of *M. falcata* L. are distributed in the much higher eastern part of Tien Shan where the climate is severe, as well as in the hills north of eastern Tien Shan (Dzhungarian-Alatau, Altai, and Sayan).

Belov (1965), the oldest researcher of the genus *Medicago* L., emphasizes the phylogenetic proximity of *M. sativa* and other blue-flowered species of alfalfa of the Central Asian region, which have many morphological characters and economic properties in common. He writes that taking into consideration the presence of one geographic area of distribution of cultivated and wild hilly forms of Central Asia and the similarity of their morphological and biochemical variability, we should relate all the cultivated and wild perennial hilly forms of alfalfa distributed throughout the vast territory of southwestern Mongolia to southwestern Central Asia to one species, viz., *Medicago sativa* L. Zhukovskii (1971) has also come to the same conclusion, considering the Tian Shan alfalfa a botanical variety or subspecies of the common alfalfa.

Tian Shan alfalfa is not an independent species and no researcher can distinguish convincingly, on the basis of specific marked characters, wild *M. sativa* subsp. *transoxana* of the Central Asian region from the saturated, backcrossed, blue-flowered *M. tianschanica* or hybrid yellow, variegated hybrid, and blue hybrid forms of this alfalfa from *M. varia*, which is a product of hybridization of these very two initial species (*M. sativa* and *M. falcata*). All the basic specific taxonomic characters of *M. sativa* and *M. varia* on the one hand and those of *M. tianschanica* on the other, either coincide or are highly similar.

If we consider the composition of the species *M. sativa* vast, as done previously when the common alfalfa was considered a species complex and wild and cultivated forms with blue, violet, cherry, cream, white, and variegated corollas of different shades were included in it, then *M. tianschanica* with similar colored flowers, except for the less numerous yellow hybrid forms, can be entirely included in the species *M. sativa*. However, the presence of yellow hybrid forms in this species does not permit us to completely relate it to *M. sativa*.

Vasil'chenko (1949), the author of the taxon *M. tianschanica*, describes it as follows: corolla 8 to 10 mm long, variously colored (lavender-blue, purple, brown, blue-green, dull pink, dull yellow, etc.); pods with one or two twists. Based on the description of corolla coloration, there is no doubt that this is an interspecific hybrid. The same is fairly true of the blue hybrid, blue-variegated hybrid, variegated hybrid, and yellow hybrid forms of the species *M. varia*.

Kul'tiasov (1967), an expert on the genus *Medicago* L., also indicates the hybrid origin of Tian Shan alfalfa. Zhukovskii writes that the Tian Shan alfalfa is a mesophytic hilly subspecies (of *M. Sativa*—A.I.) and distinguished by diversity of corolla coloration (white, yellow, blue, green, red). Based on many years cytological and genetic research, Lesins and Gillies (1972) also relate *M. tianschanica* to *M. varia*. Thus all scientists unanimously agree on the hybrid origin of *M. tianschanica*, identifying its place among the species *M. varia*, which has the same genetic base and the same ploidy level.

Therefore, under natural conditions all tetraploid perennial blue-flowered populations of alfalfa of Central Asia should be related to *M. sativa* subsp. *transoxana*, and all variegated and yellow hybrid populations with the same ploidy level to *M. varia*.

In the intermediate zone between the Central Asian (V) and Indian (IV) centers of origin of cultivated plants (Tibet, Ladakh range) lies the region of localization of one of the most important biological characters of alfalfa, facilitating spontaneous manifestation of heterosis, i.e., cytoplasmic male sterility (CMS). Carriers of CMS from the former species of Ladakh alfalfa belonging to *M. sativa* subsp. *transoxana* (Vass.) Lub. have been identified in the Soviet Union, Canada, and Poland.

The Eurasian gene center of origin and formation of cultivated plants played a decisive part in the evolution of the genus *Medicago* L., first and foremost of the subgenus *Falcago*. Here evolved about 20 species, 13 of which were retained by Lubenets in his latest classification: *M. quasifalcata* Sinsk., *M. glandulosa* David., *M. coerulea* Less., *M. hemicycla* Grossh., *M. dzhavakhetica* Bord., *M. daghestanica* Rupr., *M. rupestris* Bieb., *M. sativa* L., *M. papillosa* Boiss., *M. falcata* L., *M. glutinosa* Bieb., *M. polychroa* Grossh., and *M. cancellata* Bieb.

Species of *Medicago* L. of all known ploidy groups are found here. However, the majority are diploid, indicating the much more ancient origin of this crop in this particular center. Barring a few exceptions, almost all alfalfa species of Central Asian origin are present in the working collection of the All-Union Institute of Plant Industry.

This gene center is not rich in annual alfalfas, although no one has seriously searched for them here. The natural specific potential of annuals in the Caucasian center appears to be much richer than presently known. It suffices to mention the neighboring Crimean region which we have related to the European-Siberian gene center. According to the schemes of Vavilov and Zhukovskii, it occupies an intermediate position between the Eurasian, Mediterranean, and European-Siberian gene centers. The vegetation of the Crimean region, which is closer to the Mediterranean flora, comprises 17 alfalfa species, 9 of which are annual.

Strictly endemic to Eurasia are: *M. quasifalcata* Sinsk., *M. glutinosa* Bieb., *M. cancellata* Bieb., *M. dzhavakhetica* Bord., *M. daghestanica* Rupr., and *M. papillosa* Boiss. The last species is found only in eastern Turkey and on the southern slopes of the hills of southwestern Armenia. This species is highly drought resistant but has no prospects as fodder.

The Eurasian-Trans-Caucasian gene center boasts a concentration of the global gene pool for self-fertility, nectar productivity, nonspecific soil requirements, ploidy level, protracted plant life span, sterility, and combining ability.

The European-Siberian gene center of origin of cultivated plants was only recently identified as a separate center, and is the primary one for *M. borealis* Grossh., *M. varia* Mart., and *M. falcata* L. (the Siberian and European floodplain-steppe ecotypes). *M. saxatilis* Bieb. is endemic to this center. This is the secondary gene center for another highly polymorphic young species, *M. lupulina* L., distributed in all plant communities of this center.

The European-Siberian gene center occupies an insignificant slot in the general phylogeny of the genus *Medicago* L. and represents a small wedge of time since the unique center of the subgenus *Falcago* that formed here is secondary; the ancestors of this subgenus came from the Eurasian and Central Asian gene centers. However, this center is presently exerting considerable influence on the process of breeding because on the periphery of area of distribution of *Medicago* L. and agriculture here one finds natural and anthropogenic microcenters or, to put it simply, genome variations (carriers of germplasm) of such important characters and properties of alfalfa as winter hardiness, cold resistance, resistance to flooding, perennial growth habit, resistance to trampling by cattle, rhizomatous roots, late maturation, long daylight requirement, pre-winter rosette formation, profuse foliage, high protein content, soft stem, nonuniform fruiting, ecological adaptation, resistance to root rot and powdery mildew, self-incompatibility, source of CMS, and high crossability.

According to Zhukovskii (1970, 1970a, 1970b), the European-Siberian gene center is the primary one for species phylogenetically close to alfalfa such as *Trigonella platycarpos* L., *T. ruthenica* L., and *T. korshinskyi* Grossh. Some researchers have wrongly related these species of *Trigonella* to the genus *Medicago* L. Their region of localization is confined to the hilly ranges of Altai and Sayan as well as the steppe and forest-steppe belt of Siberia and the very unique flora of the Far East.

It has been mentioned above that the European-Siberian center, especially the Crimean region, which is floristically linked with the Eurasian and Mediterranean centers, is rich with annual species of alfalfa. Here are found: *M. orbicularis* (L.) Bartalini, *M. scutellata* (L.) Mill., *M. rigidula* (L.) All., *M. agretis* Ten. ex DC, *M. saxatilis* Bieb., *M. arabica* (L.) Huds., *M. minima* (L.) Bartalini, *M. praecox* DC, *M. denticulata* Willd., *M. lupulina* L., *M. tuberculata* Willd., *M. laciniata* L., *M. murex* Willd., *M. intertexta* Mill., and *M. tornata* Mill.

Among the subgenus *Falcago* in the territory of the European-Siberian center are found: *M. sativa* L., *M. varia* Mart., *M. falcata* L., *M. borealis* Grossh., *M. trautvetteri* Sumn., *M. difalcata* Sinsk., *M. coerulea* Less., *M. marina* L., *M. prostrata* Jacq., *M. glandulosa* David., *M. rupestris* Bieb., and *M. saxatilis* Bieb.

Other centers of origin of cultivated plants are of interest as secondary, anthropogenic gene centers of the subgenus *Falcago* (Mediterranean, North American centers) or as microgene centers characterized by botanical diversity of a limited number of species and localization of characters important for plant breeding (Andean center). Secondary gene centers have played an important role in the evolution, breeding, and spread of cultivated forms of the species *M. varia* Mart. throughout the world. A rich botanical diversity of annual species is concentrated in Australia, where the secondary center of the subgenera *Orbicularia* and *Spirocarpos* formed. The primary center of annual species is no doubt situated in Asia Minor or Central and Middle Asia and confined to the hilly belt: Tibet—Tien Shan—Caucasus—Balkans.

Geographic areas of distribution of diploid, tetraploid, and hexaploid species in the Soviet Union. The spread of perennial species of alfalfa in the Central Asian, Eurasian, and southern part of the European-Siberian centers of origin of cultivated plants in the Soviet Union is shown in Figure 14.

The following peculiarities are evident in the given scheme of localization of alfalfa species:

1. Maximum concentration of species of the subgenus *Falcago* characteristic of the Eurasian gene center.

2. Most of the species localized in the Caucasian hills are diploid.

3. In the Eurasian center tetraploid species are found either at the bottom of hilly valleys or in the foothill belt of Stavropol' territory and Krasnodar region.

4. Hexaploid species within the Eurasian-Trans-Caucasian gene center are concentrated mostly in the plains of the territory constituting an intermediate belt between gene centers VI and IX. They usually occupy lands not suitable for agricultural reclamation (stony, pebbly, sandy) and with poor water-retention capacity.

5. Diploid species of *Medicago* grow in the Caucasus along slopes of mountain ranges along the coastal belt of the Caspian Sea among xerophytic vegetation of the foothill steppe.

6. Diploid species grow everywhere in the Eurasian-Trans-Caucasian center. Sometimes their area of distribution overlaps. However, many of them retain their natural separate geographic identity. For example, *M. coerulea* extends toward the Caspian basin forming two minute centers—Caspian desert-steppe center and coastal Azerbaidzhan center. *M. papillosa* grows in the southern part of Armenia. *M. quasifalcata* is found in northern Caucasus up to the Stavropol' uplands, including the latter and occupying riverine floodplains in the western half of the territory of northern Caucasus, i.e., closer to the Black Sea. *M. daghestanica* grows in the eastern half of the central part of the Caucasian range. *M. marina, M. rupestris,* and other diploid species have a separate geographic area of distribution. *M. coerulea, M. rupestris, M. marina, M. prostrata,* and *M. quasifalcata* are situated in the intermediate belt between centers VI and IX of origin of cultivated plants or on the periphery of center VI (the Caspian desert-steppe distribution area of blue alfalfa, Azov—Black

58

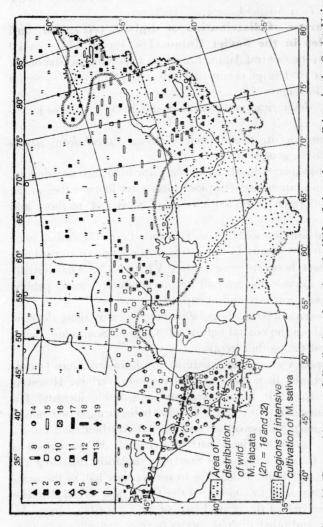

Figure 14. Geographic areas of distribution of species of alfalfa of the subgenus *Falcago* in the Soviet Union. I—area of cultivated and wild *M. varia* Mart.; II—area of cultivated and wild *M. sativa* L.: 1—*M. tianschanica* (2n=32); 2—*M. varia* (wild, 2n=32); 3—*M. glutinosa* (2n=32); 4—*M. polychroa* (2n=32); 5—*M. saxatilis* (2n=48); 6—*M. cancellata* (2n=48); 7—*M. rupestris* (2n=16); 8—*M. marina* (2n=16); 9—*M. coerulea* (2n=16); 10—*M. borealis* (2n=16); 11—*M. glandulosa* (2n=16); 12—*M. papillosa* (2n=16); 13—*M. prostrata* (2n=16); 14—*M. quasifalcata* (2n=16); 15—*M. difalcata* (2n=16); 16—*M. trautvetteri* (2n=16); 17—*M. hemicycla* (2n=16); 18—*M. daghestanica* (2n=16); 19—*M. dzhavakhetica* (2n=16).

Sea arid steppe distribution area of prostrate alfalfa, and so forth), and separated by the Caspian Sea.

7. In the Central Asian gene center, in contrast to the Eurasian center, in the hilly regions (midregion) a concentration of diploid species is not found, but rather their derivatives—phylogenetically much younger tetraploid species: *M. falcata* L., *M. varia* Mart., and *M. sativa* L.

8. Geographic areas of distribution of diploid species are situated far north in the intermediate belt between centers V and IX. *M. coerulea* Less., *M. difalcata* Sinsk., and *M. trautvetteri* Sumn. grow in the plain desert-steppe belt.

9. Diploid species of the Central Asian center have distinct separate areas of distribution: *M. coerulea* Less. has localized in the Caspian lowland of western Kazakhstan, *M. trautvetteri* Sumn. the Ustyurt zone situated west of the Mugodzhar hummocky territory, and *M. difalcata* Sinsk. in the central Kazakhstan desert hummocky belt and the southern half of the Semipalatinsk province.

10. The center of localization of the diploid species *M. borealis* Grossh. is situated on the northern periphery of the European-Siberian gene center. Along the southern border of this center, at the junction of gene centers V and VI, are distributed the diploid wild species of the subgenus *Falcago* and many annual species; they are especially evident in the European part of the USSR in the zone of contact of center IX with the Asia Minor, Trans-Caucasus, and Mediterranean centers.

Two highly polymorphic tetraploid species of alfalfa—*M. sativa* L. and *M. falcata* L.—often in competition with one another, are extensively found or cultivated in the Caucasus, the republics of Central Asia, and Kazakhstan. The first species has given rise in the extensive area of its natural growth and cultivation to several subgenera and groups of varietal types. The natural area of localization of this species in the east is restricted by the mountain ranges of the republics of Central Asia and southern Kazakhstan.

Eastern Tien Shan, Dzhungarian-Alatau, Altai, all of Siberia, and the Far East are areas of distribution of *M. falcata* L. At the junction of these two main species, which occurs in the steppe zone of the European part of the USSR (migration of *sativa* populations occurs from the Kazakh mountains to the north), desert-steppe belts of Kazakh SSR, and forest-steppe belts of Altai and Siberia, according to Bowden (1964 and 1966), Zhukovskii (1970), Ivanov (1973), and other researchers, introgressive hybridization takes place.

Role of intermediate territories in evolution and conservation of primary species. The center of introgressive hybridization is situated in the intermediate belt between centers V and VI in the south and

IX in the north, i.e., in the region of localization of hexaploid (Caucasian) and diploid (Kazakhstan) species of alfalfa with separate geographic areas of distribution. In this region, in Trans-Caucasus and Kazakh SSR, are found zones of spontaneous hybridization or strong, continually active centers of species formation and evolution which, regularly enriched by primary genetic material for the formation of new species and forms, maintain and rejuvenate it. Regions of introgressive hybridization are not merely minor centers of species formation and evolution, but rather centers of differentiation of species and interspecific taxa of alfalfa of the same or different ploidy levels. Unlike micro- and macrocenters, and primary and secondary gene centers of the origin of plants as established by Vavilov and Zhukovskii, these are local or area-specific centers of evolution organically linked with the classical centers.

In Kazakhstan, for example, several centers of introgressive hybridization have been discovered even though spontaneous hybridization between the two main species, *M. sativa* and *M. falcata*, occurs throughout the republic.

The regions of localization or local gene centers of individual wild species of alfalfa growing in the intermediate belt between centers V and IX within the territory of Kazakh SSR are concentrated in the Caspian lowland (*M. coerulea* Less.), Ustyurt plateau and Embensk sands (*M. trautvetteri* Sumn.), central Kazakhstan desert (*M. difalcata* Sinsk.), including the Semipalatinsk hummocks in the foothills of western Tien Shan (*M. tianschanica* Vass.), and hilly regions of Dzhungarian-Alatau and Saur-Tarbagatya, and the entire desert-steppe territory of the republic (*M. falcata* L.).

In the intermediate belt between centers VI and IX lie the centers of localization of *M. cancellata* Bieb., *M. saxatilis* Bieb., and *M. coerulea* Less., and in the southern steppe part of center IX, *M. falcata* L. The characteristic peculiarity of the entire intermediate belt is its arid climate.

Here per se, at the junction of the areas of *M. sativa* L. and *M. falcata* L., is situated the natural growth area of *M. varia* Mart. This polymorphic hybrid species not only maintains its area of distribution under natural conditions of the intermediate belt but also under rainfed conditions, and occupies the steppe region of the European part of the USSR, the entire highly arid zone of Kazakhstan right up to the foothills of Tien Shan, and the severe (climatewise) forest-steppe zone of Siberia extending up to the taiga belt of Yakutia and the Far East.

Along the border of centers V and IX yellow alfalfa has degenerated notably and formed local yet large groups of ecotypes, which are morphologically quite distinct from each other and confined to a definite territory: hilly belt of central and eastern Tien Shan—the alatau group of ecotypes (*alatavica*), hilly belt of Altai and southern Siberia—the Siberian group (*sibirica*), desert-steppe belt of the extensive territory of Kazakh-stan and southern Ural (northern Turan plain floristic province)—the Turanian group of ecotypes (*turanica*), and so forth.

Hence the vast intermediate territory between the southern Central Asian and Eurasian-Trans-Caucasian centers of origin of plants and the northern European-Siberian center extending from the foothills of Tien Shan to the forest-steppe belt in the north is of particular interest to resear-chers from the viewpoint of the further evolution of the genus *Medicago* L. On the one hand it is the center of localization of hexa- and diploid species, and the center of active formation and differentiation of species (which cannot be said of the hilly belt of the Central Asian center), and on the other hand it is a region of slow but annually increasing assimila-tion of the barely dispersed hexaploid and diploid species of alfalfa by the tetraploid species: *M. sativa* L., *M. falcata* L., *M. varia* Mart., *M. polychroa* Grossh., and *M. glutinosa* Bieb.

Under the influence of civilization the local gene centers of rare species degenerate quickly; their naturalness is disturbed and they gradually disappear. In the context of major transformations in the national eco-nomy, especially large-scale construction of irrigation systems, dams, laying of gas and oil pipelines, and geological undertakings that involve extensive earthworks, the process of disruption of the natural plant canopy will be increasing significantly every year. To conserve centers of locali-zation of rare species of alfalfa in regions of their active formation and differentiation, it is necessary to establish sanctuaries or protected areas and to enforce strict control over the work of these sanctuaries with the help of the Society for the Conservation of Nature.

To date it has remained a mystery why the diploid species of *Medicago* L. in the Eurasian-Trans-Caucasian center have localized in the moun-tains of Caucasus, while those in the Central Asian center have settled in the plains of the vast Turan lowland. Why have the hilly areas of Tien Shan, the Dzhungarian-Alatau, and Altai been occupied by tetraploid species of the subgenus *Falcago* and not by diploid species as in center VI ?

In noting the distribution of perennial species of alfalfa in centers of origin of cultivated plants we became aware of the fact that the classical centers of Vavilov and Zhukovskii are not always concomitantly the centers of botanical diversity and species formation. If the Eurasian-Trans-Cauca-sian center is the geographic region, center of species formation, and center of botanical diversity, then the Central Asian is just a geographic concept. This center is not distinguished for botanical diversity of species of the sub-genus *Falcago*, since they are mainly located in the foothills and plains of the vast (intermediate) territory of Kazakhstan, where the processes of introgressive hybridization are going on intensely, and where centers of species formation are maximum.

The Central Asian center is the largest center of botanical diversity of annual species, but the subgenus *Falcago* in the hills of Tien Shan is represented by only three species of the tetraploid series, which are extensively found under both natural and irrigated conditions—*M. sativa, M. falcata,* and *M. varia*. These are phylogenetically young species comparatively speaking, especially the last one.

Considering the fact that for many crops the Eurasian center is simultaneously the center of origin and center of botanical diversity, and that the processes of natural hybridization (the region of active species formation) are intensely active in the hilly valleys and foothill zone of northern Caucasus, one may assume that this center, more precisely the Caucasian section, is the only primary center of origin of alfalfa, including even *M. sativa*.

If we consider the Eurasian-Trans-Caucasian center the primary center of origin of *Medicago,* then this center must have been brought under cultivation polyphyletically, i.e., simultaneously through different channels independent of each other. It is quite possible that cultivation did not take place first in the Caucasus, but somewhere in southwest or Central Asia, perhaps simultaneously at both places. The problem of the introduction of alfalfa for cultivation is more complex and baffling than the establishment of the actual fact of its primary origin.

Centers of localization of gene pools of important breeding characters of alfalfa. Knowledge of such centers should help breeders in critically evaluating their initial material and correct selection of parental forms for the development of high-yielding varieties (Table 4).

It is evident from Table 4 that the Soviet Union is the main area of gene pools of important biological characters and properties of alfalfa. Plant breeders in various countries, especially the USA and Canada, who have achieved remarkable success in the development of high-yielding, disease-resistant, cold-tolerant, drought-resistant, and early-maturing varieties of alfalfa for intensive agriculture, as well as late-maturing, rhizomatous varieties of the pasture type with prolonged use (perennial), have long appreciated the economic importance of the wild species, ancient populations, and improved varieties of the Soviet Union. Until recently the entire alfalfa-breeding program in the USA was conducted using our Turkestan alfalfa or varieties genetically related to this ancient population. All the varieties of the rhizomatous type developed in Canada have been produced from the wild yellow alfalfa introduced in 1931 from Siberia.

Table 4. Centers of localization of gene pools of important promising biological characters of alfalfa species according to centers of origin of cultivated plants identified by Vavilov and Zhukovskii

Character	Center number (per Zhukovskii)	Region	Country, province, zone, geographic region, state, etc.
1	2	3	4
Alfalfa of subgenus *Falcago*			
Ploidy level	V, VI, V–IX, VI–IX	Soviet Union	Caucasus, Kazakhstan, republics of Central Asia, Lower Volga region
Cold resistance	V–IX, IX	Soviet Union	Western and eastern Siberia, Far East, northern and central Kazakhstan
Drought resistance	V, VI, IX	Soviet Union	Western Tien Shan, Kazakhstan, northern Caucasus, Southeast
	V, I–V, I–IV, V–VI	China	Western China
Early maturity		Southwest Asia	Iranian foothills, Kopet Dag, Afghanistan
	V, I–V	China	Sin'tszyan-Uigur (autonomous region), Khebei, Shanxi
Disease resistance	IX	Soviet Union	Eastern Siberia, northern Caucasus, central Kazakhstan
Longevity	XII	USA	Kansas, Wisconsin, Nevada, California
	V–IX, VI–IX, IX	Soviet Union	Western and eastern Siberia, Southeast, northern Caucasus, Kazakhstan
Common alfalfa, *M. sativa* L.			
Early maturity	VI–VII, VIII	Arabian east	Mesopotamia, Syrian foothills, south of Arabian peninsula

(Contd.)

Table 4 (*Contd.*)

1	2	3	4
	V, I–IV, IV–V	China	Sin'tszyan-Uigur, Tibet (autonomous regions), Khebei, Shanxi
	V, IX	Soviet Union	Republics of Central Asia and Trans-Caucasus (Tashkent-721 and 3192, Azerbaidzhan-262)
	XI	South and Central America	Peru, Mexico
Multiple cuttings, responsive to irrigation	VI, VI–VII	Near and Middle East	Irrigated lands of Arabian countries
	IV	India	Bombay, Hyderabad, Bangalore, Punjab
	X, XI	South and Central America	Mexico, Ecuador, Paraguay, Uruguay
	V	Soviet Union	Irrigated lands of republics of Central Asia and Trans-Caucasus
Heat resistance	V–VI	Southwest Asia	Iranian foothills, Kopet Dag, Afghanistan
	V–IX	Soviet Union	Kara-Kalpak ASSR, republics of Central Asia
Resistance to diseases of stems and leaves	XII	USA	Kansas, Wisconsin, California
	I–V, I–IV	China	Sin'tszyan-Uigur, Tibet, Inner Mongolia (autonomous regions)
Resistance to root rots	VI	Asia Minor	Turkey
	V, VI	Soviet Union	Korezmsk oasis, Trans-Caucasus
Salt tolerance	V, VI	Soviet Union	Central Asia and Azerbaidzhan (local varieties of the republic)
	V–VI	Iran	Teheran, Shiraz, Kermanshah
	V	Afghanistan	Gerat, Kabul, Kandhar

	VI, VIII	Middle East	Mesopotamia, south of Arabian peninsula
	V	China	Sin'tszyan-Uigur
Seed productivity	V, VI–IX, IX	Soviet Union	Republics of Central Asia, Trans-Caucasus, Ukraine, northern Caucasus (varieties)
	V, I–IV	China	Sin'tszyan-Uigur, Tibet (autonomous regions), Khebei, Shanxi
—	VI, VI–VII, VIII	Arabian east	Mesopotamia, Midian foothills, Yemen Arab Republic, People's Democratic Republic of Yemen
Yield of green mass	VI, VI–VII, VIII	Arabian east	Mesopotamia
	V	Soviet Union	Central Asia, Trans-Caucasus, Ukraine, northern Caucasus (varieties)
Foliage	IX	West Europe	France, Spain, England, Sweden
	I	China	Inner Mongolia
	VI, X	Soviet Union	Republics of Central Asia and Trans-Caucasus
Carriers of CMS (local material)	XII	North America	USA, Canada
	VI, IX	Soviet Union	Trans-Caucasus
	IX	East Europe	Poland, Bulgaria, Rumania, Hungary
	IV–V	Central Asia	Tibet (Ladakh range)
Crossability	X, XI	South America	Ecuador, Mexico, Peru, Chile (local varieties)
	XII	North America	USA and Canada (improved varieties)
	IV–VI, VIII–X, XII	Soviet Union	Republics of Central Asia and Trans-Caucasus (varieties)
	VI, VII, VIII	Arabian east, Mediterranean	Iraq, Egypt, Sudan, Libya
	IX	Europe	France

Variable alfalfa, *M. varia* Mart.

Cold resistance	IX	Soviet Union	Western and eastern Siberia, northern Kazakhstan
Drought resistance	IX	Soviet Union	Southeast, northern and central Kazakhstan

(Contd.)

Table 4 (*Contd.*)

1	2	3	4
Disease resistance	XII	USA	Kansas, Wisconsin, Nevada
	IV–V	India	Jammu and Kashmir
	IX	Soviet Union	Western and eastern Siberia
Longevity (perennial growth habit)	IX	Soviet Union	Western and eastern Siberia, Ural'sk, Central Chernozem province
Late maturity	IX	Soviet Union	Eastern Siberia, Far East
Foliage	IX	Soviet Union	Ukraine, Central Chernozem province
Winter hardiness	IX	Soviet Union	Eastern and western Siberia, Central Chernozem province
Seed productivity	XII	USA	Central and northern states
Yield of green mass	IX	Soviet Union	Ukraine SSR, Central Chernozem province, Volga Basin
	XII	East Europe, North America	Hungary, Czechoslovakia, Canada, USA
	IX	Soviet Union	Western Siberia, Ukraine. Central Chernozem province
Crossability	XII	Canada	Ottawa, Ontario, Saskachewan
	V, IX	Soviet Union	Northern Caucasus, Ukraine
Carriers of CMS (local material)	IX	Soviet Union	Central Chernozem province, central regions of Nechernozem zone of the Soviet Union

Yellow alfalfa, *M. falcata* L.

1	2	3	4
Cold resistance	V, IX	Soviet Union	Southeast, western and eastern Siberia, northern and eastern Kazakhstan
Drought resistance	V, VI, IX	Soviet Union	Southeast, central Kazakhstan

Disease resistance	V, VI, IX	Soviet Union	Northern regions of northern Caucasus, Siberia, Kazakhstan, Baltic Republics
Salt tolerance	IX	Soviet Union	Desert zones of Kazakhstan (wild forms)
Resistance to trampling and grazing	V, VI, IX	Soviet Union	Western and central Kazakhstan, Tien Shan, Kalmyts ASSR, Baltic Republics
Resistance to flooding	IX	Soviet Union	Floodplains of Ob', Irtysh, Oka, Mologa Rivers
Perennial growth	V, VI, IX	Soviet Union	Western and eastern Siberia, Southeast, northern Caucasus
Rhizomatous roots	V–VI, VI–IX	Soviet Union	Western Siberia, Kazakhstan
Late maturity	IX	Soviet Union	Western and eastern Siberia, north European part of the USSR

Trautvetter's alfalfa, *M. trautvetteri* Summ.

Grazing resistance	IX	Soviet Union	Western Kazakhstan (Ustyurt)
Winter hardiness and drought resistance	V, IX	Soviet Union	Western Kazakhstan
Duration of flowering	IX	Soviet Union	Western Kazakhstan (Ustyurt)
Perennial growth habit	V, IX	Soviet Union	Western and central Kazakhstan

Southern Kazakhstan alfalfa, *M. difalcata* Sinsk.

Winter hardiness	IX	Soviet Union	Central Kazakhstan
Drought resistance	IX	Soviet Union	Central Kazakhstan hummocky region, Tarbagatai
Pubescence of pods	IX	Soviet Union	Central Kazakhstan hummocky region, Tarbagatai

Varicolored alfalfa, *M. polychroa* Grossh.

Resistance to stem and leaf diseases	VI	Soviet Union	Foothill regions of Georgia, Armenia, and northern Caucasus
Foliage	VI	Soviet Union	Northern Caucasus

(Contd.)

Table 4 (*Contd.*)

1	2	3	4
Tian Shan alfalfa, *M. tianschanica* Vass.			
Winter hardiness	V	Soviet Union	Eastern Tien Shan
	IV–V	India	Jammu and Kashmir
Disease resistance	V	Soviet Union	Western Tien Shan
Drought resistance	V	Soviet Union	Western Tien Shan
Crescentoid alfalfa, *M. quasifalcata* Sinsk.			
Resistance to root rot	VI–IX	Soviet Union	Northern Caucasus
Perennial growth habit	VI–IX	Soviet Union	Northern Caucasus
Northern alfalfa, *M. borealis* Grossh.			
Resistance to trampling	IX	Soviet Union	Floodplain haylands and pastures of Nechernozem zone of the Soviet Union
Winter hardiness	IX	Soviet Union	Floodplain haylands and pastures of Nechernozem zone of the Soviet Union
Resistance to fungal disease	IX	Soviet Union	Nechernozem zone of European part of the USSR (floodplain haylands and pastures)
Foliage	IX	Soviet Union	Nechernozem zone of European part of the USSR (floodplain haylands and pastures)
Blue alfalfa, *M. coerulea* Less.			
Resistance to flooding	IX	Soviet Union	Volga, Ural, Uil, Sagyz, Khobda, and other rivers (floodplain haylands and pastures)
Salt tolerance	IX	Soviet Union	Caspian lowland

Disease resistance	IX	Soviet Union	Kazakhstan, Dagestan
Drought resistance	IX	Soviet Union	Western Kazakhstan
Cold resistance	IX	Soviet Union	Western Kazakhstan
Foliage	IX	Soviet Union	Caspian lowland
Seed productivity	IX	Soviet Union	Caspian lowland

Note: Dash between numbers of centers represents intermediate territory between classical centers of N.I. Vavilov and P.M. Zhukovskii.

CHAPTER II

Alfalfa in World Agriculture: Achievements and Methods of Breeding

AREA OF DISTRIBUTION OF CULTIVATED AND WILD SPECIES

The natural distribution of perennial species of alfalfa is restricted by Eurasia and extends north and south in the hilly belt along the Pyrenees—Alps—Balkans—foothills of Asia Minor—Caucasus—Tien Shan (Pamir, Tibet). According to Sinskaya (1950) only a few species enter temperate eastern Asia and the northern forest provinces of Europe and Asia. The hilly belt constituted the ancient Mediterranean province. Soviet researchers of the genus *Medicago* (A.A. Grossgeim, I.T. Vasil'chenko, E.N. Sinskaya, P.M. Zhukovskii, A.I. Belov, M.V. Kul'tiasov, P.A. Lubenets, M.I. Tarkovskii, O.Kh. Khasanov, A.M. Konstantinova, and others) usually consider this region the classical natural area of distribution of the genus. It falls in the zone of 40° L, which once again confirms the hypothesis concerning the antiquity of introduction of alfalfa for cultivation in the region of its natural growth. According to V.L. Komarova the region of the most ancient crops lies between 20° and 40° N and ascends to 2,500 m above mean sea level. The aforementioned belt is characterized by subtropical climate and is the region of the most ancient civilizations living a settled mode of life.

The most widespread perennial species of alfalfa are found within this classical area: *M. sativa*—from the Balkan Peninsula in the west to the foothills of Dzhungarian-Alatau and Tibet in the east; *M. varia* Mart.—steppe and forest-steppe zone of Eurasia; *M. falcata* L.—universal in the Old World (within the limits of the common area of the genus *Medicago*) including hilly massifs and the taiga zone; *M. tianschanica* Vass.—hilly belt of middle and Central Asia; *M. coerulea* Less.—steppe and semidesert regions of the Caspian; *M. borealis* Grossh.—taiga zone of Eurasia; *M. difalcata* Sinsk.—arid belt of Asia; and *M. hemicycla* Grossh.—the Caucasus.

The geographic area of cultivation of alfalfa is much more extensive (Figure 15). It covers all the civilized regions of the world. In the Old

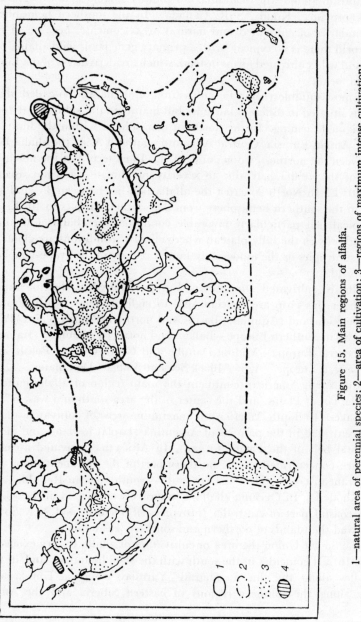

Figure 15. Main regions of alfalfa.

1—natural area of perennial species; 2—area of cultivation; 3—regions of maximum intense cultivation; 4—northern centers of cultivation.

World cultivated phytocenoses extend far north, beyond the limits of natural habitats of alfalfa (the Scandinavian countries, Kola Peninsula, Arkhangel'sk province, Komi ASSR, Canada). In the southern hemisphere the boundaries of cultivated and natural areas coincide, because in the New World there is no typical (with a primary gene pool) wild alfalfa, but weedy and wild cultivated forms instead, which are derivatives of the Eurasian wild forms.

The most suitable region for cultivation of alfalfa, the so-called alfalfa belt, is situated in different latitudes but mainly in the subtropical zone with irrigated farming. In the northern hemisphere, within the limits of Europe, Africa, Eurasia, Central Asia and southern Asia, the alfalfa belt lies between the northern tropics and 50° L. In eastern Asia the northern border of the alfalfa belt, due to severity of climate, does not ascend above 40° L. In North America the alfalfa belt lies between 35° and 50° N, but in the southern hemisphere from the southern tropics to 40° L. In the tropical belt particularly favorable conditions for alfalfa cultivation are found only in the hilly plateau where climatic conditions are closer to the dry subtropics or the moderately humid regions of the grape-vine belt of the world.

Alfalfa is cultivated throughout Europe. However, the maximum areas under this crop are concentrated in eight centers: two in France —Garonne lowland (Aquitaine Basin) and northern French plains (Paris Basin), two in southern Europe—Balkan and northern Apennine (Italian), two in central Europe—Middle Danube and Czech-Greater Polish, and two in eastern Europe—Azov—Black Sea and Volga—Don plains.

In the North American continent the main region of alfalfa cultivation is the Great Plains, and the center of the area south and west of the Great Lakes. In South America the maximum areas of cultivated alfalfa are concentrated in the pampas of Argentina (Laplat lowland and along the coastal belt of the Pacific Ocean). In Africa the cultivated areas of alfalfa are concentrated in the northern part of the continent along the Mediterranean coast and in the far south—South African Republic and South Rhodesia. In Oceania alfalfa is intensively cultivated in the southeastern coastal part of Australia (provinces of Victoria and New South Wales) and the islands of northern and southern Tasmania.

In the Soviet Union the area of cultivation of alfalfa is very extensive (Figure 16). It coincides in the south with the state boundary and in the north lies along the line Leningrad—Yaroslav'—Perm'—Tomsk, and farther along the southern regions of eastern Siberia and the Amur region.

In the taiga zone alfalfa penetrates into small areas. For example, in the European part of the RSFSR it is cultivated in Komi ASSR, and the

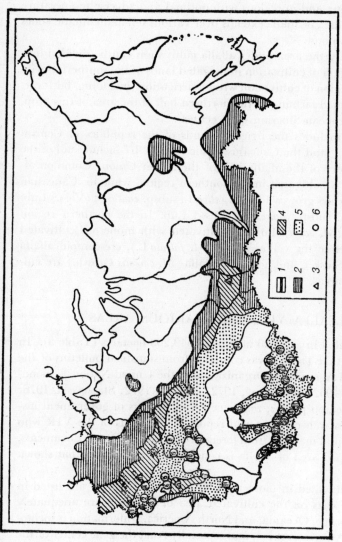

Figure 16. Schematic map of areas of cultivation and regions of commercial seed production of alfalfa in the Soviet Union.

1—northern border of cultivation; 2—zone of unstable seed production according to temperature regime or excessive humidity; 3—centers of stable commercial seed production without irrigation; 4—zone of seed production without irrigation; 5—zone of unstable seed production due to moisture deficiency; 6—centers of commercial seed production under irrigation.

Circled numbers—centers of origin of local varieties.

Leningrad and Arkhangel'sk provinces; in eastern Siberia—the lower reaches of the Angara River and Yakutian ASSR (see Figures 15 and 16).

The wide ecological plasticity of alfalfa allows its cultivation not only on irrigated lands, but very arid lands under conditions of adequate and excessive humidity, and in regions with optimal and adverse temperature regimes, i.e., the area of alfalfa extends over various soil and climatic zones and plant associations.

Conventionally the area under alfalfa cultivation can be divided into two parts: a) region of cultivation in irrigated lands of the southern Soviet Union, and b) region of cultivation without irrigation (including, however, the zone of irrigated farming in the northern half of the area of this crop, namely, the European-Siberian gene center).

Region "a" includes the irrigated lands of the republics of Central Asia, Kazakhstan, and the Caucasus, while region "b" includes all of the remaining territory of the alfalfa belt of the Soviet Union. Common alfalfa (*M. sativa*) is cultivated in the southern region, while its Caucasian and Asian subspecies grow wild—*M. sativa* L. subsp. *caucasica* (Vass.) Lub. and *M. sativa* L. subsp. *transoxana* (Vass.) Lub. In the northern region variable alfalfa (*M. varia* Mart.) is cultivated with numerous cultivated varietal types. Here the yellow alfalfa (*M. falcata* L.), crescentoid alfalfa (*M. quasifalcata* Sinsk.), and northern alfalfa (*M. borealis* Grossh.) are cultivated in small areas.

ALFALFA YIELDS IN VARIOUS AREAS

Alfalfa is cultivated in a global area of 33,649,200 hectares (Table 5). In spite of the fact that Table 5 was compiled from statistical bulletins of the FAO (Food and Agriculture Organization of the United Nations), monographs (Bolton, 1962; Maslinkov, 1972; Hanson, 1972; Staszewski, 1976; and others), research papers, reference books, reports of government institutions and research centers, field reports of scientists of the VIR who had collected initial material from foreign countries, and other documents, the world cropped area of alfalfa is considerably more than that shown here.

Alfalfa is cultivated in more than 80 countries (only 44 are listed in the Table). Reports on the cultivated area of this crop are adequately complete for Europe, Oceania, and North America. Information is incomplete for Latin America, Africa, and especially Asia, the gene center of the genus *Medicago* L., center of introduction of alfalfa for cultivation, and the region of extensive spread of the genus under natural conditions and for cultivation.

The maximum cultivated areas of alfalfa are concentrated in North

Table 5. Country and continent-wise cropped areas of alfalfa
(in thousand hectares)

Continent, country	According to Klinkowski, 1933		According to Bolton, 1962	According to Hanson, 1972	Calculated from latest reports
	1926	1929			
1	2	3	4	5	6
Europe				5,988.0	6,128.1
Austria	1.7	39.1	71.8	45.0	52.6
Belgium	12.7	9.1	13.0	7.0	10.3
Bulgaria	9.7	9.7	—	200.0	400.0
Great Britain	19.0	14.5	39.2	15.0	23.4
Hungary	175.5	151.5	192.0	326.0	398.0
German Democratic Republic	—	—	—	73.0	73.0
Greece	—	—	45.3	180.0	147.8
Denmark	32.1	15.2	24.6	18.0	22.6
Spain	75.3	77.3	118.5	200.0	188.9
Italy	599.0	—	965.0	1,977.0	1,716.0
Luxembourg	—	5.4	4.0	1.0	1.2
The Netherlands	3.2	2.7	7.1	7.0	7.0
Norway	—	—	1.6	—	1.5
Poland	1.2	—	80.0	244.0	250.0
Rumania	102.5	150.1	—	445.0	473.4
France	1,142.0	1,135.0	1,585.0	1,437.0	1,583.8
Federal Republic of Germany	272.0	285.0	—	101.0	101.0
Czechoslovakia	—	107.9	173.0	281.0	272.5
Switzerland	—	11.4	28.0	37.0	37.0
Sweden	7.7	—	20.0	15.0	18.0
Yugoslavia	5.4	64.4	151.0	359.0	350.1
North and Central America				13,142.0	13,502.1
Canada	364.0	323.9	547.0	1,989.0	2,202.0
Mexico	4.7	47.3	55.0	160.0	154.8
USA	4,570.0	—	9,870.0	10,993.0	11,145.3
South America				7,800.0	7,251.8
Argentina	7,900.0	5,830.0	10,040.0	7,500.0	6,882.6
Brazil	—	35.0	26.9	26.0	27.0
Bolivia	—	—	—	9.0	12.0
Paraguay	—	—	2.0	—	2.0
Peru	—	—	—	123.0	135.2
Uruguay	5.1	—	17.1	28.0	28.0
Chile	5.3	—	106.0	84.0	135.0

(*Contd.*)

Table 5 (*Contd.*)

1	2	3	4	5	6
Ecuador	—	—	25.0	30.0	30.0
Asia				198.0	205.3
Israel	—	—	4.1	3.0	4.3
India	—	—	16.2	21.0	20.9
Iran	—	—	—	100.0	100.0
Mongolia	—	—	—	—	1.2
Turkey	—	—	—	74.0	78.9
Africa				174.0	173.7
Algeria	—	—	—	—	5.9
South Rhodesia	—	—	—	2.0	2.0
Tunisia	—	—	—	—	2.0
South African Republic	—	—	—	172.0	163.8
Australia and Oceania				1,213.0	1,253.9
Australia	6.9	—	426.0	1,133.0	1,173.9
New Zealand	—	12.5	39.1	80.0	80.0
Soviet Union	200.0	260.0	4,050.0	4,500.0	5,134.3
Total				33,015.0	33,649.2

and South America—20,753,900 hectares or 61.6% of the entire world area. Minimum areas are found in the African and Asian continents—173,700 and 205,300 hectares respectively.

In the African region data on the cultivated areas under alfalfa is not available for ten countries, including Egypt, Morocco, Libya, Ethiopia, Sudan, Botswana, and Lesotho.

There is no data available on the cultivated areas of alfalfa in the large alfalfa-growing countries of Asia (China, Afghanistan, Syria, Iraq, Pakistan) nor for the states of the Arabian Peninsula.

In Central America the cultivated areas of alfalfa are not known for Salvador, Honduras, Cuba, Panama, Guatemala, Nicaragua, and Costa Rica. In South America alfalfa is extensively cultivated in Colombia and Venezuela. Yet for these countries as well as Guyana, Surinam, Guiana and other states of the continent, no information on the cultivated areas of alfalfa is available.

In Europe alfalfa is cultivated in an area of 6,128,000 hectares. However, information is not available on the area of alfalfa cultivation in Portugal, Albania, and Finland. Because the areas under alfalfa cultivation

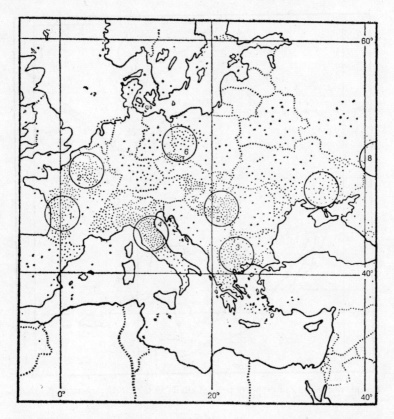

Figure 17. Density of cropped areas of alfalfa in Europe (here and in Figures 18, 19, and 20 one dot corresponds to 4,000 hectares; cited from C.H. Hanson, 1972).

Centers of intensive cultivation of alfalfa.

1—Garonne lowland (Aquitaine Basin); 2—northern French plains (Paris Basin); 3—Balkans; 4—northern Apennine (Italian); 5—Middle Danube; 6—Czech-Greater Polish; 7—Azov—Black Sea; 8—Volga—Don plain.

in these countries, especially Albania and Finland are not large, we may consider that the European continent is adequately represented in this book.

If one takes into consideration the fact that Table 5 includes no data on the areas of alfalfa cultivation for a number of leading alfalfa-growing countries in Asia, Africa, and Latin America, and more than 30 small countries in the world, then it is obvious that the figure 33,649,200 hectares is an underestimation. According to my calculations, with due consideration for the aforesaid, the total cultivated area of alfalfa in the world is

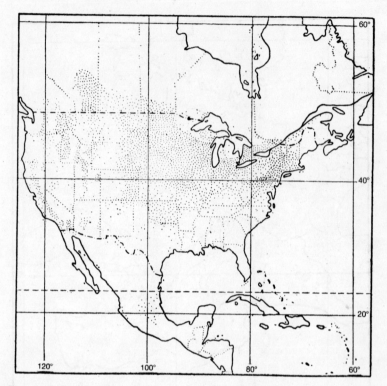

Figure 18. Density of cropped areas of alfalfa in the North American continent.

not less than 35,000,000 hectares.[1] The density of cultivated areas in different countries and continents and the regions of maximum intensive cultivation of this crop are shown in Figures 17 to 20.

In the Soviet Union the cropped area under alfalfa in arable lands is 5,134,300 hectares,[2] of which 4,610,000 hectares are harvested for hay and 520,000 for seed. Most of the area for hay is situated in the RSFSR (54%), Kazakh SSR (16%), and Ukrainian SSR (14%). These three republics account for more than 84% of the area under alfalfa for hay. They are

[1]At present no one in the world has exact data on the cultivated areas of alfalfa and alfalfa mixtures. Collecting such information is hindered by the fact that many states do not conduct statistical surveys of cropped areas of several perennial grasses, do not take into consideration the areas under cultivated haylands and pastures, and do not indicate the specific composition of grass mixtures.

[2]The total area under alfalfa cultivation in the Soviet Union, taking into consideration its cultivation outside fields of crop rotation (natural fodder lands, grazing limans, eroded lands, ridges, gullies, slopes of hilly haylands and pastures, saline lands, etc.), considerably exceeds 5,100,000 hectares and comprises not less than 6,000,000 hectares.

Figure 19. Distribution of cropped areas of alfalfa in the South American continent.

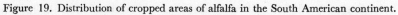

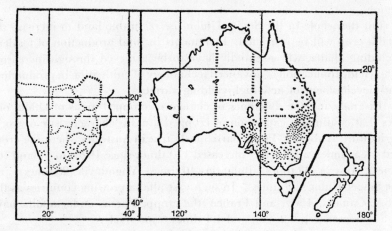

Figure 20. Density of cropped areas of alfalfa in South Africa, Australia, and New Zealand.

followed by: Uzbek SSR (5.7%), Kirgiz SSR (3.1%), Azerbaidzhan SSR (2.2%), Tadzhik SSR (1.3%), Moldavian SSR (1.3%), and Turkmenian SSR (1.0%). Less than 1.5% of the area for hay is in the Baltic republics (0.5%), Georgian SSR (0.4%), Armenian SSR (0.3%), and Belorussian SSR (0.03%).

The area of alfalfa harvested for seed is likewise unevenly distributed in the various republics. Of the 520,000 hectares harvested for seed in 1975, the RSFSR accounted for 56%, Ukrainian SSR—16.4%, Kazakh SSR—16%, Uzbek SSR—4.1%, and Kirgiz SSR—2.4%. All the remaining republics (Tadzhik SSR, Turkmenian SSR, and Trans-Caucasus, Georgian SSR, Armenian SSR, Azerbaidzhan SSR) where agroclimatic conditions are especially favorable for high seed yields in irrigated lands, accounted for just 5.0% of the harvested area of seed crop.

In the RSFSR in 1975 alfalfa occupied 2,729,500 hectares or 53% of the total cropped area in the country. Within this republic the main cropped areas are located in the southern part of the forest-steppe zone. The regions of maximum intensive cultivation of alfalfa are northern Caucasus, Volga Basin, and the Central Chernozem. Other cropped areas in descending order are: Ural Nonchernozem Zone of the RSFSR, western Siberia, eastern Siberia, and Primor'e.

In the Ukraine the maximum cropped areas under alfalfa are concentrated in the southern and eastern provinces. In Kazakhstan rainfed crops occur in the north in the grain belt, while irrigated crops of alfalfa are raised in the south in the zone of irrigated farming. In the republics of Central Asia and Trans-Caucasus alfalfa is cultivated mainly under irrigation and only insignificant rainfed areas are situated in the high hilly regions.

On the whole in the Soviet Union use of arable land to increase the alfalfa crop will be restricted. Increments in total production of fodders, including alfalfa, will essentially have to be achieved through increasing crop yield, application of advanced technology of cultivation in production, and development of new high-yielding varieties.

In analyzing the dynamics of change of cropped areas of alfalfa one sees that continuous expansion of cropped areas is characteristic of world agriculture (Table 5). This is particularly true in Australia where the cropped area under alfalfa has increased 170 times since 1926, in Poland (66 times), Austria (42 times), Bulgaria (40 times), Yugoslavia (28 times), and the Soviet Union (25 times). In such vast alfalfa-growing countries as the USA, Canada, Italy, and France, the cropped areas under alfalfa have also increased 2.4, 6.2, 2.8, and 1.4 times respectively.

However, a comparison of later data reveals a reduction in cropped areas in some countries. J. Bolton (1962), for example, points out that in

1950 to 1955 alfalfa occupied 10,040,000 hectares in Argentina. Presently, as a result of severe aphid (pulgou) epizooties the area has reduced to 3,882,000 hectares. A tendency toward further reduction of cropped area under alfalfa has been observed in that country.

In most of the developed alfalfa-growing countries the area under alfalfa has presently stabilized. Active expansion of cropped area is characteristic mainly of countries in northern and eastern Europe, which is linked with further advancement of the crop north and east. No doubt the new area of distribution of alfalfa is the result of its introduction and planned breeding.

The average hay yields of alfalfa (quintals/hectare) in different regions of the world (data for 1967 to 1974) are given below (asterisk denotes cultivation on irrigated lands):

Europe		Bolivia	180.0*
Austria	94.1*	Brazil	72.2
Belgium	109.5*	Mexico	61.8*
Bulgaria	24.8	Peru	131.0*
	100.3*	USA	28.9
			69.2*
Great Britain	48.5	Chile	27.1
Hungary	44.2	Asia	
Greece	96.7*	Israel	78.9*
Spain	200.0*	India	87.5*
Rumania	36.6	Turkey	78.2*
France	74.7	Africa	
FRG	81.2*	South Rhodesia	200.0
Yugoslavia	62.5	South African	
Australia	57.6	Republic	195.0*
Americas		Soviet Union	21.6
Argentina	79.8		57.2*

It is very difficult to calculate the average productivity of alfalfa in the world and there is hardly any need to do so. In some countries it is cultivated in irrigated lands only, in others under rainfed conditions, and in some countries with and without irrigation.

Common alfalfa is the crop responsive to irrigation. Its maximum productivity—more than 150 quintals of hay per hectare—is characteristic of countries of the subtropical belt. In the northern hemisphere Spain (200 q/ha) and within the Soviet Union the republics of Central Asia (150 to 350 q/ha) are foremost. In the southern hemisphere record productivity is characteristic for the South African Republic (195 q/ha) and South Rhodesia (200 q/ha). Bolivia (180 q/ha) is an exception in the subequatorial and tropical belt of South America. The greater part of this country, including the areas in which alfalfa is cultivated, is situated on the high-altitude plateau of Puna, which constitutes the mountain belt of the Andes (Central Cordileres). The climate here ranges from arid to moderately arid and, obviously, differs significantly from the tropical climate of the plains.

Hay yields high for the equatorial and subequatorial belt are obtained in Peru (131 q/ha). Though situated in the Andes the climate of Peru has nothing in common with the tropical climate of neighboring Brazil or states situated in the equatorial belt of the African continent.

In the temperate belt of Europe under conditions of regular irrigation high hay yields of alfalfa are harvested in Belgium (109.5 q/ha), Bulgaria (100.3), Austria (94.1), and the Federal Republic of Germany (81.2 q/ha). On the irrigated lands of the subtropical belt average hay yields (80 to 90 q/ha) are characteristic of Greece, Argentina, India, Israel, and Turkey. In the tropical belt the average hay yields of alfalfa are 10 to 30 q/ha lower than in the subtropical belt. In Brazil alfalfa yields 72.2 q/ha without irrigation; in Mexico on irrigated lands the average hay yields are 61.8 q/ha, and in the USA—69.2 q/ha.

When alfalfa is cultivated without irrigation or under conditions of irregular irrigation, characteristic of the temperate belt, average hay yields (50 to 70 q/ha) are obtained in France, southern regions of the USA, Austria, and Yugoslavia, but less (50 q/ha) in eastern Europe (Bulgaria, Hungary, Rumania, the Soviet Union), England, northern regions of the Soviet Union, and Chile.

In peripheral regions of the area of distribution of this crop (northern part of West Europe, the Soviet Union without Central Asia and the Caucasus, southern part of Argentina and Chile, prairie of Canada) it is much more difficult to obtain high hay yields of alfalfa than under irrigated conditions in the subtropical belt. Productivity of this crop in these regions is considerably lower than in the center of the alfalfa belt of the world. Here hay yields vary from 5.0 to 8.0 q/ha in the arid zone (Kazakhstan, prairie of Canada) to 30 to 50 q/ha in the moderately humid regions or conditions of irrigation.

Productivity of alfalfa varies markedly from country to country and continent to continent. It also changes from year to year within a country because it depends on several factors. The highest yields of this crop are characteristic for countries of the subtropical belt. High hay yields are also obtained in countries of the tropical belt situated in hilly massifs where the climate is closer to subtropical.

In the temperate belt the productivity of alfalfa is lower than in the subtropical belt. With the advancement of this crop in the north or, vice versa, in the south, in the tropical or arid zone its yield declines. In the first case this is due to a deficit of heat and in the second a deficit or excess of moisture.

Table 6. Average, high, and record hay yields of alfalfa (q/ha) in different soil and climatic regions of the Soviet Union

Geographic region	Average	High	Record	Reference
Baltic Republics	25–30	45–50	150.0	Smetannikova, 1967
Northwestern zone of RSFSR	20–25	40–45	138.0	Khoroshailov, 1950
Nechernozem zone of RSFSR	20–30	35–40	110.0	Smurygin, 1972
Central Chernozem region of RSFSR	25–35	40–50	131.2	Elsukov, 1950
Ukrainian SSR:				
nonirrigated	20–30	35–45	100.0	Tarkovskii, 1974
irrigated	35–45	65–80	182.9	Berezovskii, 1974
Northern Caucasus:				
nonirrigated	25–35	40–50	104.7	State Statistical Directorate, 1966
irrigated	40–55	100–120	260.0	Nichikov, 1974
Caucasus (irrigated)	35–55	85–100	142.1	Chernousov, 1972
Volga Basin:				
nonirrigated	10–20	25–35	66.2	State Statistical Directorate, 1966
irrigated	25–35	45–60	233.0	Krenitskii, 1946
Ural	15–25	30–40	83.3	State Statistical Directorate, 1966
Western Kazakhstan	4–8	10–15	50.0	Zykov, 1967
Northern Kazakhstan	6–10	15–20	70.0	Zykov, 1967
Western Siberia	15–20	30–45	115.6	Lubenets and Plotnikov, 1950
Eastern Siberia	15–18	25–35	129.8	Lubenets and Plotnikov, 1950
Far East	20–25	30–35	103.8	Lubenets and Plotnikov, 1950
Southern Kazakhstan (irrigated)	40–60	100–130	260.8	Kapyrin, 1973
Central Asia (irrigated)	55–70	100–150	350.0	Gritsenko, 1950

On the whole the yield of green mass and hay from alfalfa in most of the countries situated in various soil and climatic belts of the world are low, much lower than the potential capabilities of the crop. This is explained by a number of reasons, primary among them—low level of agronomy, and lack of inadequate development of projects for improvement of plant breeding and seed production.

Hay yields of commercial varieties of alfalfa grown in different soil and climatic zones of the Soviet Union are presented in Table 6. The data shows that the productivity of alfalfa in the Soviet Union is far from high, and certainly below the biological potentialities of the crop.

The hay yields are particularly low in rained parts of the steppe zone of the RSFSR, the Ukraine, and Kazakhstan, as well as irrigated lands of the republics of Central Asia. The reason for low yields in the steppe zone is the absence of high-yielding varieties well adapted to local conditions and resistant to drought, diseases, and pests, and suitable for intensive agriculture. On the irrigated lands in the southern Soviet Union the low yields of alfalfa are usually attributable to nonobservance of proper agronomic practices, which include a specific regime of irrigation, doses and periods of fertilizer applications, seed rate and methods of sowing, regime of cutting and grazing the crop stand, crop rotation, periods of amelioration of saline lands, methods of intercultural operations, and application of herbicides and pesticides.

An analysis conducted by the Department of Fodder Crops of VIR (P.A. Lubenets and A.I. Ivanov) showed that in all geographic regions of the alfalfa belt of the Soviet Union productivity of alfalfa in all state varietal trial farms is 30 to 40% higher on the average than in collective and state farms, and in some farms even 1.5 to 2.0 times higher than the average crop yield. It must be mentioned that the much higher yields in varietal trial farms in every zone is the direct result of high level agronomic practices. To achieve a similar yield in all alfalfa farms of our country is a difficult but nonetheless attainable goal. As for the high hay yields shown in Table 6, these represent the minimum that should be achieved in all collective and state farms of the corresponding agroclimatic zone.

The rich experience of research institutions of the Soviet Union and abroad has shown that only through the application of advanced agronomic measures can the productivity of alfalfa be increased two- to threefold in a short period of time (Grishchenko, 1950, 1956; Ivanov, 1970).

On the whole in 1974 the yield of alfalfa in the Soviet Union was 21.6 q/ha, in RSFSR—15.6 q/ha, and in Kazakh SSR—11.5 q/ha. On the irrigated lands of southern Ukraine and republics of Central Asia the hay yield reaches 40 to 50 q/ha. During 1965 to 1976 the average yield of alfalfa in the country increased 4.1 q/ha, or 21%.

Seed yield of alfalfa (q/ha) varies widely from country to country and continent to continent (data of 1969 to 1974; asterisk denotes irrigated crop):

Europe		Australia	1.56*
Bulgaria	1.25	Americas	
Greece	4.90*	Argentina	1.42
Italy	3.43*	Peru	2.23*
Poland	0.80	USA	2.00*
Czechoslovakia	0.80	Asia	
France	3.50*	Israel	3.40*
Africa		India	1.90*
South African		Turkey	1.72
Republic	3.20	Soviet Union	1.00

It can be seen that the highest yield of seeds (more than 3.0 q/ha) was obtained from irrigated lands in the subtropical belt.

Average seed yields of alfalfa (1.5 to 2.0 q/ha) for irrigated lands of the subtropical belt are obtained in southern USA, Turkey, India, Australia, and Peru.

Without irrigation or under conditions of irregular irrigation in the temperate belt, the seed yield rarely exceeds 1.0 q/ha. Such productivity is characteristic for the Soviet Union and Bulgaria. In countries of eastern Europe, especially in Poland and Czechoslovakia, the seed yield is 0.8 q/ha.

In the temperate zone seeds mature irregularly. Hence some countries (Sweden, Denmark, Great Britain, Norway, Finland, the Netherlands, Canada, and others) raise seed material in countries located in the sub-tropical belt.

In world practice some countries in the subtropical belt, for one reason or another, are compelled to import alfalfa seeds. This is particularly true of Argentina where, due to extensive aphid invasion, seed yields are very low. Mexico also imports seeds because its level of agronomy is so low and seed production has not been organized. It is very difficult to obtain viable seeds in the tropical belt. Hence some equatorial countries, in particular Brazil, Colombia, and many countries of the African continent also import seed material.

In the geographically large alfalfa-growing countries the problem of seed production is solved through organizational measures: Regions where maturation of seed crops is difficult for various reasons, are supplied seeds produced on irrigated lands in the southern regions (Soviet Union, USA, France, Italy) or in foothill valleys (Chile, Peru, Bolivia, India).

In most countries seed crops of alfalfa comprise about 10 to 12% of the total area cropped. Exceptions include Australia where seed crops constitute only 2.0% of the cropped area, Argentina—3.0%, and Chile—20%.

In the Soviet Union the area occupied by seed crops of alfalfa varies year to year from 360,000 to 520,000 hectares but on the average constitutes 9 to 10% of the total area. Seed yields in all categories of farms comprise 1.1 q/ha on the average. Seed yields in different zones on rainfed fields of the arid belt range from 0.3 q/ha to 3.0 to 4.0 q/ha on irrigated lands. On the whole the seed productivity of alfalfa in the country is not high, and 2.0 to 3.0 times lower than the biological potentialities of the crop (Table 7).

The deficit of alfalfa seeds in our country is largely due to the fact that the region without irrigation and with optimal soil and climatic conditions for the growth and development of alfalfa is very small, comprising the northern part of Moldavia and the Ukraine, and only northern Caucasus and the central regions of the chernozem belt in the European part of the RSFSR. The zone suitable for commercial seed production in the east comprises southwestern Siberia, Khakassia, and Altai.

Table 7. Yield of alfalfa seeds (q/ha) in different soil and climatic regions of the Soviet Union

Geographic region	Yields	
	Average	High
Baltic Republics and northwest RSFSR	0.5	0.8–1.0
Nechernozem zone of RSFSR	0.5	1.0–1.5
Central Chernozem region of RSFSR	0.6–1.0	1.5–2.0
Ukraine	0.7–1.0	1.8–2.5
Northern Caucasus	0.7–1.5	2.0–3.0
Volga Basin	0.4–0.8	1.5–2.0
Ural	0.3–0.8	1.0–1.5
Western Kazakhstan	0.4–0.6	1.0–1.5
Northern Kazakhstan	0.5–0.7	1.0–1.5
Western Siberia	0.3–0.8	1.0–1.5
Eastern Siberia	0.4–1.0	1.0–2.0
Far East	0.3–8.8	1.0–1.5
Southern Kazakhstan	1.0–2.0	3.0–4.0
Caucasus	1.5–2.0	2.6–3.5
Central Asia	1.8–2.5	4.0–5.0

The most important microcenters of commercial production of alfalfa seeds without irrigation are: eastern Ukraine, Central Chernozem, northern Caucasus, and Barabinsk-Khakassia. From 1.0 to 1.5 quintals of alfalfa seeds per hectare are obtained in these centers without irrigation. North of this area lies the zone of seed production that is unstable due to heat deficit, and in the south the zone of seed production is unstable due to moisture deficit. The arid belt is very extensive. It includes part of the forest-steppe, steppe, semidesert, and desert zones. In the arid belt of the Soviet Union it is possible to obtain without irrigation 0.5 to 0.8 quintals of alfalfa seed per hectare only in rare, particularly favorable years. Usually the average seed yields here are only 0.1 to 0.5 q/ha.

The main reserve for the production of sizable quantities of alfalfa seeds in the Soviet Union is the irrigated zone of the republics of Central Asia, Kazakhstan, the Caucasus, southern Ukraine, and the Volga Basin. However, this reserve is not adequately exploited, especially in the republics of Central Asia where in one year four to six cuttings of green mass could be realized and not less than 3.0 to 4.0 q/ha seeds. If the total production of alfalfa seeds in the Soviet Union is taken as 100%, then with small deviations the RSFSR provides 50% of the total yield, Ukrainian SSR—25%, Kazakh SSR—15%, and all the republics of Central Asia a mere 6.0 to 8.0%.

RESULTS AND PROSPECTS OF ALFALFA BREEDING IN THE SOVIET UNION

More than 50 research institutions are engaged in the development of new varieties of alfalfa. However, the main work is concentrated in 12 breeding centers of fodder crops located in different soil and climatic zones. Breeding work is coordinated by V.R. Vil'yams All-Union Research Institute of Fodders, while the initial material for the research institutions is supplied by N.I. Vavilov All-Union Research Institute of Plant Industry.

Considerable success in breeding alfalfa has been achieved by the VIR and its experimental stations, the Siberian Research Institute of Agriculture, Krasnoyarsk Research Institute of Agriculture, Azerbaidzhan Research Institute of Cotton, Ukrainian Research Institute of Agriculture, All-Union Research Institute of Plant Breeding and Genetics (Odessa city), Uzbek Research Institute of Cotton Breeding, Poltava Agricultural Experimental Station, Krasnokutsk Experimental Plant Breeding Station, and Tatar Research Institute of Agriculture. The following varieties are extensively cultivated in the country: Zaykevich (250,000 ha); Marusinskaya-425, Poltava-256, Veselopodolyanskaya-11, Kamalinskaya-530, Severnaya hybrid (25,000 ha); Omsk-8893, Tashkent-3192 (300,000 ha); Semirechensk local (110,000 ha); Slavyanskaya local (73,000 ha); Manjchskaya (61,000 ha); and Kizlyarsk local (20,000 ha).

On January 1, 1979, 80 varieties of alfalfa[3] were released for cultivation in the Soviet Union, of which 15 were local varieties and 65 improved varieties developed by different methods—from simple ecotype, mass or individual selection to intervarietal and interspecific hybridization (Table 8).

The released improved varieties belong to five species of alfalfa: common alfalfa—12 varieties, variable alfalfa—49, yellow alfalfa—2, crescentoid alfalfa—1, and northern alfalfa—1. Ancient varieties of the people's selection have also been released for cultivation in the Soviet Union: common alfalfa—21 varieties, variable alfalfa—53, yellow alfalfa—3, crescentoid alfalfa—1, and northern alfalfa—2.

The area of common alfalfa extends over the zone of irrigated farming (see Figure 16). Sown areas of this crop are not large here, yet the irrigated belt of the Soviet Union seems fully provided with varieties of common alfalfa: eight local varieties have been evolved and ten improved varieties developed here. But in fact this is not true. If in Azerbaidzhan SSR on a small area (90,000 hectares) five varieties have been released for cultivation including three improved varieties (ASKhI-1, Azerbaydzhanskaya-5, and Azerbaydzhan-262), in the Uzbek SSR five varieties including three improved (Tashkent-1, Tashkent-3192, and Milyutinskaya-1774), then in Turkmenian SSR and Kazakh SSR only one variety each from the local breeders (Iolotanskaya and Krasnovodopadskaya-8) has been released for cultivation, while in Kirgiz SSR not a single improved variety has been developed.

The level of breeding work on this crop in the republics of Central Asia, especially in the southern regions of Kazakhstan, Kirgizia, and Tadzhikistan is not satisfactory. Better varieties of common alfalfa in this zone are only the local population Semirechensk local (released for cultivation in ten provinces of Kazakh SSR) and the improved variety Tashkent-3192 (released for cultivation in 12 provinces of Uzbek SSR, Tadzhik SSR, and Turkmenian SSR).

Cropped areas are maximally occupied by varieties of variable alfalfa in an area new for this crop, and penetrating far north and east in the taiga belt. Four of the five local varieties of the hybrid species were evolved in steppe regions bordering the zone of irrigated farming. In the Far

[3]Not taking into account the local populations of individual provinces mentioned in the Catalog of varieties of agricultural crops released under one number as better local varieties.

Table 8. Improved varieties of alfalfa, developed by different methods, released in the Soviet Union (1979)

Method of breeding	Number of varieties	Variety
1	2	3
Common alfalfa—*M. sativa* L.		
Mass selection	2	Iolotanskaya, Krasnovodopadskaya-8
Intervarietal crossing; mass and individual selection	12	ASKhI-1, Vakhshkaya-233, Vakhshskaya-300, Azerbaydzhanskaya-5, Azerbaydzhan-262, Milyutinskaya-1774, Tashkent-3192, Kara-Kalpakian-1, Raduga, Tashkent-1
Variable alfalfa—*M. varia* Mart.		
Ecotype selection	2	Kemlyanskaya, Tibet
Individual selection	1	Kuzbasskaya
Mass selection	14	Augune II, Bolshevyaskaya Improved, Zabaikalka, Zaykevich Odessa, Manichskaya, Blue Ural, Marusinskaya-81, Marusinskaya-425, Chishminskaya-130, Krasnodarskaya Early, Irtyshskaya, Kurskaya-1, Kuibishevskaya, Karaganda-1
Intervarietal crossing; mass, individual, and progeny selections; mixed and complex hybrid populations (synthetics)	13	Flora, Chernigovskaya, Khersonskaya-1, Khersonskaya-7, Shortandinskaya-2, Omsk-192, Karabalyktskaya-18, Taiga, Barnaul'skaya-17, Biiskaya-3, Tulunskaya hybrid, Khersonskaya-9, Belorusskaya
Interspecific crossing; mass, individual, and progeny selections; mixed and complex hybrid populations	18	Veselopodolyanskaya-11, Severnaya hybrid, Yellow hybrid-191, Pavlovskaya variegated, Krasnokutskaya variegated hybrid, Iygeva-118, Variegated-57, Kievskaya variegated hybrid, Krasnoufimskaya-6

(Contd.)

Table 8 (*Contd.*)

1	2	3
		Yellow alfalfa—*M. falcata* L.
Intervarietal crossing; mass and individual selections	1	Zaykevich, Kazan-36, Kazan-64/95, Kamalinskaya-530, Kamalin-930, Kokshe, Mezhotnenskaya, Omsk-8893, Onokhoy-6
		Pavlovskaya-7
Interspecific crossing and mass selection	1	Krasnokutskaya-4009
		Crescentoid alfalfa—*M. quasifalcata* Sinsk.
Ecotype selection	1	Yellow Kuban
		Northern alfalfa—*M. borealis* Grossh.
Mass selection	1	Dedinovskaya

North, ural, western and eastern Siberia, Altai, Kazakhstan, and the Far East the released local varieties of variable alfalfa have yet to be sown. This indicates that alfalfa cultivation is comparatively new in these geographic regions. Advancement of this crop into new regions has become possible through the achievements of breeding work. Of the 53 varieties of variable alfalfa released for cultivation in the Soviet Union, 48 (90.3%) are the improved varieties developed by plant breeders.

Because of their hybrid origin and high level breeding work some of the varieties of variable alfalfa (Veselopodolyanskaya-11, Zaykevich, Marusinskaya-425, Severnaya hybrid, and others) are characterized by exceptionally high ecological plasticity. The variety Zaykevich has been released for cultivation in 29 provinces of RSFSR, Ukrainian SSR, and Moldavian SSR; Marusinskaya-425—in 16 provinces of RSFSR, Ukrainian SSR, and Kazakh SSR; Veselopodolyanskaya-11—in 15 provinces of Ukrainian SSR; and Severnaya hybrid—in 9 provinces of RSFSR.

Most of the released varieties of alfalfa have been developed in western and eastern Siberia, the Ukraine, Kazakhstan, and the Volga Basin.

Improved varieties of variable alfalfa have not been adequately bred by research institutes in northern Caucasus, Central Chernozem region of RSFSR, Nechernozem zone of RSFSR, Baltic republics, and Altai. No improved varieties of variable alfalfa have been developed under local ecological conditions of such large natural economic and agricultural regions as the Far East and Far North, even though it is a promising crop and already occupies large areas in these regions.

Wild species of alfalfa are slowly being brought under cultivation also. One variety of the crescentoid alfalfa (yellow Kuban), two of the northern alfalfa (Dedinovskaya and Saarema Kollane), and two of the yellow alfalfa (Poltava-7 and Krasnokutskaya-4009) are presently being cultivated. Cropped areas of varieties of wild species are very limited. No variety has been released for cultivation of the blue, Tien Shan, Trautvetter's varicolored, glutinous, South Kazakhstan, and other valuable species of alfalfa which are highly promising for the improvement of meadows and pastures, sloping lands, and soils subject to water and wind erosion.

Alfalfa varieties under cultivation do not completely meet the ever-increasing requirements of modern intensive farming. They lack sufficient winter hardiness and drought resistance, are susceptible to diseases, do not have a high protein content or good seed productivity, and are inadequately responsive to irrigation and fertilizers. In many regions there are no suitable meadow-pasture varieties of alfalfa.

For better satisfaction of the requirements of production, alfalfa breeding in the Soviet Union must be organized with due consideration for natural, economic, and ecological conditions as well as purpose of crop:

field-crop rotation, hay material, pasture sowing, irrigated or unirrigated, acidic, saline, and other soils not suitable for agriculture, limans, severe rainfed conditions, floodplains of rivers, high-altitude hilly regions, etc. Therefore the tasks of alfalfa breeding can be general as well as specific. The general task of alfalfa breeding is the perfection of existing varieties and development of new high-yielding ones with a series of economically valuable characters.

Specific directions in alfalfa breeding are dictated by the natural conditions of different economic regions of the Soviet Union and purpose of crop.

The Far North requires varieties that are ultra-early-maturing, winter-resistant, stem nematode-resistant, capable of growing under low positive temperatures, and able to tolerate excessive humidity, high atmospheric humidity, and considerable acidity of soil.

In the forest zone the most important direction of breeding is the development of highly nutritive varieties that are readily digestible and capable of withstanding competition when sown in grass mixtures, resistant to drenching, characterized by early spring sprouting, intense growth after cutting and grazing, resistance to canker, ring rot, and acidity of soil, responsiveness to liming and application of organic and chemical fertilizer mixtures, and with a short and uniform period of flowering.

The forest-steppe zone requires multicutting, salt-tolerant, high-yielding varieties that are resistant to bacterial diseases, with high winter resistance, drought resistance, and seed productivity.

In the steppe and semidesert regions the breeding of alfalfa must take into consideration such important properties as drought resistance, cold resistance, salt tolerance, resistance to viral diseases and root rots, responsiveness to application of phosphate fertilizers and trace elements, use of autumn-winter precipitation, and nonshedding of seeds.

Regions of irrigated cultivation require fast-growing, multicutting varieties with a high protein content and essential amino acids, which are characterized by a long vegetative period, erect bush, thin stems, profuse foliage, resistance to pests and diseases, salt tolerance, heat tolerance, and responsiveness to irrigation and application of large doses of chemical fertilizers.

For sowing in pastures the new varieties must be perennial, resistant to frequent grazing and trampling, with high sprouting ability, rhizomatous roots, well-developed rosette of basal leaves, and deep root neck.

For sowing in floodplain soils it is necessary to develop lodging-resistant, perennial varieties capable of withstanding prolonged flooding and high soil water table.

High-altitude hilly regions require early-maturing, cold-tolerant varieties with a negative induction to a long day and lack of particular soil requirements.

The following methods of breeding are promising:

1. Individual, mass, and ecotype selection (especially for wild species);

2. Intervarietal and interspecific hybridization under conditions of free and controlled pollination;

3. Identification of high-yielding and quality biotypes, development of complex hybrid populations through free, selective cross-pollination of better varieties, admixture of the resultant biotypes in biomechanical mixtures and evaluation of progenies for crossability;

4. Clonal hybridization with use of backcrossing;

5. Development of high-yielding varieties on the basis of polyploidy and mutagenesis;

6. Development of heterotic varieties on the basis of CMS and self-incompatibility involving wild tetraploid and diploid species as one of the parents.

At present, in the Soviet Union, of the 82 released varieties of alfalfa, 45 (55.1%) were developed through intervarietal and interspecific hybridization and 37 (44.9%) by the method of ecotype, mass, and individual selection. All varieties evolved through hybridization were obtained through free, uncontrolled pollination. Use of the most promising, albeit genetically complex methods of plant breeding, linked with the development of synthetic polyploid mutant varieties, as well as heterotic hybrids on a sterile base, with fixing of important economic characters in the progeny did not receive wide application in the development of alfalfa varieties. In contrast to red clover, to date not a single alfalfa variety has been developed in the Soviet Union by complex genetic methods of plant breeding, even though research into methodology has been conducted on a small scale in the VIR, the All-Union Research Institute of Fodders, Siberian Division of the Academy of Sciences of the USSR, VSGI, Institute of Genetics and Plant Breeding of the Academy of Sciences of Azerbaidzhan SSR, and other research institutes.

Neglect of such an approach to the breeding of this crop has been fully justified when one has obtained a good variety at minimal cost; why then undertake complex methods requiring costly equipment and highly qualified personnel?

Today the identification of promising ancient varieties is almost complete; cataloging wild populations continues since at the present stage of development of agriculture wild forms are promising for cultivation in regions with severe growth conditions. In field crop rotations the best wild populations usually yield to released improved varieties with respect to productivity.

According to Konstantinova (1972, 1974), Novoselova and Cheprasova (1974), Kuleshov (1974), and other authors, hybridization should be considered the main breeding method for perennial grasses including alfalfa. High-yielding intervarietal hybrids have been obtained in Uzbek SSR (Tashkent-1, Tashkent-3192, Milyutinskaya-1774), Tadzhik SSR (Vakhshskaya-233, Vakhshskaya-300), and Azerbaidzhan SSR (ASKhI-1, Azerbaydzhanskaya-5, Azerbaydzhan-262).

Interspecific hybridization holds great promise in alfalfa breeding. In the Soviet Union 19 varieties developed by this method have been released for cultivation. Many varieties have been evolved using natural interspecific hybrids or by improving the released interspecific varieties. Better interspecific hybrids are—Severnaya hybrid, Zaykevich, Marusinskaya-81, Marusinskaya-425, Omsk-8893, Flora, Omsk-191, Omsk-192, Taiga, Veselopodolyanskaya-11, Khersonskaya-1, Khersonskaya-7, Khersonskaya-9, and Kokshe.

Through interspecific hybridization winter hardiness, drought resistance, productivity, and disease and pest resistance are increased, and the nutritive qualities of the fodder likewise improved. This method is widely used not only in the Soviet Union but also in the USA, Canada, Sweden, England, Denmark, the Netherlands, Finland, Australia, New Zeeland, the Federal Republic of Germany, the German Democratic Republic, Czechoslovakia, and Poland.

While using the method of distant hybridization, the breeding process must be based on scientifically selected initial material, involving the diploid wild species, in particular the blue, Trautvetter's northern, South Kazakhstan, and crescentoid alfalfas, which are presently hardly used even though they are carriers of gene resistance to trampling. Success of breeding work also depends on the selection of the cultivated parent, which must carry per se a series of useful traits: high yield potential, responsiveness to irrigation and fertilizers, early maturity, high sprouting ability, non-shedding seeds, uniform flowering, and responsiveness to high-level agronomy. Selection of parental forms should be done with due consideration given to the geographic, ecological, and biological properties of the plant to ensure better heterosis.

Soviet researchers are very interested in the new, more complex genetic methods of alfalfa breeding developed and extensively tried in the New World and widely accepted in West Europe.

Among the new trends in breeding the most promising is the method of development of synthetic varieties by polycross tests. This method strives to preserve the effect of heterosis through free pollination of genotypes in the course of several successive generations. This is achieved by unification of initial components with high general crossability. In developing synthetic varieties different initial material can be used as genotypes—inbred lines, clones, families, biotypes, and entire populations. The positive property of synthetic varieties is their high plasticity, which ensures increased resistance to adverse environmental conditions.

A synthetic population is distinguished from a variety developed by mass selection, which also comprises the sum of genotypes, and from a variety developed through pure line selection when several promising lines are used as initial material so that the population is formed of components already tested for crossability. However, identification of genotypes with high crossability is also the basic task of breeding synthetic varieties. Almost any initial material in polycross nurseries having high crossability can serve as the base for a new synthetic variety.[4]

Crossability is established by different methods depending on the initial material and manner in which the hybrids are used. The simplest method is the crossing of genotypes with each other in a system of polycross, or with one or several testers in topcross. Diallele crossings as a method of evaluation of crossability envisaging all possible combinations of the control cross between parental forms (under strict isolation) are the most cumbersome but nevertheless the most reliable.

Experience in other countries has shown that in developing synthetic varieties genotypes of any degree of inbreeding may be used, but it is better that the components not be related since closely related material reduces productivity. It is also important to consider the quality of clones (lines, varieties) included in the synthetic variety. This question remains controversial. However, in order to avoid excessive inbreeding in much later generations, according to most researchers, it is necessary to use not less than four parental forms.

The program of breeding synthetic varieties is simple but can be highly diverse. The polycross test method enables us to increase the productivity of synthetic varieties compared to the initial parental forms by 4.0 to 52.0% and compared to the released varieties—up to 15%. The theoretical basis for breeding alfalfa by polycross test has been successfully determined in the USA, Canada, France, Sweden, England, Belgium, Hungary, and other countries.

The most promising breeding method wherein the highest effect of heterosis is achieved is the method of obtaining heterotic hybrids on a sterile base or crossing self-incompatible plants. In this case the productivity of hybrids is ensured by preservation of initial genotypes because their

[4]The term "synthetic variety" has become a fashion today and is often misappropriated; any variety of grass is called synthetic which has been developed by different methods from two or more parental forms through free pollination without identifying the general crossability of the parents.

pollination takes place under strict control. With the discovery of CMS and the identification of different types of sterility, the use of heterosis has become economically profitable and feasible for several fodder crops.

Heterotic hybrids have several advantages over synthetic varieties: Complete absence of inbreeding, which appears in successive generations of synthetic varieties; exclusion of natural selection and biological admixture from breeding work because purity of the hybrid is ensured by strict limitation of filial progenies, and so forth. It is assumed that hybrid varieties of alfalfa, due to the autotetraploid nature of the plants, will be more heterogenic than hybrid varieties of corn.

Commercial heterotic hybrids of alfalfa have not yet been bred in any country. It is expected that the productivity of heterotic hybrids will be 20 to 30% more compared to the released varieties.

In the Soviet Union the first sterile plants of alfalfa were identified in 1964 at the Maikopskaya and Kubanskaya Experimental Stations of the All-Union Research Institute of Plant Industry (VIR) under the guidance of Professor P.A. Lubenets. After preliminary multiplication this valuable material was sent to leading plant-breeding institutions of the Soviet Union and Bulgaria. In our country male sterile plants or their seeds from free pollination have been obtained by VIK (Moscow), VSGI (Odessa), VNIIZKh (Tselinograd), Poltavskaya Agricultural Research Station, and other institutions. At present research on the breeding of heterotic hybrids on a sterile base and self-incompatibility are being conducted by more than ten research institutes in the Soviet Union. From 1975 to 1979 highly productive, wilt-resistant, interspecific heterotic hybrids for further breeding work were identified at the Maikopskaya and Kubanskaya Experimental Stations of VIR.

Research on the problem of heterosis in alfalfa is basically methodological. In 1968 the Department of Fodder Crops of the VIR published the first methodological guidebook on identification and multiplication of sterile plants. In the same decade appeared the first publications of the department on methods of selection of parental forms to ensure maximum effect of heterosis. In 1970 a more comprehensive methodological guide on the use of heterosis of first-generation hybrids of alfalfa was published, which had been edited by A.M. Konstantinova. Subsequently, several methodological publications on the breeding of heterotic hybrids of alfalfa on a sterile base have appeared on the market.

It is recommended that work on the development of heterotic hybrids be conducted in phases: 1) identification and selection of promising initial material for breeding for heterosis; 2) determination of crossability of identified varieties, biotypes, plants; 3) identification and multiplication of plants with sterile pollen; 4) development of sterile lines; 5) identification of heterotic hybrids on a sterile base and their evaluation; and 6) primary seed production of hybrids.

According to the data of the Department of Fodder Crops of VIR, under conditions of northern Caucasus the most productive heterotic hybrids were obtained by crossing sterile plants of medium-maturing varieties with fertile plants of early-maturing, multicutting, tall varieties from Mexico, Ecuador, India, Iraq, Egypt, and Peru. Heterosis increases if parental forms belong to different species or are interspecific hybrids (Yellow Kuban × Slavyanskaya local). The most promising sterile plants have been identified from the wild varicolored alfalfa species (Catalog number K-16659, K-16691), cultivated varieties of the variable alfalfa—Ladak, Kubanskaya, Novokuban, Marusinskaya-425—and complex interspecific hybrids—Ladak × hybrid Yellow Kuban × Slavyanskaya.

Considering the high heterogeneity of hybrids in the first and subsequent generations, hybrids with fixed heterosis are obtainable. Constant heterozygosity of hybrid populations is ensured by preferential synopsis of homologous chromosomes with similar alleles and their transfer to different poles during meiosis. This phenomenon of pseudolinkage fixing of heterosis has been labeled the "Miryuta effect" after the author who first observed it. This phenomenon explains a number of other phenomena in the genetics of autopolyploids: Why are one and the same characters in a number of alfalfa varieties inherited according to the autotetraploid scheme, but in other varieties according to the diploid? P.A. Lubenets believes that the most distinguished heterotic hybrids of alfalfa, outyielding the standard (control) variety in the first and subsequent generations, possess permanent heterozygosity. The author states that such hybrids can be propagated vegetatively.

Research on hybrid seeds of alfalfa, using self-incompatibility, is underway in the experimental network of the VIR, VNIISKh of the Southeast, VSGI, VIK, Poltavskaya Experimental Station in the Research Institute of Irrigated Farming of Ukrainian SSR, Azerbaidzhan Research Institute of Cotton, Kazakh Research Institute of Meadow-Pasture Management, Alma-Ata Agricultural Institute, Siberian Division of the Academy of Sciences of the USSR, and other institutions.

In the All-Union Research Institute of Agriculture (VNIISKh) of the Southeast six self-incompatible plants were identified and from them four hybrids obtained which surpassed the control variety by 13 to 20% in productivity. In the VSGI 22 plants have been identified with high indexes of this character (from 92 to 100%), of which only two proved totally self-incompatible. Seven heterotic hybrids have been developed which excel the control variety in yield of green mass by 16 to 24%. At the Maikopskaya Experimental Station of VIR 11 hybrids have been developed from crossing self-incompatible plants, outyielding the control variety by 20 to 57% in production of green mass. The most productive hybrids (increase in yield 48 to 57%) were obtained from crosses of two pairs: Slavyanskaya local × local alfalfa from Ecuador (K-8471) and local alfalfa from Yugoslavia (K-19935) × Tashkent-1. Plant breeders in Canada have been more successful in this direction and were the first in the world to produce and multiply the self-incompatible variety of alfalfa Ellerslie-1 (No. 201).

To date the method of polyploidy has not yielded positive results in the breeding of alfalfa; nevertheless it is considered promising while working with diploid species and is widely used for overcoming noncrossability of several species and for obtaining high quality initial material. The breeding process for the production of polyploid varieties involves the following stages: 1) selection of lines of definite genetic make-up at the diploid level; 2) doubling of chromosomes; 3) evolution of polyploids; 4) use of better forms in hybridization; and 5) multiplication of high-yielding plants and hybrids. This method proved particularly promising in the breeding of clover and cereal grasses. In the Soviet Union the released tetraploid VIK variety of red clover was developed by this method. AN-tetra-1 is the second promising variety. In the Siberian division of the Academy of Sciences of the USSR three populations of tetraploid red clover varietal analogues are under trial—Zyryanovskii local, Osinovskii local, and Masayaninskii local.

In alfalfa breeding the polyploidy method could be of great importance for the development of varieties with high seed productivity, especially if for the initial material (male or female parent) diploid annual species are used, which are capable of producing seeds under adverse weather conditions during the vegetative phase.

Achievements in the development of new varieties of fodder crops by subjecting the plants to mutagenic factors are less significant than the use of polyploidy. Nevertheless this, too, is a promising method. The reports available suggest that through mutagenesis it is possible to increase resistance to diseases, especially to powdery mildew and rust of alfalfa, and grain shattering, and to increase root growth and improve chemical composition. The method of mutagenesis makes it possible to obtain great diversity of useful variability rapidly (Dubinin, 1961; Dubinin and Shcherbakov, 1965; Busbice et al., 1972).

It is necessary to improve alfalfa breeding in our country for important economic properties: increase of protein content and essential amino acids, resistance to specific (for each zone) diseases and pests, high seed productivity, uniformity of flowering, root growth, responsiveness to fertilizers, high drought resistance, winter hardiness, saline tolerance, low percentage of cellulose in roughage, and attractiveness of plants for frequent visitations by honeybees and other pollinators through providing various alluring backgrounds.

MAIN DIRECTIONS IN BREEDING WORK IN LEADING ALFALFA-GROWING COUNTRIES

Alfalfa is under intense study from various aspects in Australia, England, Bulgaria, Hungary, Denmark, India, Italy, Canada, the Netherlands, New Zealand, Poland, the USA, France, the Federal Republic of Germany, Czechoslovakia, Sweden, the South African Republic, and Japan. Here I have briefly described the most important directions in research on breeding being conducted on alfalfa in the leading alfalfa-growing countries of different continents of the world.

Europe. Alfalfa is cultivated and studied in every country and has been sown on an area (excluding the Soviet Union) of more than 6,000,000 hectares. Europe played a decisive role in the spread of this crop throughout the world. *M. sativa* is cultivated in the subtropical belt and *M. varia* north of the subtropics. *M. falcata*, *M. varia* (*M. media*), and *M. lupulina* are found more often under wild conditions.

England. Major cropped areas of alfalfa are concentrated in the southeastern part of the country and used for the preparation of vitaminized grass meal. The leading research center for breeding of this fodder crop is the Institute of Plant Breeding at Cambridge, which participates in the activities of the National Seed Development Organization (NSDO).

To date no high-yielding, disease- and pest-resistant improved commercial varieties of alfalfa have been developed in England. Improved varieties from western France are therefore grown here on a large scale. The local varieties (English Early and others) are not winter hardy and their seed yield negligible. At present several promising varieties are being multiplied—Maris Kabul, Maris Phoenix, and Sabilt—which exhibit early maturity (three cuttings), resistance to ring wilt (*Verticillium albo-atrum*) and bacterial wilt (*Corynebacterium insidiosum*), rapid growth, and rhizomatous roots. The initial material for these varieties were improved varieties of the Flamande type from France, rhizomatous hybrids from Canada, and wild species of the Eurasian and Mediterranean gene centers.

The important conditions for breeding here are the development of varieties suitable for pastures with a high coefficient of digestibility of green and coarse fodders capable of withstanding crop competition (especially when sown in grass mixtures with *F. arundinacea*), which grow vegetatively from early spring to late autumn. For the purpose of selection of initial material, a large collection of alfalfa from many countries of the world was studied in the Institute of Plant Breeding. Specimens were identified with respect to early maturity, resistance to diseases, winter hardiness, chemical composition, and productivity. Efforts to compile an interspecific classification of the said specimens (Hawkins and Zaleski) were not successful.

Evaluation of wild species of alfalfa obtained from the Soviet Union revealed great prospects for breeding in England in a number of characters. For example, in *M. glutinosa* the root neck is situated below the soil surface, which increases resistance to intensive grazing and trampling and makes this species particularly valuable for pasture use; *M. coerulea* is resistant to drought and the stem nematode (*Ditylenchus dipsaci*); *M. quasifalcata* is distinguished by very profuse foliage and productivity; and *M. hemicycla* is resistant to bacterial wilt, low temperature, and increased humidity.

Research has shown that *M. sativa* is readily crossed with *M. glutinosa* (60% hybrids) and *M. falcata* (52%) but more difficult to cross with *M. varia* (28%). Productivity of the hybrids of the first generation is less than that of the control variety, but backcrosses with the French variety even in the first generation are distinguished by profuse foliage, high crude protein content, and resistance to diseases. Hybrids of *M. hemicycla* × *M. quasifalcata* are particularly promising. It is recommended that selection be delayed to the second or third generations (Evans et al., 1966).

Bulgaria. Alfalfa is cultivated on an area of 400,000 hectares and is the main fodder crop of the country. The main cropped areas are concentrated in Razgrad, Pleven, Velikotyrn, Plovdiv, and Rusen regions.

Breeding work with alfalfa has been undertaken comparatively recently—early 1960's—and is mainly conducted in two research centers: Institute of Fodder Crops (Pleven) and Institute of Breeding of Cereals and Legumes (Rusen).

In the Institute of Fodder Crops three, first in Bulgaria, varieties have been developed through hybridization with free cross-pollination: Pleven I, Pleven II, and Pleven III. Without irrigation, these varieties slightly outyield the control—the old local population Dunavka and the French variety, Du Puits—which occupy 80% of the area under this crop. Since 1970 this Institute has conducted research on clonal breeding and inbreeding, use of CMS in breeding work (first hybrid plants with CMS were obtained from the VIR), evaluation of promising lines for resistance to ring wilt using artificial infection in fields, removal of noncrossability between promising wild species, and genetics of quantitative characters.

In the Institute of Cereals and Legumes alfalfa breeding is based on the development of synthetic varieties by the polycross method. There are several promising numbers in the varietal trial nursery which outyield Dunavka in the production of green mass and seeds (Maslinkov et al., 1972; Angelov, 1976).

Hungary. More than ten varieties of alfalfa have been developed in the country, among which the most popular are Tichantuli, Synalfa, Tapioszele, and Nagyszenasi. Research is conducted in the Institute of Plant Industry (Kompol't) and in the Institute of Agro-Botany (Tapioszela).

The chemical composition of clones and their resistance to diseases and pests, in particular *Verticillium albo-atrum* (wilt, vascular micosis) and *Ascochyta imperfecta* (leaf spot) are under study. Because seeds of alfalfa are difficult to obtain, self-fertilization and self-pollination of flowers are also, being studied, and artificial rearing of the alfalfa leaf-cutter bee (*Megachile rotundata*) has been organized. The most important problem of breeding—development of heterotic hybrids on a CMS base—has already been successfully solved (Balázs, 1960, 1961; Janossy and Sulyok, 1964; Bócsa and Buglos, 1974).

Denmark. Until recently this country was not interested in developing its own varieties of alfalfa, relying mainly on improved varieties from Sweden, France, the Federal Republic of Germany, and England for sowing in crop rotation, meadows, and pastures. Now theoretical research is conducted on all aspects and high-level methodology employed. Alfalfa is studied in the University of Veterinary and Agricultural Sciences (Odense) and in the Institute of Economics and Plant Industry (Kolding).

Research by Danish scientists on the biology of flowering in alfalfa has established that under field conditions plant crossing is as high as 74 to 87%. High positive correlations have been found between self-fertility and self-fertilization. These scientists recommend that this fact be considered in tests of polycross and topcross. Separation of plants by a distance of 150 m results in 25% hybrids.

It has been shown that for pollination in hothouses it is better to use bumblebees (*Bombus* spp.) rather than the alfalfa leaf-cutter bee (*M. rotundata*). Bumblebees pollinate 85% of the flowers, while the alfalfa leaf-cutter bee pollinates only 30 to 35%. Two valuable modifications of flowers—"unprotected stigma" and "open keel"—have been identified and are being multiplied.

In working out methods of alfalfa breeding positive correlations have been established between vegetative growth, early flowering, and seed setting. Highest yields of green mass have been obtained from synthetics derived from inbred lines compared to clonal synthetics.

At present, inducing artificial infection, scientists are working on the development of lines resistant to *Verticillium albo-atrum*. Other aspects under study are the causes of sterility in plants, polycotyledony and the nature of its heritability, chemical control measures against weeds of alfalfa, and so forth (Johansen, 1968, 1968a; Nielsen and Andreasen, 1970).

Italy. Alfalfa is cultivated on an area of 1,716,000 hectares, which is the largest cropped area of alfalfa for countries of Europe. The main cultivated areas are concentrated in the northern and central regions of the country (see Figure 17).

Alfalfa is under study in several research institutions of Italy. However, the most in-depth and all-round studies are conducted in the Institute of Fodders (Lodi) and in the Faculty of Plant Breeding of the University of Perugia. Theoretical research in the University is devoted to unraveling the role of self-pollination and selection in breeding alfalfa, variability of quantitative characters, and interspecific hybridization. It has been established that inbreeding drastically reduces plant vigor. Yield of seeds is liable to far greater fluctuation than plant height. The inhibitory effect of self-pollination does not intensify from generation to generation. Inbreeding is prominently manifested in S_2. Certain restoration of plant vigor is observed in subsequent generations. It has been established that in alfalfa the inevitable selection of stronger plants (the most heterotic forms) retards the process of homozygosis. Self-pollination as a method of breeding is recommended only when plant vigor in synthetic varieties considerably covers productivity of initial parental forms. Synthetics with 6, 10, and 12 clones have been developed.

A study of the crossability of *M. sativa* (2n = 32), *M. glutinosa* (2n = 32), *M. coerulea* (2n = 16), *M. hemicycla* (2n = 16), and *M. falcata* (2n = 32) has shown that if diploid species are used as the female parent, then the entire progeny is tetraploid. Triploids occur (very rarely) only in the cross *M. sativa* × *M. hemicyla*. Hybrids promising for productivity are obtained in crosses of tetraploids *M. sativa* × *M. glutinosa*. The efficacy of honeybees as pollinators of alfalfa has been proven in hothouses, etc.

Genetic-breeding research is being conducted in the Institute of Fodders on the development of synthetic varieties of alfalfa with the use of self-pollination and dense sowing. P. Rotili, I. Zannone, and G. Gaussmann consider that the method of plant breeding based on the use of wide-spaced crops, extensively practiced in the world, is outdated and inefficient. In their opinion, wide-spaced crops exclude interspecific competition of plants at the earliest stages of development of a new variety.

The method developed by Italian researchers envisages evaluation of seedlings in hothouses with a pot area of 4.0 cm × 4.0 cm with subsequent transplantation in the field at the rate of 150 seedlings per square meter. Plant vigor is determined on the basis of plant mass. The selected plants are self-pollinated up to S_4, propagated by cloning, and subjected to diallelic crossings (17 series). At the level of hybrids F_1 synthetic varieties (F_2) with two, four, and eight lines and double interline hybrids are developed.

Simultaneously clones are evaluated for carotene and chlorophyll content. To study the rate of photosynthesis the density of plants is increased up to 350 per square meter. It has been proved that the higher the homogeneity of genotypes, the higher the productivity of synthetics. It is recommended that alfalfa breeding be conducted only in densely sown crops under interspecific competition because the development of characters and crossability of clones and lines change depending on area of plant feeding (Rotili, 1974; Rotili and Zannone, 1971, 1971a, 1973).

The Netherlands. A good level of development of animal husbandry (55% of the agricultural production) requires a well-organized scientific solution to the fodder problem. Alfalfa plays a leading role in the fodder balance of the country. It is sown in meadows and pastures, especially polder meadows, and is the main crop for preparing highly nutritive concentrated feeds. This country has no improved varieties of its own and hence varieties from Sweden (Tuna), Belgium (Harmignies), France (Flamande, Du Puits), the Federal Republic of Germany (Old Franconian) are sown. Research is conducted in the Institute of Field Crops and Fodder Grasses (Wageningen).

Breeding for nodule bacteria to increase the efficacy of symbiosis has been successful. It has been established that virulence, intensity of nitrogen fixation, and synthesis of physiologically active substances depend on the degree of interaction between nodular bacteria and host plant, which eventually determines the productivity of the fodder crop. Plant breeders are working on the development of high-yielding, early-maturing, multicutting, winter-hardy varieties resistant to trampling, verticillosis, and rust.

Poland. Valuable research on heterosis of alfalfa is being conducted in the Institute of Plant Breeding and Genetics at Rajikov.* It has been proven that cytoplasm plays a decisive role in the transmission of CMS. The opinion of Soviet scientists has been confirmed that plants with male sterility as well as plants with reduced fertility of pollen are inherent to all populations since this is a regular process of evolution. Plants with reduced fertility of pollen are not inferior to fertile plants in size of vegetative organs and develop seeds well after self-pollination or fertilization by viable pollen. Strengtheners of sterility and restorers of fertility have been identified. At present the main method of breeding is the polycross test (Staszewski, 1970, 1975).

Research is being conducted in colleges of agriculture on the development of lines resistant to bacterial, ring wilt, and fungal diseases, as well as canker and anther mold. Doses, periods, and methods of application

*Proper spelling of place names given in this section could not be ascertained in some cases—General Editor.

of pesticides are under study for the control of weed infestation of seed crops of alfalfa.

France. The area under alfalfa is 1,583,800 hectares. This crop is grown everywhere. Two centers of intensive cultivation of alfalfa, of the eight found in the European continent are located in France (see Figure 17).

Every aspect of alfalfa is studied in France. The main research and breeding centers are the Experimental Station of the State Agronomical Institute at Lausanne and the Central Experimental Station of Plant Breeding and Genetics (Versailles) where theoretical problems are considered.

The achievements of plant breeders in this country are well known throughout the world. For example, the Flamande type Du Puits is found in every continent of the world and even today is widely used in breeding programs in many countries. French varieties are still being exported to England, the Netherlands, Austria, Belgium, Switzerland, Japan, 'the Federal Republic of Germany, Africa, Australia, and Oceania.

The first improved varieties were developed by the method of hybridization and selection: Flamande de Bosse, Flamand du Nor, Europe, Prima, Elga, Hybride de Grecy, Hybride de Millefeuille, Du Puits, Boreal, and Warote. New high-yielding, disease-resistant varieties have been obtained from Flamande varieties: Etoile du Nord, Emeraude, Florimond, Depre, Gamma, Omega, Glacier, and Du Marais de Luson.

Soon the methods of alfalfa breeding in France changed. Emphasis was given to the development of hybrid synthetic varieties and new schemes of breeding and selection worked out. Preference was given to tall, early-maturing, erect plants with good bush habits. The new variety had to have high productivity, multicutting growth habit, and resistance to spot disease and ring wilt. Varieties Luciole, Cardinal, and Orca combine such characters.

Today the main method of alfalfa breeding is that of pure lines. Initially homozygous progenies are studied and later crossed. Self-pollination is practiced for four to five generations. Fertility of plants reduces with prolonged inbreeding. Plant vigor lost through inbreeding is restored through crossing of homozygous lines. Researchers are hopeful that the new hybrids will exhibit hereditary stability and increased vigor, as a result of which productivity will increase 30 to 40% compared to mass selection varieties.

Studies of the problems of biology of flowering in alfalfa have shown that the captive honeybee does not work effectively in crops. The pollen carried by the insects remains viable for no more than 24 hours. The French scientists recommend a quick change of pollinator plants during artificial pollination in isolation chambers. Much of their research is devoted to agronomic problems, control of pests, diseases, and weeds, association between species and varieties of alfalfa and *R. melioti*, effect of trace elements and growth substances on the growth and development of seed, photoperiodicity, water regime, chemical composition, anatomy and morphology of plants, applied genetics, heritability and variability of quantitative characters, polyploidy, mutagenesis, and other problems (Demarly, 1968; Guy, 1972, 1975, 1976; Guy et al., 1975).

Federal Republic of Germany. Many crops of alfalfa are concentrated in the southwestern part of the country. This crop is cut two to three times during its vegetative period and the plants maintained in the fields for a period of two to three years. Research is conducted at Stuttgart University and the Bavarian Institute of Plant Breeding.

The maximum acreage under cultivation of this crop is occupied by the Old Franconian population of alfalfa and the improved varieties Altfranken Schmidt-Steinbach, Arnim, Triesdorfer, and Luna. These varieties are very low in seed productivity and hence seeds are multiplied at a cooperative base in the USA (California) and in other countries.

The problems being successfully solved here include: Tolerance of alfalfa varieties to soil acidity, polyploidy, methods of breeding for heterosis, biology of flowering and pollination, chemical control methods against diseases and pests, fertilizer applications, and effect of intensity of cuttings of winter hardiness of plants (Simon, 1967, 1967a).

Czechoslovakia. The varieties Hodoninska, Kasticka, Nitranka, Uudava, Palova,* Prerovska, Stupicka, and Taborka are extensively sown in the country. They are characteristically low in seed productivity. Research is conducted at the Institute of Plant Industry (Prague-Ruzin), Institute of Fodders (P'eshtyani), and in colleges of agriculture.

It has been established that wild honeybees and bumblebees are the most effective pollinators of alfalfa. Mechanical opening of flowers does not increase the seed set and does not affect seed productivity and method of sowing. Maximum seed yields are obtained at a plant density of 450 to 600 plants per square meter. Researchers are also studying the resistance of plants to diseases and pests, effect of insecticides on seed productivity of species and varieties, activity of improved lines of nodular bacteria in fixing nitrogen in the soil, methods of obtaining hybrid seeds, and other problems.

Sweden. The main problem under study by plant breeders and alfalfa specialists in Sweden is the development of early-maturing, winterhardy, stem nematode and ring wilt-resistant, perennial, high-yielding varieties

---

*An obvious misprint in the Russian original. There are two established varieties—Polava and Palava—and it is not clear which one is intended—General Editor.

of alfalfa capable of stable seed yields every year under conditions of northern latitudes (56° to 60° N).

Breeding work with this crop is conducted by the Swedish Seed Production Society at Svalef Station under the Institute of Plant Breeding, while varietal trials are organized at experimental stations in Ultun, Skon, Gotlands, Kalmar, and Ostermland.

The quick-sprouting, winter-hardy Swedish varieties Mega and Tuna (I-0611) are used in breeding programs in many countries of West Europe. From the variety Tuna (selection from German alfalfa) and lines I-0602 and I-0614 (selections from the variety Grimm) a new variety I-0615 has been developed and its multiplication organized in Israel. The variety Alfa has been improved through multiple selection of plants resistant to the stem nematode; an analogue of the latter variety—Alfa II—contains 80% resistant plants (versus 5.0% in the initial population). The re-established variety Vertus has a combined resistance to the stem nematode and wilt.

Very recently a new variety, Sverre (SV-0643), was evolved from the varieties Alfa, Tuna, and I-0615, which has a combined resistance to verticillosis and the stem nematode. With respect to winter hardiness, productivity, disease resistance, and intensity of sprouting, this variety excels the varieties Vertus, Tuna, and Alfa II. It has been recommended for cultivation in the southern part of the country. For northern regions a new variety, Netun, not only resistant to the nematode, but also with greater winter hardiness has been evolved from the variety Tuna by selection of plants resistant to the nematode.

Interesting research is underway in Sweden on polyploidy and mutagenesis of alfalfa, winter hardiness, resistance to diseases and pests, chemical composition and digestibility of crude fodders, effect of seeds produced in southern latitudes on productivity of varieties in northern latitudes, and application of herbicides for the control of weeds in alfalfa crops (Julen and Julen, 1962, 1974; Torssell and Bingefors, 1961).

America. Alfalfa is cultivated in all countries of the American continent. Of the 33,000,000 hectares occupied by this crop in the world, New World countries account for 19,450,000 hectares or 60.8%. This continent is a pioneer in the development of breeding methods for alfalfa, notably polycross, topcross, breeding for inbred lines, and breeding for heterosis making use of CMS. This continent plays an important role in research on the cytology and genetics of alfalfa, development of breeding methods for resistance to diseases and pests using artificially infected fields, development of rhizomatous varieties, and so forth. Well-planned research is conducted in Argentina, Bolivia, Canada, Mexico, Paraguay, Peru, the USA, Uruguay, Chile, Ecuador, and other countries (see

Figures 18 and 19). Particularly noteworthy are the studies on alfalfa conducted in the USA and Canada.

Canada. According to Heinrichs (1967, 1973, 1973a) alfalfa is cultivated in all the provinces of Canada. In 1970 it was cultivated on an area of 2,201,644 hectares. The largest areas occur in the provinces of Manitoba, Saskatchewan, Ontario, Alberta, and British Columbia, where it is sown in both neutral and highly calcareous soils.

For large-scale production throughout the country varieties of a hybrid species (*M. varia* Mart.) are cultivated, which are divisible into two types: standard and Flemish. Varieties of the first type are characterized by slow growth, resistance to diseases, long dormancy period, drought resistance, winter hardiness, perennial growth habit, and rhizomatous roots or taproot system. Among the released varieties of this type are: Beaver, Grimm, Ladak, Rambler, Rhizoma, Ranger, Roamer, Vernal, Braylander, and Narragansett. They are cultivated under severe soil and climatic conditions—dry prairies at the northern border of crop distribution. Varieties of the second type—Alfa, Glacier, Du Puits, Mega, and Saranac—are closely related to the French alfalfas (the Flamande base)[5] in origin. They are distinguished by blue flowers, fast rate of spring growth and sprouting after cutting, much higher yields in the second and third cuttings, good uniformity of plant stand, and erectness; however, they have a lower resistance to diseases, drought, and low temperatures. All varieties of the Flemish type were brought to Canada from West Europe and the USA. They are cultivated in regions with a much milder climate and under irrigation.

The most important research centers studying alfalfa and other perennial forage crops are the Central Experimental Farm of the Department of Agriculture in Ottawa (Ontario), research centers of the Universities of Alberta (Edmonton) and Ontario, and experimental stations situated in the provinces of Ontario, Saskatchewan, Alberta, and Manitoba.

Canadian researchers were the first in the world to pay attention to rhizomatous forms of alfalfa; they developed breeding methods and evolved varieties with this valuable character. Rhizomatous varieties made it possible to extend the cultivation area of this crop to new regions, namely, dry prairies, which led to the immediate solution of several national problems: Reclamation of new areas through inclusion of dry areas in agricultural crop rotation, increase of animal husbandry pro-

---

[5]Du Puits and Glacier were evolved in France and Alfa and Mega in Sweden. The Swedish varieties were developed through selection from varieties of West European origin closer to the ancient populations of French alfalfa. Saranac was developed in the USA by the backcross method from the varieties Alfa (Sweden), Du Puits, and Flamande (France).

duce, increase of productivity of natural fodder lands, and development of perennial varieties with increased survival capability due to greater resistance to drought, diseases, and low temperatures. Rhizomatous varieties Rhizoma, Rambler, Roamer, and Braylender are excellent initial material and are being used in breeding programs in several countries throughout the world.

Canadian researchers pioneered work on genetic methods of alfalfa breeding for heterosis, utilizing CMS, self-incompatibility, and inbred lines. The sterile plants identified by them were multiplied and sent to various agricultural institutions in the USA (Lubenets, 1961; Bolton et al., 1962; Guy, 1972, 1975, 1976; Guy et al., 1975).

Canadian researchers have played a significant role in the study of genetics and cytology of alfalfa. A pioneer in this field is K. Lesins, who has raised an excellent genetic collection at the Central Experimental Station of the University of Alberta and successfully solved the problems of applied genetics, taxonomy, chromosome morphology, and evolution of individual species of alfalfa over a period of several decades. The directions of his research and that of his school have been described in the section "Evolution of the Genus *Medicago* L., Subgenus *Falcago* (Reichb.) Grossh."

Achievements of Canadian geneticists include numerous crosses between species with different chromosome numbers, study of karyotypes in wild species and hybrid forms, compilation of idiograms of chromosomes of all species, artificial production of polyploid series in cultivated groups of taxa, and development of genetic bases for breeding this crop built on the inheritance of important characters and their progeny evaluation. At present these geneticists are interested in the problem of heritability of chlorophyll, polycotyledony, resistance of aerial and underground parts to diseases and pests, and mode of inheritance of 18-S protein (fraction No. 1) responsible for tympanitis (abdominal dropsy), a disease of cattle.

On artificially infected fields at the experimental stations of Letbridge and Winnipeg scientists conduct evaluation, identification, and multiplication of alfalfa clones for resistance to bacterial wilt, apical bud rot, winter rot, root rot, and the stem nematode (Hawn and Hanna, 1967).

Like other countries in the temperate belt, the most important problem in Canada is how to increase seed productivity of alfalfa. For the first time attention has been directed toward the alfalfa bee (*Megachile rotundata* Fabr.), which pollinates plants of this crop in the prairie region. Meanwhile the leaf-cutting bee is being successfully multiplied under artificial conditions and even exported to other countries.

Much research has been devoted to the problems of agronomy of alfalfa. The problem of cultivation of this crop is solved separately in each province with due consideration given to the peculiarities of soil and climate. There is a general ban on cutting and grazing of alfalfa in Canada from September 1st to October 15th since plants cut in this period lack sufficient nutritive reserves and do not overwinter well.

USA. Alfalfa is the most important fodder crop in the USA and is cultivated on an area of 9,864,332 hectares. This country holds first place in the world for cropped area of alfalfa. The main regions of its cultivation (60%) are concentrated in the northern half of the central part of the country. Varieties of two species are cultivated: *M. sativa* L.—mostly the irrigated zone of the southern area, and *M. varia* Mart.—northern area and dry regions of the central part of the country.

Alfalfa is comprehensively studied in the USA and all the major aspects of the biology of this crop covered. Significant success has been achieved in working out methods for the development of synthetic varieties and heterotic hybrids, utilizing inbred lines and CMS in the breeding of alfalfa for immunity, and in applied genetics of individual species. On a somewhat smaller scale than in the Soviet Union research is also conducted in this country on introduction, taxonomy, evolution, breeding for cold resistance, and bringing wild species under cultivation.

The study of alfalfa in the USA is concentrated in agricultural research centers in the states of Maryland, Utah, and California, at experimental stations, in numerous research centers of universities, and in federal, state, and private seed-production companies and firms.

The extensive spread of alfalfa in this country is associated with the introduction of the "Chilean clover" (derivatives of the "common") and varieties Ladak, Grimm, Turkestan, Kossak, Hairy Peruvian, African, and Indian. However, cultivation of alfalfa on rainfed lands, particularly in the region of the Great Plains was nevertheless limited due to inadequate resistance of the introduced material to drought, low temperatures, and diseases. In the early 1940's the first two bacterial wilt-resistant varieties were developed: Ranger—for northern regions of the Great Plains, and Buffalo—for the central regions. Later, with the perfection of methods of artificial infection of plants with pathogens and the creation of numerous congenial infection backgrounds, plant breeders developed more than 30 new varieties resistant to bacterial wilt and other diseases, including several promising varieties and hybrids with concomitant compound resistance to several diseases and pests. Varieties from the first group which have won recognition include Vernal, Moapa, Zia, Williamsburg, Narragansett, Lahontan, Saranac, and Cayuga, and from the second group Cody, Caliverde, Bamo, Dawson, Atra, Kansas, Tim, Apex, Cherokee, Tuman, Teton, Hayden, Victoria, WL-214, WL-306, WL-504, WL-508, and others.

Cytological research in the USA presently covers a wide range of problems: gametogenesis and development of the embryo, crossing of diploids with tetraploids, cytology of haploids, diploids, triploids, tetraploids, hexaploids, and aneuploids.

Genetic and plant-breeding research is mainly devoted to proving the autotetraploid nature of cultivated alfalfa, heritability of characters depending on the nature of crossing of parental forms, development of methods for breeding synthetic varieties, analysis of use of diallele crosses, efficiency of different types of selections for important characters and their heritability theory of synthesis of polyhybrid varieties and their multiplication, use of inbreeding in the development of synthetic varieties, and theoretical basis for the development of hybrid varieties from homozygous lines and CMS.

American scientists had widely resorted to phenotype selection during the early stages of alfalfa breeding. This was later replaced by the polycross method. However, if a character is a highly heritable one, then the phenotype selection is much more effective than the polycross method. If the character to be improved is characterized by low heritability, or low to moderate heritability, then for its fixation the polycross method is better suited. High-yielding alfalfa varieties such as Apex, No. 520, Scout, Cardinal, Washoe, Bokosa, Dawson, Fremont, Titan, Victoria, and Weevlchek have been developed by the polycross method.

In developing synthetic varieties it is essential to remember that all of them allow a certain degree of inbreeding, depending on number of individuals in Syn. 0 and most often appearing in generation Syn. 2. It requires not less than four parents (clones, plants) to avoid the harmful effect of inbreeding in subsequent generations, and an equal number of parents if they themselves are partially inbred. Double-clone synthetics have proven less productive than multiclone ones, although synthetics from two parents have been developed in France (varieties H. de Crecy, H. de Millefeuille, Luciole).

Contrarily, from the viewpoint of suppression of inbreeding in subsequent generations, inclusion of more than 16 parents in a synthetic variety is less effective. But if the genetic relationships between parents are not known, for complete suppression of the undesirable effects of inbreeding it is appropriate to include more than 16 parents since inbreeding will nonetheless prevail if the parents are phylogenetically closely related.

The new synthetic variety Dawson, resistant to bacterial wilt and leguminous aphids, and the variety Atra-55, highly responsive to irrigation and with high seed productivity, comprise eight clones. The new synthetic variety WL-215, comprising 25 clones, possesses compound resistance to the most common diseases and pests in the USA. The variety

Moapa, resistant to the spotted alfalfa aphid, was developed from nine plants, while the variety Cody, also resistant to the alfalfa aphid, was developed from 22.

The most important trend in plant breeding is the use of backcross. To reduce the effect of inbreeding during backcross it is necessary to conduct hybridization with unrelated plants of the parental population. Examples of successful breeding by the backcross method are the varieties Caliverde, Caliverde-65, Saranac, Iroquois, and Aralachy.

Comprehensive and extensive research has been conducted in the USA on the use of clones in plant breeding. Considering the difficulty of clonal evaluation of parents, it has been shown that if the character is a highly heritable one there is no need to exhaust material and manpower for vegetative propagation to ensure its fixation. Recurrent phenotype selection, costing far less, yields better results anyhow.

It has also been proved experimentally that hybrid varieties of alfalfa have certain advantages over synthetics for the following reasons: Complete exclusion of inbreeding (followed for synthetic varieties); elimination of the undesirable effects of natural selection and biological contamination of population due to limitations on the practical use of seed generations; and complete utilization of the effect of nonadditive genes. The autotetraploid nature of alfalfa ensures a much higher heterogeneity of hybrid varieties compared with hybrid varieties of corn in which homozygotes are formed during self-pollination or during crossing of sibs.

American researchers were the first to breed for attractiveness of alfalfa clones in order to lure a large number of wild pollinators and honeybees to alfalfa fields.

Artificial intensity of visitation of bees is achieved by increasing the pollen and nectar contents of the flowers by synchronization of flowering of seed crops and activity of bees, reducing the length of the corolla tube, and so forth. Based on such research a new branch of entomological industry is rapidly coming to the fore. Under the guidance of G.E. Bohart and W.P. Stephen a method has been developed to multiply the solitary leaf-cutting bee (*Megachile rotundata*) and cocoons of this pollinator have become an item of commerce. They are exported to Denmark, Hungary, France, and other countries of West Europe. These scientists suggest that use of synthetic clones of alfalfa and their pollination by the solitary bee result in seed yields of up to 20 quintals per hectare.

The agronomic problems of alfalfa under rainfed and irrigated conditions, methods of breeding for individual characters, study of biological properties of important organs, multiplication of seeds and seed control, technology of preparation of concentrates, breeding for individual chemical components of biomass, physiology of resistance to adverse environmental factors, water requirements, mechanization of all work from sowing to harvesting of seeds and seed processing, chemical methods of weed and pest control, etc. have been adequately dealt with in numerous publications by American researchers.

Africa. Very little information is available about the cultivation of alfalfa in countries of the African continent even though it is an important fodder crop in the Arab world, states of the eastern coastal part of the continent, and in the south. The most comprehensive reserach occurs in the South African Republic.

Republic of South Africa. The subtropical climate of this country provides ideal conditions for alfalfa cultivation, and it has been cultivated since 1850 [according to Heinrichs et al. (1972) since 1863]. Maximum areas of alfalfa are concentrated in the Cape and Orange provinces and the southern coastal region (see Figure 20). Scientists assume that certain grass mixtures preserved to date are 80 years old. Seed production is concentrated in the Cairo region. Alfalfa is mainly cultivated under natural precipitation, although irrigation is also widely practiced.

Research work with this crop is conducted in the experimental institutions of the Directorate of Agricultural Research (Pretoria), Middleburg Research Institute, College of Agriculture, and Stellenbosh University.

The best variety of the country is the South African Standard. This is a product of natural selection of the early introductions—varieties Provence (France), Hunter River (Australia), and Chinese (Tibet, China). The South African Standard has assimilated the best characters of the initial introduced varieties, is well adapted to local climate and soils, and today is the unbeatable local variety in terms of productivity.

Today the breeding program envisages development of a variety better adapted to local ecological conditions and excelling the Standard in productivity and protein content, and possessing compound resistance to drought, frost, and diseases. On studying the genetic composition of the population of the Standard variety, scientists discovered high heritability of plant height, foliage, nitrogen content, diameter of crown, and yield of green mass. Genetic diversity of the variety South African Standard makes it possible to successfully accomplish the proposed breeding program.

High doses of lime (40 q/ha) and superphosphate (12 q/ha) are favorably reflected in increased yields of alfalfa. At the research center in Dokkane the addition of 0.25 kg/ha molybdenum increased seed yield, while spraying with molybdenum increased hay yield by 63%. In Natal province alfalfa is mixed with grasses of the cold season (fescue, ryegrass, cock's foot, brome grass) and grasses of the warm season (perennial teff,

Paspalum wide, crab grass, kikuia, Nile grass). Pure crops of alfalfa are less productive.

Interesting experiments are underway on the digestibility of various types of fodder, technology of preservation of alfalfa, and fattening of animals depending on quantum of feed and quality of products fed.

Research on increasing seed productivity of alfalfa in Cairo has shown that with wide-row sowing (70 cm) the yield of seeds is 6.0 q/ha versus only 4.0 q/ha with the broadcast method. It has also been noted that green seeds germinate better, are less susceptible to molds, contain harder seed coats, are distinguished by higher viability, and produce fewer abnormal seedlings compared to the much larger brown seeds. Scientists recommend that the state standards for sowing qualities of seeds of alfalfa should take into consideration the color of the seeds.

Asia. This region gave the world alfalfa in the old days, but unfortunately is neither distinguished by volume of cropped area, nor by theoretical research.

India. Alfalfa is not among the leading fodder crops in India. It is mainly cultivated in irrigated lands of the plain provinces—Uttar Pradesh, Punjab, Madhya Pradesh—and the hilly regions of northern India. The popularity of this crop has recently increased with farmers because it gives high fodder yields in early spring—summer, exceeds Egyptian clover in yield in winter, and provides protein-rich hay and green mass after harvesting. Local farmers call it "berseem".

In northern India alfalfa is a leading fodder crop. Grass stands in the hilly haylands and pastures can remain for as long as 40 to 50 years if used properly.

The main research centers for studying alfalfa are the Fodder and Grassland Research Institute (Uttar Pradesh), agricultural universities in both Uttar Pradesh and Haryana, and plant-breeding experimental stations under the Department of Agriculture, Ministry of Agriculture.

Alfalfa breeding in India is undertaken according to a preplanned program involving specialists of various disciplines: plant breeders, entomologists, phytopathologists, and veterinarians. At the experimental station in Sirsa two alfalfa varieties have been developed—Sirsa-8 and Sirsa-9. The breeding program gives much importance to the problem of increasing the resistance of alfalfa to downy mildew, rust, and the leguminous stem borer. In Uttar Pradesh research is underway on artificial development of hexaploids by crossing colchicine-induced octoploids with natural tetraploids.

Agronomic research has shown that the yield of alfalfa increases if the interval between cuttings is 42 to 50 days. The most favorable conditions for the growth of this crop in the plains obtain from February to May.

Increasing the seed productivity of alfalfa is a serious problem in India because the local honeybee (*Apis indica* F.) is not a very effective pollinator of crops.

In northern India three types of alfalfa are grown in the hilly pastures: Jharkhand, Kargil, and Owlback. Jharkhand is erect and reaches 1.2 to 1.5 m in height, with a thick stem and broad leaves. Its yield potential for two to three cuttings is 75 to 100 q/ha green mass per season. Kargil is distinguished by a creeping habit, with a 60 to 90 cm long, slender, and tender stem. It is cut only once, at the end of the vegetative season, and yields 25 to 38 q/ha green mass. Owlback is an intermediate type. These three types of alfalfa are grown on hilly slopes with poor, stony soils and deficit water. The first cutting occurs in the third year of growth after the plant root system is well established. Density of plant stand is maintained by natural shedding of seeds.

Japan. Alfalfa is used for increasing the productivity of natural pastures in the cold regions of the islands. The crop is studied by the National Agricultural Experimental Station (Hokkaido), Agronomy Faculty of Hokkaido University, and National Institute of Animal Husbandry.

Japan has no improved alfalfa varieties of its own. The French variety Du Puits and the Canadian rhizomatous varieties Rhizoma and Rambler are cultivated. The most productive is the variety Du Puits.

Research has shown that the rate of sprouting of the aerial plant parts depends on the degree of development of lateral roots and total mass of root system ($r = +0.93$). Root mass correlates well with carbohydrate content. Varieties which intensively use reserve nutrients at the commencement of sprouting accumulate more carbohydrates in subsequent periods of plant growth. Double cutting of alfalfa in September reduces carbohydrate reserves and causes yield losses in subsequent years. The greater the proportion of alfalfa in grass mixtures, the higher their productivity.

Australia and Oceania. The main producers of alfalfa in this part of the world are Australia and New Zealand (see Figure 20).

Australia. Perennial species of alfalfa are cultivated on an area of 2,000,000 hectares in the coastal regions of the eastern, southern, and southwestern parts of the country where precipitation is high (550 to 650 mm). The first local variety, Hunter River, evolved at the beginning of the century from the French (Provence) and probably Spanish and North African populations, belongs to the Mediterranean type and occupies 99% of the cropped area.

Alfalfa is studied mainly in the research centers of the National Academy situated at Canberra, Brisbane, and Deniell (Queensland), the experimental station at Trangie (New South Wales) and Adelaide

(South Australia), and the Agricultural Research Institute of Adelaide University.

Breeding work with alfalfa was begun in the National Academy in 1954 and 14 years later (1968) the first national improved variety, Cancreep, was released (Canberra Creeping, alfalfa from Canberra), which included the best characters and properties of the initial parental forms. Cancreep is a complex hybrid between the maternal varieties Hunter River (Australia), Hairy Peruvian (Peru), and African (Egypt), and the paternal variety Rambler (Canada). The new variety made it possible to extend alfalfa cultivation from the humid coastal belt to the continental interior right up to the semiarid zone with an annual rainfall of 300 to 350 mm, because it possesses characters such as rhizomatous roots, resistance to grazing and trampling, dwarf habit, and much higher winter hardiness, drought resistance, and resistance to wilt and other diseases compared to the maternal varieties. In contrast to the paternal variety Rambler it exhibits early maturity, rapid growth, good responsiveness to irrigation, and short winter dormancy (Daday, 1962, 1968, 1968a).

Launching of the breeding program was preceded by an evaluation of varieties introduced in this continent and well known in other countries—Du Puits, Caliverde, Indian, Rambler, African, Hairy Peruvian, Saladina, and others. These varieties were studied in various soil and climatic zones of the country and were compared with the national standard variety, Hunter River. It was established that the variety African is distinguished by high productivity in the summer period and Hairy Peruvian in the cold period of the year, while Du Puits is distinguished for productivity throughout the entire vegetative period. Variety Rambler is characterized by a slow growth rate, low productivity, and a long period of winter dormancy. Not a single variety introduced in Australia satisfied the plant breeders because they did not combine high resistance of plants to grazing and trampling with perennial sprouting, winter hardiness, multicutting, and high productivity. It was this situation which motivated Australian researchers to develop the new variety, Cancreep. However, the pace at which this new variety is being brought under cultivation is incredibly slow. Released for cultivation in 1968 it is grown today on an area that does not exceed 10 hectares.

Important research is underway in the continent on the identification of winter-hardy plants with artificial freezing of seedlings in refrigerated chambers, and heritability and variability of chemical composition in dormant (during winter) organs. It has been found that cold resistance is linked with the duration of the period of winter dormancy and length of day; cold resistance in hybrids is inherited according to the law of averages; the electrostatic potential of cold resistance is inversely proportional to the intensity of winter growth; cold resistance has polygenic heritability, and so forth. The nature of segregation of progeny in F_1 in diallele crosses has shown that it is very difficult to combine winter hardiness with intensive winter growth in one hybrid, but nevertheless it is possible (Greenham and Daday, 1957, 1960; Palmer, 1960, 1967).

In addition, scientists have also established that acidic reactions of the soil solution (pH 5.5 to 6.0 and below) suppress the growth processes of alfalfa by inhibiting formation of nodules on the roots and, therefore, large doses of lime or phosphate must be applied to reduce the toxic effect of aluminum in the soil solution.

Rotational grazing of grass stands at intervals of eight to nine weeks facilitate conservation of alfalfa in pasture grass mixtures, especially in the case of mixed sowing of late clover.

The greater part of the research in Australia is devoted to problems of disease and pest control. Dieldrin at a rate of 1.12 kg/ha or heptachlor at a rate of 2.24 kg/ha is applied to the soil for weevils. To control the turnip moth, which damages seed crops, scientists recommend an oil emulsion of DDT (25%), and for the flower midge treatment of crops with the chemical Supergam at a rate of 100 to 130 kg/ha or Lidenal at 20 to 40 kg/ha. Preparations 2,4-D and 2,2-D-PA are recommended for the control of weeds.

New Zealand. The production of alfalfa is concentrated in South Island in regions with an annual rainfall of 900 to 1,180 mm.

The central part of the island receives 590 to 790 mm of rain. Summer drought and prolonged frost in winter are quite common here. Northern alfalfa is cultivated in the island in the region of the Central Plateau where the average rainfall per annum is 1,575 mm.

Alfalfa is studied by the National Research Center (Lincoln), Raukur Agricultural Research Center of the Department of Agriculture, Biological Department of the Lincoln Institute, and Massei University.

Three varieties of alfalfa have been developed in the country: Marlborough—a selection from the early Australian introductions of French alfalfas; Wairau—a selection from the varieties Marlborough (New Zealand), Grimm, and Ontario Variegated (introduced from the USA); Glutinosa—a rhizomatous variety developed in Lincoln Institute utilizing local alfalfas as well as varieties such as Rambler (Canada), Argentine (Argentina), Chanticleer, and Saladina (Spain).

The maximum area in New Zealand is occupied by the variety Wairau, although its growth rate is reduced during the cold season compared to the Australian standard variety (Hunter River). The breeding program envisages development of a new, highly productive variety, better adapted to the local climate.

117

Comprehensive research is underway in New Zealand on the grazing regime of pure alfalfa crops and grass mixtures, liming and subsequent inoculation of soils with nodular bacteria, regime of irrigation and doses of chemical fertilizers, technology of preparing grass meals and briquettes, and treatment of seed crops with insecticides (Palmer, 1960, 1967).

CHAPTER III

Introduction, Breeding Evaluation, and Use of the World Collection of Alfalfa

Biologists throughout the world unanimously recognize the renowned Soviet scientist, founder of the All-Union Institute of Plant Industry, Nikolai Ivanovich Vavilov, as one of the propounders of the doctrine of initial material. In his classical work *Selektsiya kak Nauka* (Plant Breeding as a Science) he wrote: "The concept of initial material, that is, the origin of cultivated plants, must be the basis for plant breeding."[1]

Vavilov scientifically established the botanical, geographic, and ecological principles of the study of initial material. He outlined the prospects of utilization of local varieties, wild flora, as "extraregional and extraterritorial" initial material in plant breeding. He made significant contributions to the theory of introduction, and considerably enhanced the fundamental research of the eminent evolutionist, Charles Darwin, and the propounder of the doctrine of acclimatization of plants, I.V. Michurin.

One of the significant contributions to the theory of introduction made by Vavilov was the discovery of centers of origin and centers of diversity of cultivated plants and their wild relatives associated with ancient centers of civilization.

Vavilov discovered the law of homologous series of hereditary variability of characters that made it possible *de novo* to evaluate the principles of ecogeographic crossings, selection of parental components, and methods of evaluating hybrids. Today Vavilov's concepts concerning initial material are being expanded by his disciples and by the All-Union Institute of Plant Industry (VIR). Scientists of the VIR are mobilizing plant resources in the "centers of Vavilov," conducting in-depth studies of initial material, and providing a theoretical basis for plant breeding that incorporates the problems of evolution, taxonomy, introduction, immunity of plants, and applied genetics of cultivated plants.

The main task of the VIR and its extensive experimental network is

[1]N.I. Vavilov. 1960. Izbrannie trudy v pyati tomakh (collected works in five volumes). AN SSSR, Moscow, vol. 2, p. 16.

the mobilization of plant resources—their all-round study, multiplication, and supply to plant-breeding institutions. As a result of organizational measures work on the mobilization of plant resources of the world, initiated under the guidance of Vavilov, advanced considerably in the 1970's. At present the collection of VIR comprises 270,000 varietal specimens of various agricultural crops and their wild relatives, representing 1,800 plant species. This unique gene bank has served as the spearhead for the development of more than 2,000 varieties and hybrids, of which 929 have been released for cultivation today and occupy about 80,000,000 hectares in agricultural production. The entry of specimens in the world collection confirms that the rates of collection of initial material in the tenth Five-Year Plan were 20 to 30% higher than in the years 1971 to 1975 (Brezhnev, 1967, 1974, 1975).

Planned work on the introduction and evaluation of fodder crops was initiated in the VIR in 1922. For over half a century scientists of the Department of Fodder Crops have collected initial material from wild flora, identified valuable local populations of fodder crops in various regions of the Soviet Union, and included in the collection improved varieties of many foreign countries.

The world collection of alfalfa housed in the All-Union Institute of Plant Industry is at present the richest genetic collection in the world. The botanical and ecological diversity of alfalfa stored in the national gene bank of the Soviet Union reflects fairly well its entire world potential. The collection comprises more than 2,000 specimens, including improved varieties as well as local and wild populations from 70 countries of all the continents of the globe. The Soviet Union, Turkey, Iran, and Afghanistan

Table 9. Composition of VIR alfalfa collection as on January 1, 1978

Geographic region	Perennial species				Annual species		Region-wise
	M. sativa and M. varia	M. falcata	Other wild species				
			No. of species	Specimens	No. of species	Specimens	
Asia	951	91	14	113	25	52	1,207
Europe	556	92	11	66	20	61	775
America	264	5	—	—	4	8	277
Australia	19	—	—	—	11	16	35
Africa	39	—	—	—	1	1	40
Total	1,829	188	—	179	—	138	2,334

Table 10. Countries with maximum number of specimens of perennial species of alfalfa in the principal catalog of the VIR collection*

Country	Number of		Percentage of entire collection
	Species	Specimens	
Entire collection	—	2,196	100
Soviet Union	17	1,309	61.0
USA	3	171	8.0
Turkey	1	70	3.3
Bulgaria	2	49	2.3
France	1	46	2.1
Italy	2	38	1.8
China	4	36	1.7
Afghanistan	1	36	1.7
Iran	1	26	1.2
Hungary	1	25	1.1
Yugoslavia	1	25	1.1
Canada	3	23	1.1
Czechoslovakia	1	19	0.9
Argentina	1	16	0.7
Federal Republic of Germany	3	15	0.7
Australia	1	12	0.5
Rumania	2	11	0.5
Peru	1	11	0.5
India	1	10	0.5
Spain	1	9	0.4
Egypt	1	5	0.2

*The temporary catalog of the Department of Fodder Crops lists 800 specimens under multiplication. Individual species are well represented in the collection of the Soviet Union (17 species) and Australia (12 species).

are the most comprehensively represented in the collection since the primary centers of origin of alfalfa species are located in these countries. Several improved and local varieties are stored in the collection from countries whose territory converges toward the primary centers of origin of cultivated plants (China, Bulgaria, Italy, France), as well as from countries where alfalfa breeding is practiced at a higher scientific level, resulting in the establishment of secondary (improved, artificial) gene centers of cultivated species of *Medicago* L.

Data on the enrichment and continental and countrywise composition of the VIR alfalfa collection is presented in Tables 9 and 10.

INTRODUCTION, CONSERVATION, AND ECONOMIC AND ECOLOGICAL CHARACTERISTICS OF SPECIES OF PERENNIAL ALFALFA OF KAZAKH SSR

Collection of Initial Material

In his classical work *Botaniko-Geograficheskie Osnovy Selektsi* (Botanical and Geographic Principles of Plant Breeding) N.I. Vavilov wrote that a large number of grass and leguminous herbaceous species of annual and perennial plants in our country deserve serious attention as initial material for introduction for cultivation. This pertains first and foremost to wild species of *Medicago* L., which are distinguished not only by high nutritional properties, but also by wide ecological variability as well as intrapopulation variability.

In the evolution of the genus *Medicago* L. diploid and tetraploid species of alfalfa of Kazakh SSR play an important role and, without exception, constitute valuable initial material for breeding and practical use. Considering the ever-increasing depletion of germ plasm throughout the world, the All-Union Institute of Plant Industry has intensified the pace of mobilization of plant resources within our country and abroad. Toward this end in 1969 seven permanent field-study groups were organized to survey the main natural economic regions of the Soviet Union. One of them, the Kazakhstan expedition, undertakes regular collection of initial material from Kazakh SSR and regions of the Central Asian and European-Siberian gene centers bordering the republic (Figure 21).

The soil and climatic conditions of Kazakhstan are extremely heterogeneous. Wide variations in ecological conditions promote rich specific and especially interspecific diversity of alfalfa.

Before the organization of permanent field-study groups the plant resources of Kazakhstan were mainly surveyed by geobotanists and florists. The history of these undertakings, initiated almost 200 years ago by P.S. Palass who surveyed Altai and the northeastern part of Kirgiz territory in 1771, has been recounted in *Botanika v Kazakhstane* [Botany in Kazakhstan (1959)] and other publications.

In the study of the genus *Medicago* in Kazakhstan and the republics of Central Asia (until 1925 these constituted a unified territory known as Kirgiz territory) significant contributions have been made by Soviet botanists: G.P. Sumnevich, A.I. Belov, V.M. Golodkovskii, I.T. Vasil'chenko, M.V. Kul'tiasov, I.V. Larin, O. Kh. Khasanov, V.P. Goloskokov, and others. These botanists played an important role in determining the geographic areas of individual species and their origin in relation to the evolution of the genus, verification of its taxonomy, identification of the

122

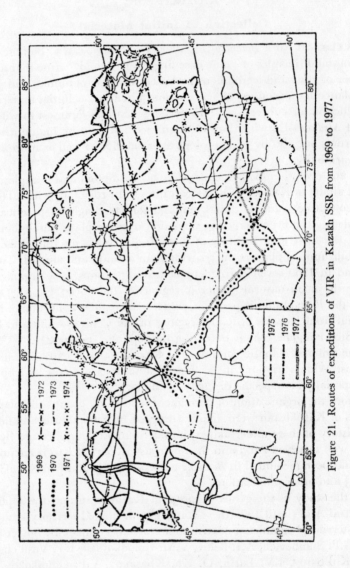

Figure 21. Routes of expeditions of VIR in Kazakh SSR from 1969 to 1977.

centers of hybridization, and determination of how wild species could be utilized for cultivation. However, the research of these botanists was strictly floristic, given their professional orientation.

The shortcoming of floristic research is the absence of agronomic characteristics of wild fodder plants which are most promising for introduction for cultivation. The vegetation of Kazakhstan was quite thoroughly studied by geobotanists in the past but never assessed by agronomists, plant breeders, and plant scientists, i.e., by agricultural specialists entrusted with the task of solving practical problems related to an increase in agricultural production.

The first major agronomic survey of the natural fodder lands of Kazakhstan was conducted in 1936 by the agricultural expedition of the Academy of Sciences of the USSR. The creative culmination of the work of this expedition was a monumental work entitled *Sel'skoe Khozyaistvo Rudnogo Altaya* [Agriculture of Rudnoi Altai (1940)]. In 1938 the plant breeding-agronomic expedition of the Siberian Research Institute of Agriculture, comprising N.V. Tsitsin, V.Yu. Voitonis, and E.G. Priimak, surveyed the Altai and desert-steppe zone of Kazakhstan. This expedition collected seeds and herbs of wild perennial grasses promising for introduction in agriculture and use in plant breeding and identified their centers of distribution. Ecological classification of the collected material was done later. In the same year, in the northern part of Kazakhstan, field studies were undertaken by the Omsk Agricultural Institute (N.A. Plotnikov) which collected specimens of yellow alfalfa and other grasses useful for cultivation. Similar expeditions were conducted in western, northern, and central Kazakhstan during the prewar period, and in southern and eastern Kazakhstan in the postwar years.

The specialists who participated in these expeditions conducted successful breeding work with the introduced material. Nearly all of the alfalfa varieties released for cultivation in the republic (especially those of cereal grasses) such as Karaganda-1, Blue Ural, Tibet, Shortandinskaya-2, Kokshe, Semirechensk local, Karabalykskaya, Irtyshskaya local, and Krasnovodopadskaya-8 were developed from the ancient varieties of folk selection or through hybridization of the improved material with local varieties and indigenous or wild populations introduced in the republic.

The systematic survey of the diverse geomorphology and vegetation of the territory of Kazakhstan proposed by the N.I. Vavilov All-Union Research Institute of Plant Industry was conducted in several stages and has been more or less accomplished.

The expeditions of 1969 to 1978 crossed the dry deserts of Mangyshlak, Caspian lowland, Ustyurt plateau, clay deserts of Dzhezkazgan and Betpak-Dala; the high-altitude hilly regions of western and eastern Tien

124

Shan, Dzhungarian-Alatau, southern and Rudnoi Altai, the hillocks of Mugodzhar, Semipalatinsk, and northern and central Kazakhstan; the sands of the Volga-Ural and Ural-Embensk interfluves; the sandy massifs of Kyzyl-Kum, Muyunkum, Sary-Ishikotrau, and Bol'shaya and Malya Barsuiki; and the territories of Mugodzharo-Irtysh and Chu-Alakol'sk subprovinces constituting the extensive North Turan floristic transitional province.

Thus almost the entire territory of Kazakhstan was surveyed from 1969

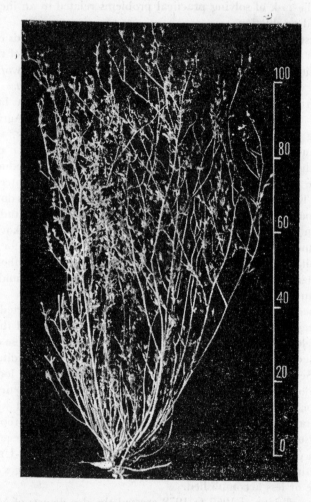

Figure 22. Blue alfalfa (*M. coerulea* Less., 2n=16). Plants erect, tall (up to 140 cm) with profuse foliage. Second terrace of floodplain of Ural River, meadow (Ural province, Taipakskii region, state farm "Essensaiskii").

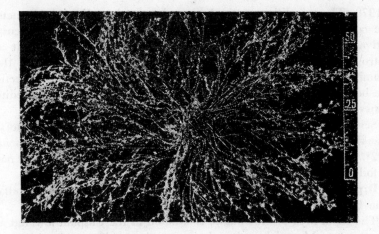

Figure 23. Blue alfalfa (2n=16). Plants with good foliage, compact bush. Willow grove in floodplain of Ural River, flooded for short duration by meltwater (Gur'evskaya province, village Kulagino, state farm "Put'Il'icha").

Figure 24. Trautvetter's alfalfa (2n=16). Tall (up to 3.0 m), with sparse standing plants, almond-leaf, willowlike poor foliage, wild population. Clay floodplain of the Ili River, Koktal (Taldy-Kurgan province, Panfilovsk region, collective farm "Usharal").

to 1978. The expedition parties traversed more than 200,000 kilometers. The collection of the institute was enriched with 3,578 specimens of cultivated plants and their wild relatives (not including the fruit and subtropical crops). Fodder plants (2,446 specimens) and among them leguminous herbs—alfalfa—comprised the main bulk of the collection. The best specimens of wild species of alfalfa collected by the expedition parties from 1969 to 1978 are pictured in Figures 22 to 25.

Seven species of alfalfa of the subgenus *Falcago* grow in the territory of Kazakhstan, of which three are diploid and four tetraploid (Lubenets, 1972). All these species can be used for increasing the productivity of natural fodder lands.

Diploid species. Blue, Trautvetter's, and South Kazakhstan alfalfa occur in the low-lying areas of the desert and semidesert belt.

The main area of blue alfalfa is situated in the Caspian lowland and extends up to Mugodzhar. Populations of blue alfalfa growing in western Kazakhstan are of two types: floodplain and sandy. The first type is characterized by tall plants (from 120 to 150 to 200 cm), semispreading bush, salt tolerance, high tillering habit, medium foliage, poor pubescence, disease resistance, high seed productivity, and small but well-twisted (three to five twists) pods. The second type is more xeromorphic, with small prostrate brushes, poor foliage, and narrowly lanceolate or linear pubescent leaflets (Figures 22 and 23).

Trautvetter's alfalfa is localized in the hills of Mugodzhar on the Ustyurt plateau, in the southern part of the foothills of Dzhungarian-Alatau, and centers of introgressive hybridization situated in western Tien Shan. It grows in the floodplains of small rivers, at the bottom of water sources, low-lying areas of plains, along hilly slopes at the edges of forest massifs, along railway lines, and in kitchen gardens. In places with a good water supply wild populations have an erect, rarely spreading bush. Foliage poor, leaflets small, elongated, linear, pubescent. Trautvetter's alfalfa is characterized by high salt tolerance, drought resistance, winter hardiness, and disease resistance. The most productive populations of this species grow in the Aktyubin province, in the hills of Mugodzhar, on the Ustyurt plateau, and in the basin of the Bol'shaya Khobda River, as well as in southern Kazakhstan in the floodplain of the Ili River (Figure 24).

The South Kazakhstan alfalfa occupies extensive dry steppe, semidesert, and desert zones of the republic. Its wild populations are mainly concentrated north of Lake Balkhash. Large centers, according to V.B. Kuvaev —ecocenters, of this species of alfalfa from which seeds for commercial use are possible, occur in Dzhezkazgan, Karaganda, Turgaisk, southern Kustanaisk, Semipalatinsk, Pavlodarsk, Vostochno-Kazakhstansk, eastern Kokchetavsk, and northern Dzhambul provinces. This is the most drought-

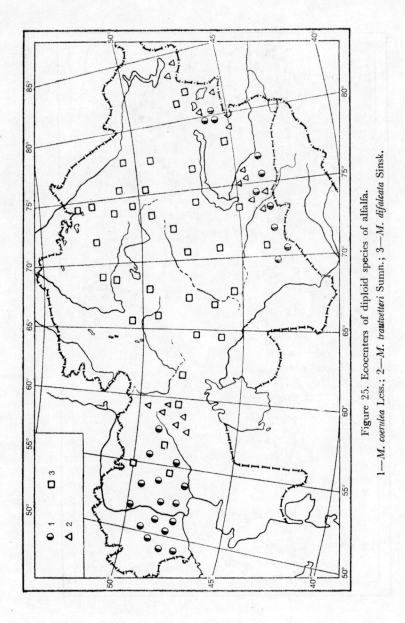

Figure 25. Ecocenters of diploid species of alfalfa.

1—*M. coerulea* Less.; 2—*M. trautvetteri* Sumn.; 3—*M. difalcata* Sinsk.

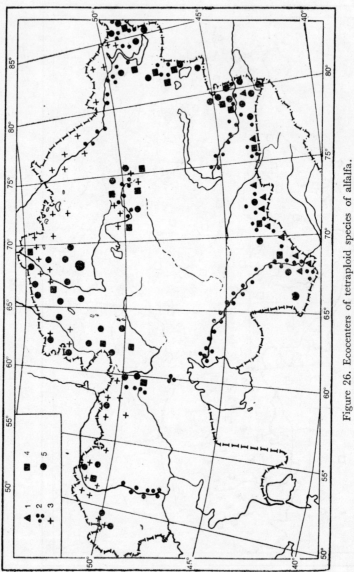

Figure 26. Ecocenters of tetraploid species of alfalfa.

1—*M. tianschanica* Vass.; 2—*M. sativa* L.; 3—*M. varia* Mart. (cultivated); 4—*M. varia* Mart. (wild); 5—*M. falcata* L.

resistant species of the subgenus *Falcago* of those found in Kazakh SSR. In the northern part of the republic the area of the South Kazakhstan alfalfa is restricted by cultivated lands, and in the south by irrigated fields under crop rotation where wild diploid species cannot compete with fast-growing populations of common alfalfa, Trautvetter's alfalfa, Tian Shan alfalfa, and even yellow alfalfa. The alfalfa areas of the subgenus *Falcago* in Kazakh SSR are delineated in Figures 25 and 26.

Tetraploid species. Common cultivated alfalfa, variable alfalfa, crescentoid alfalfa, and Tian Shan alfalfa, with a few exceptions, do not grow in the desert belt.

Common alfalfa is cultivated on irrigated lands in Chimkent, Dzhambul, Alma-Ata, and Taldy-Kurgan provinces. Under wild conditions it grows in the lower reaches of the foothills of Tien Shan, extending far into the highly fertile plains, and with assured moisture along irrigation channels and tree plantation belts, floodplains of rivers, interrows of fruit orchards, bottom of dried water sources, and along railway lines.

Variable alfalfa is cultivated in the desert and steppe zones of Kazakhstan. In the natural phytocenosis of central Kazakhstan (desert belt) it is found only as a weed mixed with wild flora in anthropogenic (secondary) cenoses formed on artificial earth embankments (quarries, dams, lowlands, bridges, deep roadside ditches, irrigation canals, etc.). Under conditions of usual water supply (natural cenosis) it cannot compete with the more drought-resistant diploid species, South Kazakhstan alfalfa. In the arid zone variable alfalfa grows very rarely under wild conditions and that, too, only in places with better water supply compared with other microcenters of the surrounding landscape. One of the largest areas of natural growth of variable alfalfa is the Mugodzhar hillocks.

Wild populations of variable alfalfa have appeared recently in the desert belt of Kazakhstan. This is a product of natural hybridization of wild-growing, yellow-flowered species of different ploidy levels with tetraploid species of common alfalfa introduced here for cultivation. Small weedy populations of variable alfalfa, often represented by solitary plants, are those forms of cultivated varieties which were released here or were brought here from neighboring regions for cultivation but became wild.

The geographic area of distribution of the crescentoid alfalfa is the most extensive. In Kazakh SSR it grows among all plant formations. In the arid zone yellow alfalfa grows in the floodplains of rivers, bottom of dried water sources, edges of reservoirs among sandy dunes, and fringes of forests in low hill valleys. Ecocenters of this species are situated in the forest-steppe zone, floodplains of large rivers, and the hilly belt including Kokchetavsk hillock. Hilly productive forms of wild populations of cres-

130

centoid alfalfa are maximally concentrated in the mountains of Altai, Tien Shan, and Dzhungarian-Alatau.

Tian Shan alfalfa is found only in the hilly valleys of the extreme southern part of Kazakhstan, in mountain passes, and on slopes of hilly ridges (Figure 27).

The species composition of the subgenus *Falcago* (Reichb.) Grossh. alfalfa collected by the Kazakhstan expedition of the VIR is shown in Table 11. Maximum saturation of natural phytocenoses with wild species of alfalfa is characteristic for southern (56 specimens) and especially western Kazakhstan (69 specimens). The flora of this geographic region is significantly distinguished from that of other regions of the republic by richness and diversity of natural populations of species of *Medicago* L. This is explained by a number of factors: geomorphological heterogeneity

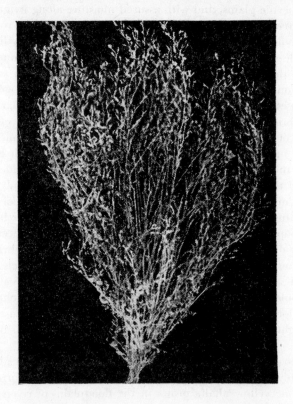

Figure 27. Tian Shan alfalfa (*M. tianschanica* Vass., 2n=32). High-yielding population with strong solitary bushes growing along irrigation canals in fruit orchard at an altitude of 1,200 to 1,400 m above mean sea level.

Western Tien Shan Kirgiz ridge (Dzhambul province, Lugovsk region, Sugoty area).

of the territory, continuous belt, different types of soils, sharp climatic transitions, excess or, contrarily, deficit of water resources, poor economic development of the territory, and so forth.

Ecobiological Characteristics of Specimens

Botanical and breeding descriptions of better wild specimens of alfalfa, most promising for breeding and cultivation in the areas of their natural growth, are given in Table 12.

Centers of Introgressive Hybridization

Field surveys of the territory of western Kazakhstan have shown that in the hills of Mugodzhar lies a strong center of introgressive hybridization. Areas of distribution of *M. coerulea* Less., *M. sativa* L. (cultivated and weedy forms), *M. falcata* L., and *M. difalcata* Sinsk. (*M. ochroleuca* Kult.) are contiguous in this center. The products of their hybridization are *M. trautvetteri* Sumn. and *M. varia* Mart.

Studies of the places of natural growth and cytological analysis have confirmed the hypothesis of hybrid origin of the first species, to say nothing of the second species, which is a product of crossing of common alfalfa and yellow alfalfa. Populations of *M. trautvetteri* spread over a vast area of *M. falcata* and the two often grow side by side with other species in almost one and the same phytocenosis. In the latter case distinct hybrid characters are evident in such populations. Their phenotype resembles the variable alfalfa. It is understandable that some researchers have crossed these two species, mistaking the common hybrid form of *M. varia* for *M. trautvetteri*.

Pure, phenotypically quite uniform plant stands of Trautvetter's alfalfa with diploid chromosomes are found rarely. Such stands are localized near centers of introgression in places of high natural isolation (narrow hilly clefts, low-lying areas in the desert plateau of Ustyurt). They are wild populations occupying a small area, uniform with respect to blue flowers, and possessing other distinctive morphological characters such as compactly pressed or erect shape of bush, low foliage, pigmentation of stem, pubescence, thin stems, prolonged period of flowering (from May to September), and so forth. These rare populations have a precise distribution area and unfortunately disappear due to rapid development of civilization; they originated from the natural crossing of diploid species—*M. coerulea* Less. and *M. difalcata* Sinsk. (*M. ochroleuca* Kult.). P.A. Lubenets considers the pale yellow alfalfa a synonym for *M. tianschanica*. In my opinion it belongs in the series of *M. difalcata*, especially since its geographic area does not correspond absolutely to just the blue-flowered hilly species, but concomitantly the plain desert-steppe area of the South Kazakhstan alfalfa.

Table 11. Species composition of the subgenus *Falcago* (Reichb.) Grossh.; alfalfa collected by the Kazakhstan expedition of VIR in different regions of the republic from 1969 to 1977

Species	Western Kazakhstan	Northern Kazakhstan	Central Kazakhstan	Eastern Kazakhstan	Southern Kazakhstan	Total
M. sativa (2n=32)	—	—	3	9	24	36
M. varia (2n=32)	5	6	2	—	4	17
M. tianschanica (2n=32)	—	—	—	—	6	6
M. falcata (2n=32)	27	1	21	3	13	65
M. trautvetteri (2n=16)	22	—	—	4	8	34
M. coerulea (2n=16)	13	—	—	—	—	13
M. difalcata (2n=16)	2	14	10	11	1	38
Total	69	21	36	27	56	209*

*Remaining specimens of alfalfa belong to other subgenera.

Table 12. Characteristics of the better wild specimens of alfalfa collected by the expedition from 1969 to 1977 from the territory of Kazakh SSR

Origin	Habitat	Description of plant
1	2	3
	Common alfalfa—*M. sativa* L.	
Dzhambul province, Lugovsk region, Algabas village, Sugoty area	Home gardens, foothills of Kirgiz ridge. Along irrigation channels, roadside ditches, and low-lying places among tree plantation belts	Bush semiprostrate, large, 90–100 cm tall, with 10–15 branches; leaflets oval-cuneiform, foliage moderate; maturation of pods uniform; profuse fruiting; pod medium sized (5.87 ± 0.06) with 0.5–1.5–2.0–2.5 twists (1.85 ± 0.08)
Dzhambul province, Lugovsk region, Algabas village	Western Tien Shan, Kirgiz ridge. Tree plantation belts, along railway lines in foothill part of valleys. Depression between hills	Bush prostrate; stem 70–90 to 120–130 cm long; leaflets elongated-oval, foliage moderate; stems slender, long, tender, slightly pigmented, glabrous; corolla violet; pods small (2.0–3.0 mm) with 2.5–3.5 twists, or medium sized (4.0–6.0 mm) with 2.0–2.5 twists; fruiting profuse; disease resistant
Dzhambul province, Chuisk region, beet state farm at border with Frunze province	Chuisk canal. Along irrigation channels and tree plantation belts in foothills of Kirgiz ridge. Legume-cereal herbage	Bush erect, 70–80 cm tall, foliage profuse; leaflets roundish-oval, cuneiform, obovate; stems thick, rough at base; corolla violet of different hues; pods large, with 1.5–2.0–2.5–3.0 twists; fruiting profuse; disease free; broom-rape found in grass stand
Eastern Kazakhstan province, Zaisan region, Michurin state farm, varietal trial field	Zaisan plain. Along irrigation channels and tree plantation belts	Plants erect, height 80–90 cm; 5–7 branches in bush; corolla violet; early maturing; pods small, with 2.5–3.5 twists; maturation of pods uniform

(Contd.)

Table 12 (*Contd.*)

1	2	3
Eastern Kazakhstan province, Zaisan region, Michurin state farm	Fruit orchard at foothills of northern slopes of Saur ridge. Along irrigation channels and among tree plantation belts	Bush semiprostrate, large, 80–100 cm tall, with 12–17 branches; leaves oval-cuneiform foliage moderate; maturation of pods uniform; fruiting profuse; pod medium sized (5.67 ± 0.05) with 0.5–1.5–2.0–2.5 twists (1.55 ± 0.03)
Eastern Kazakhstan province, Markakol'sk region, "Gornovskii" state farm	Kurchumsk ridge. Hilly plateau. High-altitude herbage; 1,800 m above mean sea level. Yellow alfalfa predominates	Bushes strong, up to 100 cm tall, erect, also prostrate; stems rough; pod with 1.5–3.5 twists, mostly small; early maturing and cold resistant
	Variable alfalfa—*M. varia* Mart.	
Eastern Kazakhstan Province, Markakol'sk region, "Gornovskii" state farm	Kurchumsk ridge. Alpine pasture; 1,600 m above mean sea level. Solitary plants scattered in low-lying places among alpine herbage and yellow alfalfa	Bushes small, 40–50 cm tall, erect, with good foliage; stems thick, rough; leaflets oval, elongated-lanceolate, small, pubescent; corolla violet, red-violet, small; pods with 1.5–2.0–3.0–3.5 twists (2.57 ± 0.05), small (4.23 ± 0.05)
Easter Kazakhstan province, Markakol'sk region, "Karaoil'skii" state farm, Arkhipovka village	Hilly ravines and depressions up to 2,000 m above mean sea level	Plants sharply distinguished in form depending on altitude of locality; small at 1,500–2,000 m, and large, up to 100 cm in height, below 1,500 m; many transitional large-podded forms found in population; cold resistant
Eastern Kazakhstan province, Kurchumsk region, Kurchum village	Foothill plain. Depression among semidesert wormwoods	Bushes large, mainly erect, 80–120 cm tall; branches numerous; foliage profuse; early maturing; pods with 1.5–2.0 twists

Dzhezkazgan province, Shetsk region, north of Aksu-Ayuly village	Southern slopes of hillock. Streams on passes with interrupted phytocenosis	Bush strong, erect, 80–120 cm tall; 12–18 thick, rough, but green branches; foliage moderately profuse, leaflets large, cuneiform; corolla violet; pod large, with 2.0–3.0 twists; seed productivity very high
Aktyubin province, Chelkarsk region, "Aktogaiskii" state farm	Gravelly floodplain of Zhuldak River in eastern environs of Mugodzhar. Herbage	Bush strong, semiprostrate, 70–80 cm tall; leaflets small, elongated-lanceolate; foliage good; branches slender, up to 70 in a bush; corolla violet-lilac; pods falciform, rarely with up to 0.75 twist
Aktyubin province, Mugodzhar region, environs of station Emba	Floodplain of Emba River (colluvial soil, silty clay)	Bush highly prostrate or semi-erect, prostrate in case of long-stemmed plants, usually stems 60–80 cm long; bushes with very long stems also known (130–160 cm long) (along borders near irrigated gardens); 8–15 branches in bush; foliage moderate, leaflets elongated-cuneiform; corolla dirty violet, pods falciform
Aktyubin province, Baiganinsk region, plateau Ustyurt, Shushkakul' area	Short-duration floodwater current of Shagan (colluvial soil, loamy)	Bush strong, erect to semi-erect, 90–120 cm tall; 20–30 branches in bush; leaflets lanceolate, dorsally pubescent; corolla whitish to violet-lilac; pods falciform
Ural'sk province, Chapaevsk region, environs of Kolovorotnoe village	Herbage (soil, sandy-loam). Plants of variegated alfalfa grow in same cenosis with blue alfalfa	Tall plants, up to 90–170 cm; foliage moderate, leaflets medium sized, elongated-lanceolate; corolla greenish-yellow, whitish, to violet; pods falciform with 0.75 to 1.0 twist
Tselinograd province, Vishnevsk region, "Krasnozerskii" state farm	In plains (sandy soils). Steppe legume-cereal herbage	Plants solitary, very strong; tillering profuse; bush up to 110 cm tall; pods small, with 1.5–2.5 twists; fruiting profuse; seed dispersal not seen

(Contd.)

Table 12 (*Contd.*)

1	2	3
	Yellow alfalfa—M. falcata L.	
Eastern Kazakhstan province, Markakol'sk region, Buran	Dune sands in floodplain of Irtysh River. Solitary bushes of alfalfa and white sweet clover grow in depressions between dunes. Not far from tugai riverbed forests	Bushes large, 120–180 cm tall, with 50–70 and more branches; stems at base thick and rough but flexible and tender in upper portion; foliage moderate; corolla yellow; pod falciform, large (12.83±0.08); fruiting profuse; flowering period highly protracted; racemes small
Alma-Ata province, Kegensk region, "Kegenskii" state farm	Eastern Tien Shan, southeastern slopes of Kegensk pass in hills of Ketmen-Alatau. High-altitude crops (1,800–2000 m above mean sea level). Among natural vegetation around plowed fields	Bushes dense, up to 1.0 m tall; stems soft, green even at fruiting stage, slender, 9–18 to 30 branches in bush; foliage moderate; pods large, falciform; typical pasture population characterized by high winter hardiness and resistance to trampling by cattle
Taldy-Kurgan province, Andreevsk region, "Leninskii" state farm	Western slopes of Dzhungarian-Alatau. Hilly fodder land, unirrigated fruit orchard. Rich legume-cereal-grass mixture. Altitude 1,300–1,500 m above sea level	Bush highly prostrate; branching only in upper part; stems long, 70–90 cm and more (120–150 cm), slender, glabrous in lower portion; from 7–12 to 35 branches in bush; foliage good; leaflets lanceolate or narrowly linear, sometimes pubescent; corolla yellow; pod falciform, large; fruiting profuse
Karaganda province, Egindybulaksk region, environs of Egindybulak village	Slopes of central Kazakhstan hillocks. Water current in passes and at foothills. Among herbage	Bush highly prostrate, from 70–80 to 120 cm long; branches many, pigmented; leaflets small, lanceolate, pubescent; pod falciform, medium sized
Eastern Kazakhstan province, Zaisan	Foothills of Saur. Hilly valleys. Tree	Bushes erect or semiprostrate, 75–90 cm tall, with 12–15

region, Michurin state farm, vegetable varietal trial field	plantations along reclaimed northern slopes of ridge	branches; leaflets ovate-lanceolate, foliage moderate; pod from slightly curved to 0.66 turn; fruiting profuse; corolla yellow; disease resistant
Eastern Kazakhstan province, Bol'shenarymsk region, Uryl' village	Bol'shaya Narymsk ridge. Hilly pasture, northern slopes, tall grass meadow (1,500 m above mean sea level)	Plant strong, with good foliage; stems long, flexible, pigmented, up to 120 cm long; stems supported by branches that cling to grass stand of other plants; pod curved, with sausagelike segmentation, pubescent; early maturing and cold resistant
Eastern Kazakhstan province, Markakol'sk region, "Kal'dekirskii" state farm	Pass through Kurchumsk ridge. In depressions of intrahilly plateau on dark hilly meadow soils; small bushes of alfalfa	Plants 50–60 cm (also up to 100 cm) tall with 7–12 branches; bush semiprostrate and erect; leaflets oval-cuneiform; corolla yellow, or pale yellow; medium sized; pod falciform; disease resistant
Aktyubin province, Irgiz region, "Nurinskii" state farm	Steep bank of Lake Airkul' (soil dark, sandy loam)	Bush strong, erect, 60–90 cm tall; leaflets large, cuneiform, rarely oval-lanceolate, slightly pubescent; foliage good; corolla large or medium, yellow; pods falciform, rarely up to 0.75 twist
Aktyubin province, Irgiz region, "Taupskii" state farm	Steep bank of Tel'kara River (soil dark, sandy loam)	Bush prostrate, with 6–12 branches 50–60 cm long; stems rough; leaflets large, cuneiform, pubescent; foliage good; corolla pale yellow; pods falciform
Aktyubin province, Irgiz region, state farm named after Kalinin	Floodplain of Irgiz River (soil sandy loam). Herbage	Plants 60–100 cm tall, with 15–35 branches on the average, but sometimes 60–70; stems rough; leaflets large, cuneiform; foliage moderate, rarely profuse; corolla yellow, flowers medium sized; pods falciform, up to 0.75 twist

(Contd.)

Table 12 (*Contd.*)

1	2	3
	South Kazakhstan alfalfa—*M. difalcata* Sinsk.	
Semipalatinsk province, Zharminsk region, "Shermetevskii" state farm, brigade No. 2	Low hills. Chingiz-Tau ridge. Artificial depression amid sheep's fescue—feather grass steppe	Bush large, semiprostrate, 80–100 cm tall, with 50–80 branches; leaflets slender, elongated, pubescent; foliage poor; pod straight or slightly curved, medium sized (10.16±0.13); fruiting profuse; disease resistant
Semipalatinsk province, Abaisk region, Zhdanov state farm	Semipalatinsk hillocks. Hilly valley, fodder land. Alfalfa predominant in depressions. Meadow-steppe grasses associated: St. John's wort, sorrel or dock, garden burnet, crazy weed, wormwood, sheep's fescue, and others	Bush dense or spreads markedly; alfalfa plants occupy lower tier of grass stand; stems slender, flexible, highly pigmented in lower portion, 60–70 cm long; with 12–18 branches; leaflets narrow, almost linear, pubescent; foliage poor; corolla pale and whitish-yellow, medium sized; pod straight, with persistent dry petals, pubescent, long and slender or short and wide; many seeds in pod; fruiting good; disease resistant
Semipalatinsk province, Abaisk region, "Kainarskii" state farm, 8th settlement	Chingiz-Tau ridge. Hilly fodder land. Sheep's fescue—feather grass steppe, depression	Bush compact, with 12–15 branches; stems slender, fragile, pigmented, 80–90 cm long; foliage poor; leaflets lanceolate; corolla pale yellow; pods straight; fruiting profuse
Semipalatinsk province, Abaisk region, Tel'man state farm, Sarzhal village	Valley in between hills. Fodder land. Alfalfa—feather grass association in depressions	Bush compact, with about 30 branches; stems 50–70–90 cm long; foliage poor; leaflets almost subulate, very narrow, pubescent; corolla pale yellow; pod straight or slightly curved, with persistent dry petals
Kokchetavsk province, Kzyltusk region, "Kairat" state farm	On plains in depressions between water intake tanks (brown soil). Grass stand sparse	Bush semi-erect or prostrate, highly branched; stems slender, up to 50–100 cm long; foliage not profuse; leaflets almost linear; pod straight, pubescent, with

		segmentation corresponding to number of seeds; seed productivity high; drought resistant and winter hardy
Kustanaisk province, Uritsk region, "Sorochinskii" state farm	In depressions and on small slope (brown soils). Forms extensive thickets	Plants with good tillering, semi-erect, up to 60 cm long; stems slender; foliage poor; leaflets very small; pods small, straight or slightly curved, not thick and flat, black and dark gray; seed maturation not uniform; seed dispersal observed
Taldy-Kurgan province, Sarkand region, "Semirech'e" collective farm	Dry slopes of foothills of Dzhungarian-Alatau. Fodder land. Herbage (1,700–1,800 m above mean sea level)	Bush erect, from 70–80 cm to 1.0 m tall; stems highly pigmented; foliage moderate; leaflets lanceolate, narrowly linear, almost subulate; pod straight; seed productivity high; drought and cold resistant
Semipalatinsk province, Ayaguzsk region, Chingiz-Tau ridge	Desert steppe association with predominance of summer cypress and ebelek. Precipice	Bush erect or slightly prostrate, with 9–11 branches, 40–60 cm tall; stems pigmented; foliage poor; leaflets subulate, lanceolate, pubescent; pod straight

Trautvetter's alfalfa—*M. trautvetteri* Sumn.

Aktyubin province, Baiganinsk region, northern point of Ustyurt plateau	Short-duration floodwater current, Sarsai dry bed of Shagan in Shushkakul' area (colluvial soil, heterogeneous, solonetz, sandy-clayey, in depressions mostly heavy)	Bush strong, erect to semi-erect, with 20–30 branches; 90–120 cm tall; leaflets lanceolate, dorsally pubescent; corolla from whitish to violet-lilac; pods mostly falciform (78.2%), medium sized (9.76±0.16). Drought resistance, winter hardiness, and salt tolerance high
Alma-Ata province, Dzhambul region; environs of Uzunagach village	Foothill valley, with number of small rivulets. Among rich legume-cereal-grass mixture (1,000–1,200 m above mean sea level)	Bush semiprostrate, very strong, 70–80 cm tall; 14–16 branches; stems thick, rough; foliage moderate; corolla violet; pods with 0.75 twist; seed productivity moderate

(*Contd.*)

Table 12 (*Contd.*)

1	2	3
Aktyubin province, Baiganinsk region, northern point of Ustyurt plateau	Short-duration floodwater current, Koksai dry river bed of Shagan (colluvial soil, solonetz, sandy loam)	Bush compact; stems slender, green, flexible, tender, flexible; flowering highly protracted; 90% of corolla violet and lilac; pods falciform, with 0.75–1.0–1.5–2.0 twists; very valuable population of pasture type.
Aktyubin province, Baiganinsk region, northern point of Ustyurt plateau	Short-duration floodwater current, Sarsai dry river bed of Shagan (colluvial soil, heterogeneous, solonetz, sandy-clayey, in depressions mostly heavy)	Bush strong, erect to semi-erect, 90–120 cm tall; 20–30 branches; leaflets lanceolate, dorsally pubescent; corolla from whitish to violet-lilac; pods generally falciform; drought resistance and winter hardiness very high
Taldy-Kurgan province, Panfilovsk region, "Usharal" collective farm	Clayey floodplain of Ili River. Tugain forests. Solitary plains among high grass, xerophytic second growth or post-spring	Plants very large; branches of first and second orders protrude from dense grass stand and lie on branches of tall grasses and apices of shrubs; stems slender, flexible, from 120–150 to 220 cm long, highly branched in apical part, glabrous in lower part, weakly foliate in upper part; leaflets small, highly susceptible to powdery mildew; corolla blue, small; pod generally with 1.0–1.5 twists, small

Blue alfalfa—*M. coerulea* Less.

1	2	3
Ural'sk province, Taipaksk region, "Essensaiskii" state farm	Second terrace of floodplain of Ural River. Depressions among small shrubs and herbage (soils light, sandy loam)	Plants 80–140 cm tall; tall plants usually prostrate; leaflets elongated-lanceolate; foliage moderate; corolla violet; pods with 2.5–3.0–3.5–4.5–5.0 twists (3.78 ± 0.26), small (3.96 ± 0.19)

Gur'ev province, Indersk region, Kulagino village, "Put' Il'icha" state farm	Willow grove in floodplain of Ural River flooded for short while by spring thaw (soil dark gray). Alfalfa grows in depressions	Bushes with densely set rosettes, 50–70 cm long; flowers small, corolla violet-red; pods small, with 3.0–5.0 twists
Gur'ev province, Kzylkoginsk region, environs of Miyaly village, state farm named after Abai	Dry valley hayland (soil sandy loam). Alfalfa grows in depressions	Bushes of medium strength, 40–90 cm tall; foliage poor; leaflets narrowly lanceolate, almost linear; corolla violet; pods with 2.0–5.0 twists
Ural'sk province, Taipaksk region, "Essensaiskii" state farm	Second terrace of floodplain of Ural River (soil sandy loam). Alfalfa grows in depressions among herbage	Plants 80–140 cm tall; foliage moderate; leaflets elongated-lanceolate; corolla violet; pods with 2.0–5.0 twists

Tian Shan Alfalfa—M. tianschanica Vass.

Chimkent province, Sairamsk region, Aksu-Dzhabagly	Western Tien Shan, Talassk ridge. Hilly hayland (1,800–2,000 m above mean sea level). Meadow herbage	Bush erect, 50–60 cm tall, with 8–12 to 15 branches corolla from bright yellow and white to dark violet; pods with 1.0–1.5 twists, rarely with 0.75, 2.0 and 2.5 twists; pod large (6.75 ± 0.17); seed productivity moderate; cold resistant; disease resistant
Dzhambul province, Lugovsk region, Sugoty area	Western Tien Shan, Kirgiz ridge. Fruit orchard (1,700–1,800 m above mean sea level). Along irrigation channels	Bush strong, semiprostrate, 70–90 cm tall, but sometimes up to 130 cm; 15–19 to 30–50 branches; leaflets elongated-oval and obovate, medium sized; foliage profuse; corolla from bright violet and lilac to dark violet and dirty white; pods with 1.5–2.0 twists, rarely 0.75 to 1.0 twist; fruiting profuse; disease resistant
Chimkent province, Sairamsk region, Aksu-Dzhabagly sanctuary	Western Tien Shan, Talassk ridge. Hilly hayland (1,800–2,000 m above mean sea level). Herbage	Bush erect, 50–60 cm tall; 9–12 to 15 branches; foliage moderate; winter hardiness, drought resistance, and disease resistance high; corolla from bright yellow, almost white, lilac and violet to dark violet; pods with 1.0–1.5 twists; seed productivity moderate

(Contd.)

Table 12 (*Contd.*)

1	2	3
Alma-Ata province, Talgarsk region, environs of Talgar town	Trans-Ilian Alatau. Foothill valley, home gardens (800–1,000 m above mean sea level). Herbage	Bush semiprostrate and prostrate, 60–80 to 100 cm tall; 15–20 to 25–30 branches; leaflets oval and elongated-oval, rarely cuneiform; foliage profuse; pods large and medium sized, with 1.0–1.5 and 2.0 twists; corolla violet; fruiting profuse

Thus *M. trautvetteri* is a species rarely found at the diploid level which was spontaneously selected for blue flowers. Its distribution area coincides with the area of blue alfalfa. In spite of differing greatly in pod shape from the blue alfalfa, this species has many common morphological characters: pubescence, pigmentation, shape of leaflets, color of corolla, shape of bush (hillocky populations), ecological adaptation to conditions of growth, and so forth.

Numerous tetraploid populations, morphologically resembling the diploid *M. trautvetteri*, are usually less homogeneous in phenotype. They are derivatives from natural hybridization of species of once rarely different ploidy levels, in which at least one parent should have been tetraploid. Here the variations can be highly diverse: *M. falcata* × *M. sativa*, *M. coerulea* × *M. falcata*, *M. difalcata* × *M. sativa*, and so forth. All derivatives from these crosses are tetraploid forms of alfalfa, which morphologically are almost identical to the polymorphic species *M. varia* Mart.

The rarely found diploid level natural populations of *M. trautvetteri* and all the diverse forms of tetraploid level natural hybrids are nothing more than products of introgressive hybridization. In Kazakhstan five strong, constantly active centers of introgression have been discovered, even though natural hybridization between the two main species, *M. sativa* and *M. falcata*, occurs everywhere.

The following are centers of introgressive hybridization: Mugodzharo-Ustyurt (I), Tien Shan (II), central Kazakhstan (III), Dzhungaria (IV), and eastern Kazakhstan (V). Interaction in the second center has resulted in *M. tianschanica*, *M. trautvetteri*, and *M. varia*, while in the other centers mainly *M. varia* has developed (Figure 28).

The centers of introgression not only constantly enrich themselves with primary genetic potential for the origin of new species, but also maintain and renew this potential. They constitute a unique forging anvil for the emergence of new forms and species, which improve directly under specific edaphic conditions with due consideration to geomorphology and ecology. Centers of introgression are centers of evolution and differentiation of species and intraspecific taxa of alfalfa of different ploidy levels. In contrast to the macro- and microcenters, and the primary and secondary centers of origin of cultivated plants established by N.I. Vavilov and P.M. Zhukovskii, these are the local microcenters of evolution of plants organically linked with the classical centers of origin of cultivated plants. The discovery of centers of natural hybridization, especially centers of natural introgression, and an understanding of the processes occurring in them, will considerably elucidate not only our concept of the evolution of the genus *Medicago* L., but also the theory of origin of all plant species.

Conservation of Endemic Species

To conserve valuable fodder crops we recommend the establishment of state preserves in the hills of Mugodzhar in the sands of the Bol'shaya Barsuki (on the territory of the Aral Experimental Station of VIR), in the forest massif of the Kokchetavsk hillocks, and in Dzhungarian-Alatau on the land of the Lepsinskii forest farm (Andreevsk region of Taldy-Kurgan province). For conservation of endemic diploid alfalfa species local preserves with strictly controlled hay cutting and cattle grazing should be appropriately delineated on haylands and pastures of state farms (Table 13).

Anatomy of Aerial Vegetative Organs of Wild Species of Alfalfa

A large number of studies have been devoted to the anatomical features of alfalfa. According to the data of L.V. Dmitrieva and E.Ya. Il'inaya, considerable changes in the internal structure of leaf and stem of alfalfa are observed depending on the whorls (tiers) and age of the plant as well as various conditions.

Common alfalfa (*Medicago sativa* L.) has been the primary object of studies. The anatomical characters mentioned for the leaf and stem of *M. sativa* are common for other alfalfa species, both wild and cultivated. Comparative anatomical studies with due consideration of wild perennial species are inadequate.

We studied the leaves and stems of 18 specimens of perennial alfalfa growing in the steppe, desert, and hilly regions of Kazakhstan and two specimens raised in the experimental fields of the Pushkin Laboratory of VIR. All the specimens (diploid and tetraploid) were from ten species. According to the subdivision of alfalfa into two groups on the basis of color of the corolla, among the studied alfalfas six species had yellow flowers and four blue (*M. coerulea*, *M. varia*, *M. tianschanica*, and *M. sativa*). The material (middle portions of axillary shoots) was fixed in 70% ethyl alcohol and examined according to the universally recognized method. To study the leaf structure transverse sections were prepared of the central leaflet of the compound trilobate leaf, while lateral leaflets were used in preparing slides of the epidermis.

The studies revealed that the leaves of all species of alfalfa are basically similar in internal structure. The distinguishing features relate mainly to adaptability to different habitats and to a lesser extent their taxonomic position. In the leaf structure of the specimens studied, in addition to mesomorphic characters (dorsoventral sparse mesophyll, spongy parenchyma, sinuate epidermis), we also observed a good number of xeromorphic characters: thickening of walls (especially outer) of

Table 13. Most suitable regions for organizing conservation of endemic diploid species of alfalfa in the territory of Kazakh SSR

Zone	Region	Habitat
1	2	3
	M. trautvetteri Sumn.	
Western Kazakhstan	Mugodzhar hills. Aktyubin province, Mugodzharsk region	Hilly ravines, forest fellings, haylands in depressions of flood-plains of small rivers
	Ustyurt plateau. Aktyubin province, Baiganinsk region, Shagan area	Deep water currents (sai) falling into Lake Shushkakul' in the territory of state farm named after Abai
	Aktyubin province, Khobdinsk region, basin of Bol'shaya Khodba River	Haylands along floodplains of Bol'shaya Khobda River
Eastern Kazakhstan	Foothills of Dzhungarian-Alatau, Taldy-Kurgan province, Panfilovsk region, Koktal	Clayey floodplain of Ili River. Shrub pasture of "Usharal" collective farm
	M. coerulea Less.	
Western Kazakhstan	Caspian lowland. Gur'ev province, Kzylkoginsk region, state farm named after Abai, "Komsomol'skii", and "Sagizskii"	Haylands in floodplain of Ural, Uil, and Sagiz Rivers, in low-lying areas of dune sands
	Caspian lowland. Gur'ev province, Makhambetsk region, floodplain of Ural River from Sorochinka village to Kulagino village	Haylands along Baksai River and right coastal part of floodplain of Ural River; second terrace of left coastal part of floodplain of Ural River among herbage

(Contd.)

Table 13 (*Contd.*)

1	2	3
	Ural'sk province, Taipaksk region, flood-plain of Ural River, "Essensaiskii" state farm	Haylands along left bank of Ural River and region of Malykh ozer (small lakes) (upper reaches of Uil River)

M. difalcata Sinsk.

1	2	3
Central Kazakhstan	Kazak low hills. Karaganda province, Karkaralinsk region, "Intaly" state farm	Dry valley meadow with strong symptoms of alkalinity. In grass mixtures among wheatgrass, wormwood, and Russian thistle
	Kazak low hills. Karkaralin hills. Forest massif, "Karkaralinskii" state farm	Slopes of hills among trees and forest fringes
	Chingiz-Tau mountains. Semipalatinsk province, Zharminsk region, Arkat village, Farm No. 2	Hilly hayland, in depressions among wheatgrass and wormwood
	Kazak low hills. Semipalatinsk province, Abai region, state farm named after Abai	Haylands in interknoll valley. Depressions among wheatgrass and crested wheatgrass
Northern Kazakhstan	Kokchetavsk province, Kzyltusk region, state farms "Tolbukhinskii", "Kairat" named after Chapaev, and "Alaba-tinskii"	Dry valley meadows on plain or slopes of hills among herbage

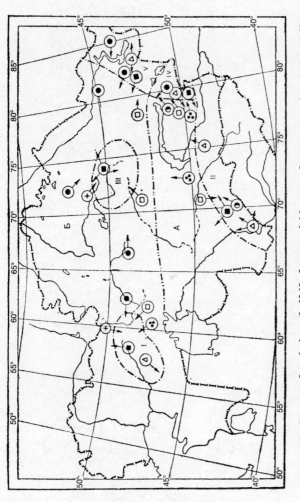

Figure 28. Centers of evolution of alfalfa forms and biotopes of common and variable alfalfa.

I—Mugodzharo-Ustyurt; II—Tien Shan; III—Central Kazakhstan; IV—Dzhungaria; V—Eastern Kazakhstan. Biotopes: A—common alfalfa (cultivated and wild); Б—variable alfalfa (cultivated).

Remaining legend same as in Figure 14. Arrows show direction of introgression.

epidermal cells, elongated and elongated-oval outline of epidermal cells, slightly depressed stomata, prevalence of close-set palisade parenchyma, and palisade chlorenchyma cells well developed in the petiole of some species.

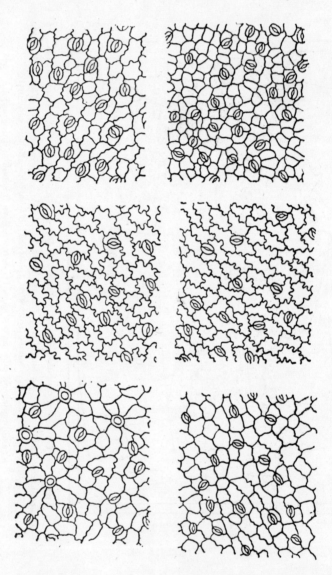

Figure 29. Lower (left) and upper (right) epidermis of the alfalfa leaf (×280). Top—*M. tianschanica*; center—*M. sativa*; bottom—*M. difalcata*.

The upper and lower epidermis of the alfalfa leaf consists of cells with different outlines of the cell walls—from straight-round to sinuate to some degree. Usually the most sinuate cell walls are seen in cells of the lower epidermis. Along with species in which the cell walls of the upper and lower epidermis of the leaf differ in configuration, we also came across species in which the outlines of these cells were uniform on both surfaces (Figure 29): highly sinuate in common alfalfa and some specimens of crescentoid alfalfa (Leningrad province), slightly sinuate, almost straight in most of the steppe specimens, crescentoid (K-800, Kazakhstan), and hybrid alfalfas (K-886). Many minute crystals of calcium oxalate are dispersed throughout the epidermis of some species.

The leaves of most species of alfalfa are covered with simple, one- to three-celled nodular hairs of different lengths, and rarely with glandular hairs; the underside of the leaf is usually more pubescent. In plants of arid habitats the leaves are densely pubescent. The highly elongated apical cell of the simple hairs is often bent over the leaf surface and, consequently, the hairs pressed down.

The species examined exhibited two concomitant types of stomatal apparatus: anomocytic (stoma surrounded by an uncertain number of cells indistinguishable from other epidermal cells in size and shape) and anisocytic (stoma surrounded by three subsidiary cells, of which one evidently smaller than the other two). Stomata are more numerous on the upper side of the leaf, ranging from 150 to 200 and more per unit of leaf surface. The guard cells of the stomata on the underside of the leaf are somewhat larger than those on the upper surface. Twin stomata are also found (Table 14).

The upper and lower epidermis in a transverse section of the leaflet of alfalfa is single layered, externally covered with cuticle, often giving a serrated appearance to the surface, which is particularly well expressed on the abaxial bulge and along the edges of the blade. The outer walls of the epidermal cells are highly thickened in the species studied by me, and the stomata situated at the level of the epidermal cells, but sometimes elevated or slightly depressed in relation to them (see Figure 29).

The most perceptible structural changes arising from the effect of various ecological factors appeared in the mesophyll of all the alfalfa species studied. The species differ in ratio and situation of the palisade and spongy parenchyma constituting the mesophyll (Figure 30). In some leaf blades the palisade tissue is confined to the adaxial side only and lies along both sides of the leaf. Palisade tissue adjoining the lower epidermis consists of one to two rows in which the cells are distinguished from typical palisade parenchyma by lesser height and sparser distribution. In most specimens of alfalfa the palisade cells occupy one row from the underside of the leaf.

Table 14. Anatomical characteristics of leaf of some wild alfalfa specimens, collection 1968–1969

Species and origin of specimen	Habitat	Thickness, μm		Length of guard cells, μm		No. of simple hairs per mm²		No. of stomata per mm²		
		Blade	Palisade tissue	Upper	Under	Upper	Under	Upper	Under	Total
						Side of leaf				
1	2	3	4	5	6	7	8	9	10	11
Common alfalfa Variety Tibet (standard)		236	115	23.7	26.0	Absent	5.7	132	118	250
Wild specimens										
Yellow alfalfa Ural'sk province, Furmanovsk region	Dry valley pasture with wormwood predominant; in depression, solitary bushes of alfalfa	—	—	17.6	20.3	23.1	58.5	342	195	537
Yellow alfalfa Aktyubin province, Khoboinsk region	Dry sai (river bed) with sandy soil, herbage; grows on steep slopes and bottom of ravine	329	158	19.0	21.8	Absent	17.1	280	202	482
Blue alfalfa Aktyubin province, Uilsk region	Semidesert landscape with sandy loam soil, green wormwood predominant in grass mixture; alfalfa in small depressions	—	—	19.0	20.5	6.0	23.4	232	173	405

Variable alfalfa Ural'sk province, Kysykkamyssie lakes	Watersheds between lakes that dry up in summer and become overrun with wheatgrass; wormwood, black-eyed Susan, summer cypress, sometimes reed also found here	—	—	19.4	22.7	46.5	68.1	228	139	367
Blue alfalfa Gur'ev province, Indersk region	Willow grove flooded by spring meltwater; second terrace of floodplain of Ural River, light sandy loam; grows in ravines and depressions	—	—	18.0	21.8	1.2	35.4	234	129	363
Semitwisted alfalfa Armenian SSR	Slopes of Loriskov upland; solitary plants among herbage	271	133	23.6	25.5	Absent	3.6	197	155	352
Blue alfalfa Ural'sk province, Taipaksk region	Second terrace of floodplain of Ural River, ravine (soil dark, colluvial, loam-rich). Herbage	312	164	19.7	21.7	Absent	11.7	185	135	320
Blue alfalfa Dagestan ASSR	Caspian sandy dunes, in depressions	262	132	24.5	26.4	Absent	10.5	172	137	309
Trautvetter's alfalfa Aktyubin province, Baiganinsk region	Water current of Shagan flooded by meltwater in Shushkakul'sk hollow of Ustyurt plateau (soil colluvial, sandy loam)	290	150	24.5	26.0	Absent	13.5	155	127	282

152

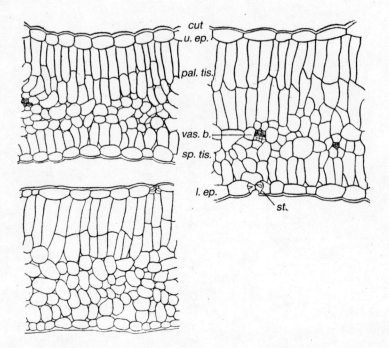

Figure 30. Transverse section of alfalfa leaf.
Top: left—*M. difalcata* Sinsk.; right—*M. sativa* L. subsp. *transoxana* (Vass.) Lub.
Bottom—*M. falcata* L.
cut—cuticle; u. ep.—upper epidermis; pal. tis.—palisade tissue; vas. b.—
vascular bundles; sp. tis.—spongy tissue; l. ep.—lower epidermis; st.—stoma
(× 280).

Moreover, this row may comprise only of radially elongated cells or palisade cells and the spongy parenchyma may alternate among them. Palisade tissue is prominent in transverse sections of leaves of all the species examined. When the mesophyll is dorsoventral in structure (K-843 and K-36105, yellow and common alfalfa, Leningrad province), it comprises a well-differentiated palisade tissue (two rows of cells) and loose spongy tissue (three to four rows of cells). In the highly xeromorphic specimens (K-790, K-800, and K-889) we found increased volume of palisade tissue mainly on the adaxial side of the leaf, the result of greater elongation and density of palisade cells.

On the abaxial side of the leaf the midrib forms a bulge, the greater part of which is occupied by the angular collenchyma. The vascular system is represented by collateral bundles of different size passing through the leaf. The vascular bundle of the midrib is the largest; sclerenchymatous fibers in the forms of a small arch adjoin the phloem and sometimes also the xylem of this bundle. Sclerenchyma is also characteristic for the large veins spread in the mesophyll; it occupies a peripheral position from the side of both the phloem and xylem of the bundle. Mechanical tissue is not present in the smallermost veins. All veins are surrounded by a single-layered lining of parenchymatous cells containing rhombic crystals of calcium oxalate in some specimens.

The petiole in transverse section is more often in the shape of a semi-circle (triangle) with a groove on the adaxial side. It varies in shape in different alfalfa species from equilaterally round to elongated at the base of the triangle. The epidermal cells have a thick outer wall covered with cuticle that appears serrated on the surface. The mechanical tissue is represented by one row of collenchyma in the abaxial bulge and by scleren-chymatous fibers on the upper and lower sides of the vascular bundles. The chlorenchyma (two to three rows of round cells) is situated along the periphery of the petiole (subepidermally). In some species (K-790 and K-889) the chlorenchyma is highly developed in the petiole, probably as an adaptation to very dry and arid conditions. The chlorophyll cells, especially on the adaxial side and the bulges of the petiole are similar in shape to the short cells of the palisade parenchyma (Figure 31). In a number of species the cells in the petiole situated above the sclerenchymatous vascular bundles contain rectangular and rhombic crystals of calcium oxa-late. The vascular system of the petiole in all the specimens studied com-

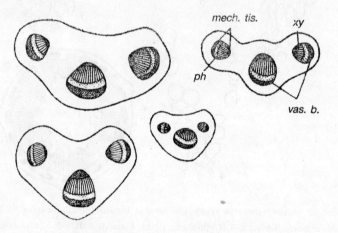

Figure 31. Schematic transverse section of alfalfa petiole.
Top: left—*M. sativa* L. subsp. *transoxana* (Vass.) Lub.; right—*M. falcata* L.
Bottom: left—*M. sativa* L. (cultivated); right—*M. tianschanica* Vass.

154

prises three collateral bundles: the largest central bundle is located toward the abaxial side and the two smaller bundles in the bulges.

There are many things common in the stem structure of alfalfas growing under different ecological conditions. The stem of the species studied is slightly quadrangular in transverse section and the small corners filled with angular collenchyma. The single-layered epidermis is covered with cuticle with various-shaped ridges on the surface. The cells of the epidermis are small, with highly thickened tangential walls, especially along the edge of the stem. The stomata, with minute cuticular excrescences are slightly sunken (somewhat below the upper level of the epidermal cells). A layer of three to four rows of chlorenchyma cells lies below the epidermis and is interrupted only at the corners by angular collenchyma. In certain species (Tian Shan alfalfa, steppe alfalfa K-790) the subepidermal row of cells differs from the underlying chlorenchyma; the contents of its cells are lighter in color and the outer cell walls with weak angular thickenings similar to the collenchyma; three rows of typical chlorenchyma underlie the subepidermal row of cells. In most of the specimens of steppe

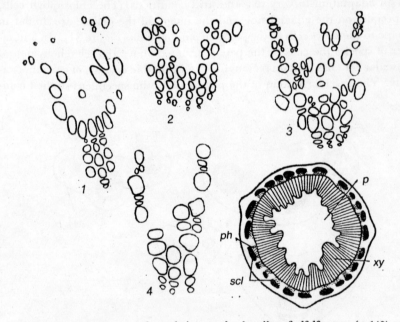

Figure 32. Arrangement of vessels in vascular bundles of alfalfa stem (×140). 1—*M. difalcata* Sinsk.; 2—*M. falcata* L. (wild, Kazakh SSR); 3—*M. tianschanica* Vass.; 4—*M. falcata* L. (cultivated).

Bottom: right—transverse section of South Kazakhstan alfalfa (*M. difalcata* Sinsk.); ph—phloem; xy—xylem; scl—sclerenchyma; p—pith (×21).

alfalfa (K-801, K-790, and K-913) the chlorenchyma is much better developed along the edges of the stem and does not consist of round or round-oval cells, but rather of palisade-type cells which are elongated in a radial direction (Figure 32). This chlorenchyma is analogous to the one observed in petioles of some alfalfa species and is an indicator of the greater xeromorphic nature of these plants.

In all the species studied the chlorenchyma is followed by a starch sheath (endodermis) in which the cells are more or less oval and often elongated tangentially. The cells of the endodermis are arranged in one row above the sclerenchymatous arches of the bundles, but in the interstices in two to three rows. Sclerenchymatous portions are distinguished by their tangential extension, number of rows, and thickness of cell walls. The cells of the cortex directly adjoin the sclerenchymatous arches and contain large rhombic crystals of calcium oxalate.

The vascular system of the stem is annular. In some species the borders of individual collateral bundles in the ring are distinctly visible, while in others they are less distinct or not seen at all. Vascular bundles in the ring are not distinguishable by size and the primary xylem retained in most. Phloem patches are similar in structure in all species of alfalfa. Secondary xylem (wood) is more extensive than the cortex. The width of the xylem region varies from species to species: In some species (Shishkin alfalfa, steppe alfalfa K-913 and K-801) the xylem region is wider with a small pith, while in other species (crescentoid and common alfalfa, Leningrad province; Tian Shan and yellow alfalfa from Kazakhstan) just the opposite is seen. In most of the specimens studied the vessels are orderly arranged in the secondary xylem of vascular bundles. In such cases two radial strands are distinctly seen in each bundle which comprise one (rarely two) vessel throughout the entire xylem tissue below the cambium. Both strands are joined by a group of vessels near the primary xylem. In some species (two specimens of steppe alfalfa) the secondary xylem vessels are scattered.

Differences are also observed in the size of vessels and thickness of walls of the libriform fibers. Sclerenchyma patches are situated above the phloem groups. The peripheral pith or medulla (perimedullar zone) differs considerably from the central pith in size of cells; the parenchymatous cells of the pith increase in size toward the center. The perimedullar zone consists of much smaller cells; in some species these cells contain starch grains (crescentoid alfalfa K-800 and K-887; hybrid alfalfa).

In many of the specimens studied the peripheral cells of the medulla are characterized by porosity (yellow alfalfa K-849, steppe alfalfa K-801, Tian Shan alfalfa). The cavity in the center of the stem is sometimes barely perceptible but often very distinct (Figure 33).

156

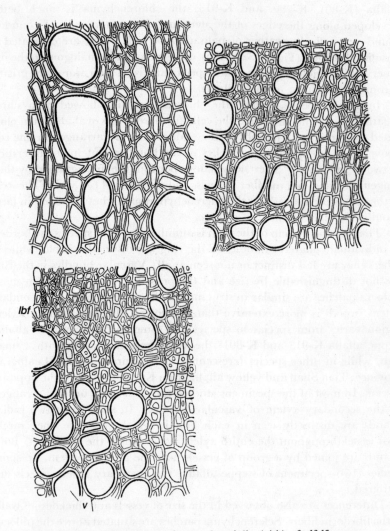

Figure 33. Transverse section of part of medulla (pith) of alfalfa stem.
Top: left—*M. falcata* L.; right—*M. tianschanica* Vass. Bottom—*M. sativa* L. subsp.
transoxana (Vass.) Lub.; v—vessels; lbf—libriform (×280).

A comparative anatomical study of the stem and leaves of perennial alfalfas growing under different ecological conditions (hilly and desert regions of Kazakhstan, Ural and Leningrad provinces) reveals that the diversity of habitat conditions is responsible for differences in the anatomical structure of alfalfas which have adapted to such conditions.

The most perceptible changes occur in the leaf blade. In most of the specimens studied xeromorphic characters are predominant in the leaf structure (rectangular epidermal cells; denser pubescence; thickening of outer wall of epidermis; compact cells of palisade parenchyma); such specimens exhibit a transitional structure. Only a small number of specimens have a mesomorphic structure (sinuate epidermal cells; dorsoventral mesophyll, loose spongy parenchyma).

Palisade tissue is predominant in the mesophyll of all the alfalfa specimens studied and consists of compact cells. Differences appear in the extent of palisade tissue, number of rows, and height of cells. The spongy parenchyma is distinguished by volume, number of rows, size of intercellular space, and shape of cells adjoining the lower epidermis; the latter are either round, similar to cells in the remaining rows (in dorsoventral mesophyll) or radially elongated (Palisade type).

Small changes in the structure of the petiole of alfalfas of different habitats pertain mainly to the parenchyma.

In the stem structure of the studied species, in addition to features in common, significant differences in the structure of the cortex and medulla have also been observed which, as in the leaf, reflect the influence of ecological factors and do not constitute supplementary characteristics of the species.

A comparison of the anatomical structure of the stem and leaves of alfalfa species made it possible to establish several similar features. True distinguishing features which could be of diagnostic importance were not found. The same anatomical feature may be present in specimens of alfalfa belonging to different species.

An analysis of the anatomical characteristics of the dorsal and ventral sides of the leaf of cultivated and wild alfalfas conducted at the Aral Experimental Station revealed that the transpiration apparatus of wild species is well adapted to hot climate.

The leaflets of some species have a large number of stomata per unit surface (yellow alfalfa from Ural'sk province No. 65 has 342 stomata versus 132 in control; blue alfalfa from Ural'sk province No. 32—232 stomata; Trautvetter's alfalfa from Aktyubin province No. 63—228 stomata) and high or medium pubescence on the underside of the leaf (yellow alfalfa and variable alfalfa from Ural'sk province—58.5 and 68.1 hairs per mm^2 respectively). Because of the well-developed palisade and spongy tissue the leaflets of other populations are distinguished by an unusually thick leaf blade: yellow alfalfa from Aktyubin province 329 μm versus 236 μm in control; blue alfalfa from Ural'sk province No. 33—312 μm, semitwisted alfalfa from Armenian SSR—271 μm. Some of the wild specimens are characterized by very small guard cells of the stomata. The diurnal course of rate of transpiration, pigment content, and presence of vitamin C in the leaves of plants of wild alfalfa species are given in Table 15.

Agrobiological Characteristics of Introduced Material

Many years of study of the initial material collected by the Aral Experimental Station of VIR under hot, rainfed, and irrigated conditions revealed that wild populations of alfalfa without corresponding breeding treatment lag behind improved varieties in productivity. Only a few, in the case of prolonged exploitation of the grass stand, surpass the standard in yield of hay and seed (Table 16). Moreover they represent valuable initial material for breeding for other important biological and economic characters: perennial growth habit, drought resistance, winter hardiness, salt tolerance, resistance to disease and pests, rhizomatous root development, prolonged period of vegetative growth, resistance to trampling and grazing by cattle, high protein content in the leaf and stem, slender stem, no requirement for soil fertility, resistance to prolonged flooding, and so forth (Table 17).

For convenience of comparison of experimental data obtained during a study of cultivated and wild specimens of alfalfa, agrobiological characteristics of wild populations and variability of important economic characters and their correlation are given in the section below pertaining to the world collection of alfalfa, since these same characteristics are discussed therein. It should be noted that this rich initial material is presently being studied by many institutions of genetics, plant breeding, and botany in the Soviet Union and abroad.

BREEDING EVALUATION OF THE WORLD COLLECTION OF ALFALFA

Initial Material and Methods of Study

We studied the collection of alfalfa in two geographic areas in 1961—the Aral Experimental Station (desert zone) and Shortandin Auxillary Center (steppe zone). Evaluation of specimens for frost resistance, photoperiodism, effect of growth substances, and content of protein and pigments, as well as statistical analysis of experimental data, chromosome count, study of water regime of plants, and anatomical studies were conducted not only at the aforementioned centers, but the corresponding departments of the Institute and the Pushkin Institute of VIR (taiga zone).

The Shortandin Auxillary Center functioned up to 1975 under the Plant Breeding Center of VNIIZKh and was located in the steppe zone of northern Kazakhstan. The climatic peculiarities of this region are lack of

Table 15. Content of pigments and vitamin C in leaves of various alfalfa species and varieties in the first cutting of a second-year crop in the vegetative phase, 1969

Species, variety, specimens	Vitamin C mg/100 g green mass	Sum of pigments mg/g green mass	Chlorophyll		Carotene	Lutein	Xanthophyll	
			a	b			1	2
					mg/g raw matter			
Variable alfalfa Karaganda	98.9	0.306	0.136	0.134	0.022	0.012	—	0.002
Common alfalfa Tashkent-3192	91.7	0.321	0.204	0.078	0.019	0.013	0.002	0.005
Yellow alfalfa Krasnokutskaya-4009	97.8	0.272	0.168	0.065	0.019	0.014	0.003	0.004
Blue alfalfa Wild (Dagestan ASSR)	100.4	0.237	0.145	0.053	0.019	0.012	0.002	0.007
Varicolored alfalfa Wild (Stavropol' territory)	85.3	0.216	0.100	0.088	0.022	0.009	—	0.002
Tian Shan alfalfa Wild (Chimkent province)	108.2	0.308	0.070	0.097	0.021	0.014	—	0.005
Semitwisted alfalfa Wild (Armenian SSR)	85.3	0.300	0.167	0.082	0.026	0.018	0.002	0.004

Table 16. Most productive wild specimens of alfalfa collected from western Kazakhstan during a study under conditions of irrigation (Aral Experimental Station of VIR, 1970–1973)

Species, sample, and origin	Yield of green mass kg/m^2				
	1970	1971	1972	1973	Four-year average
Blue alfalfa					
Ural'sk province, Taipaksk region, pasture	1.28	2.27	4.07	2.26	2.44
Gur'ev province, sands of Miyaly village	0.94	2.34	3.10	2.50	2.22
Gur'ev province, sands of Raigorodok village	0.72	1.96	1.78	2.28	1.68
Trautvetter's alfalfa					
Aktyubin province; Baiganinsk region, pasture along water current of Shagan	0.79	2.08	3.52	1.93	2.08
Aktyubin province, Chelkarsk region, pasture	0.56	1.68	2.63	2.03	1.72
Yellow alfalfa					
Ural'sk city, floodplain of Ural River	0.56	1.82	4.38	2.92	2.42
Ural'sk province, Chapaevsk region, floodplain of Ural River	0.67	1.86	3.87	3.17	2.39

Table 17. Disease-resistant wild specimens of alfalfa identified for productivity and other economic characters under rainfed conditions (Aral Experimental Station of VIR, 1974–1975)

Serial no. in VIR Catalog	Species, origin of specimens	Plant height before cutting, cm	Foliage	Winter hardiness	Green mass per m²		No. of seeds per m²
			percent	percent	in % of neighboring standard		
					1974	1975	1974
	Blue alfalfa						
15198	Gur'ev province	69	42	100	159	135	147
35009	Ural'sk province	68	45	100	129	187	128
36051	Ural'sk province	70	40	100	122	220	116
	Common alfalfa						
30706	Tadzhik SSR	66	47	100	95	117	81
1410	Eastern Kazakhstan province	49	45	100	100	200	86
1427	Eastern Kazakhstan province	43	49	100	83	175	73
	Yellow alfalfa						
24727	Kyzyl-Orda province	51	43	100	85	160	82
36751	Ural'sk province	40	45	100	91	126	82
	Tian Shan alfalfa						
34628	Chimkent province	53	49	100	147	59	109
	Trautvetter's alfalfa						
34631	Aktyubin province	60	38	100	129	58	100

stability, contrast, short frostless period (sometimes up to 70 to 80 days), high wind velocity, and drought.

The Aral Experimental Station is located in the desert zone of western Kazakhstan, precisely at the northern edge of the sandy massif of the Bol'-shaya Barsuki (northern Aral). The average annual precipitation in this region is only 150 mm. As for humidity, this is one of the most arid regions of the Soviet Union.

The various collections in these study centers are periodically renewed. The subgenus *Falcago* was represented in the nurseries by 14 species, and 123 varietal types and ecotypes within both cultivated and wild species identified by P.A. Lubenets (1972). The collection included improved and local varieties of the Soviet Union, the USA, Canada, France, Sweden, Hungary, England, Czechoslovakia, Bulgaria, Italy, Yugoslavia, Argentina, German Democratic Republic, Egypt, Federal Republic of Germany, Australia, Spain, Mexico, Ecuador, Chile, Uruguay, Syria, Sudan, Kenya, Algeria, Poland, Rumania, Peru, Mongolia, and other countries, as well as numerous wild populations collected from the territories of the Soviet Union, Turkey, Pakistan, China, Iran, Afghanistan, India, and other countries situated in the belt of ancient civilizations, whose territories lie in the primary gene centers of alfalfa—Eurasian and Central Asian centers—or adjoin them. Since 1961 more than 15,000 alfalfa specimens have been evaluated in the collection nurseries. The little-studied perennial wild species of the yellow, glutinous, Tian Shan, Trautvetter's, crescentoid, South Kazakhstan, northern, semitwisted, glandular, varicolored, and other alfalfas are represented in the collection only by specimens of native origion.

The nurseries were laid in periods normal for alfalfa. In northern Kazakhstan spring and summer sowing were done, while in western Kazakhstan sowing was done under both rainfed and irrigated conditions. Intercultural crop operations, counting, and observations for growth and development of specimens were done according to the methods of the Department of Fodder Crops of VIR. In studying the collection each specimen was evaluated for such important economic characters and properties as productivity, resistance to diseases and pests, winter hardiness, drought resistance, vegetative period, foliage, chemical composition, seed set, plant height, rate of growth in spring and postcutting, responsiveness to irrigation, variability of characters and correlations between them, reaction to photoperiod, anatomical structure of leaflets and stem, water regime, pigment content, reaction to treatment with growth substances, and so forth. Statistical analysis of the experimental data was done in the computer center of the VIR. Physiological and biochemical research was conducted according to methods developed by Soviet scientists.

Vegetative Period

In northern Kazakhstan the seedling phase of different species and varieties of alfalfa may continue for 13 to 55 days with spring sowing and 7 to 27 days with summer sowing. The duration of the seedling phase depends on air temperature and soil moisture, and survival of the seedlings on their resistance to the effect of dry winds and frosts (Table 18).

In irrigated lands in western Kazakhstan seedlings appear in seven to nine days in varieties of common alfalfa and variable alfalfa. Wild species are slower to germinate and the seedling phase in them five to ten days longer. Under rainfed conditions the time of seedling emergence depends largely on climatic conditions in spring and the presence of reserves of productive moisture in the upper soil layer. Under normal conditions seedlings emerge 15 to 20 days after sowing. In cold and windy weather or on drying of the upper soil layer the seedling period is protracted to over a month. Absence of spring precipitation and the early onset of drought cause severe thinning of seedlings. Sometimes crops sown under rainfed conditions perish completely.

In the steppe zone the seedling phase sets in early (13 to 15 days) in spring sowing of the improved varieties of Kazakhstan, the republics of Central Asia, Azerbaidzhan SSR, northern Caucasus, Ukrainian SSR, Latin American countries, Canada, and the USA. Increase in duration of the seedling phase (complete seedlings appear 18 to 25 days after sowing) is seen in the varieties and specimens of the Lower Volga region and Siberia, Central Volga region, Central Chernozem zone of the RSFSR, Nechernozem zone of the RSFSR, the Baltic republics, and other regions. Seedlings appear late (after 25 to 30 days) and nonuniformly in the improved varieties of the yellow, crescentoid, and northern alfalfa. The seedling phase commences very late (after 30 to 55 days) in wild specimens of the yellow, South Kazakhstan, blue, Trautvetter's and northern alfalfas. In the little-known Caucasian species—glutinous, varicolored, and semitwisted, and in the Central Asian wild species—Tian Shan alfalfa—seedlings appear quickly (13 to 17 days after sowing) and uniformly. Under favorable weather conditions and good soil moisture (summer sowing of 1961) the time of seedling emergence is halved.

In northern Kazakhstan the spring of 1961 was unfavorable for seed germination (sowing April 26). Strong dry winds, several wet snowfalls after sowing, and frosts up to 2°C continued until May 9th. However, in spite of the protracted cold spring seedlings of varieties and specimens of common alfalfa of different groups of varietal types appeared early and the range of variability of this character was less (13 to 18 days) than in variable alfalfa, which is resistant to unfavorable environmental factors (13 to

Table 18. Vegetative period of various alfalfa species and varieties in the first year of growth with different times of sowing (Shortandin Auxillary Center of VIR, 1961)

Species, variety, specimens	Number of days from sowing to commencement of phase:					
	Seedling	Budding	Flowering	Seedling	Budding	Flowering
	Spring sowing			Summer sowing		
Shortandinskaya-2 (standard)	15	69	97	9	35	60
Common alfalfa						
Khiva local	15	71	92	8	34	58
Milyutinskaya-1774	15	72	92	8	37	60
Variable alfalfa						
Dolinskaya-2	15	71	97	8	35	57
Poltava-256	18	74	99	7	37	57
Hybrid (Canada)	15	73	91	7	36	58
Vernal (USA)	15	75	89	7	35	59
Omsk-8893	18	79	98	9	40	66
Kamalin-930	18	81	103	10	37	66
Marusinskaya-81	20	82	106	10	37	67
Onokhoy-6	20	77	100	11	42	89
Yellow alfalfa						
Maikopskaya yellow	20	71	101	13	44	75
Krasnokutskaya-4009	28	82	110	15	44	88
Wild (K-29126)	49	92	119	21	49	93
Crescentoid alfalfa						
Yellow Kuban	28	82	110	16	47	89
Northern alfalfa						
Dedinovskaya	30	84	111	17	45	89
Glutinous alfalfa						
Wild (K-2625)	15	74	97	9	37	56
Tian Shan alfalfa						
Wild (K-13035)	17	75	92	12	39	58
Varicolored alfalfa						
Wild (K-30094)	13	75	107	10	39	60
Semitwisted alfalfa						
Wild (K-16650)	17	76	95	13	36	60
Blue alfalfa						
Wild (K-12820)	20	79	105	14	45	84
Trautvetter's alfalfa						
Wild (K-34631)	32	84	106	18	44	89

Table 19. Duration (in days from sowing) and variability of seedling phase in species, varietal groups, and varieties of alfalfa with different periods of sowing (Shortandin Auxillary Center of VIR, 1961)

Species, varietal groups, varietal types, variety, populations	Spring sowing				Summer sowing			
	Range of variability	Average duration ($\bar{x}\pm m$)	Accuracy of experiment (R), %	Coefficient of variability (V)	Range of variability	Average duration ($\bar{x}\pm m$)	Accuracy of experiment (R), %	Coefficient of variability (V)
1	2	3	4	5	6	7	8	9
Common alfalfa, group of varietal types								
Latin American	13–15	14.5±0.21	1.5	5.7	7–8	7.7±0.11	1.5	5.9
Central Asian	14–18	15.9±0.37	2.3	7.7	7–10	8.4±0.28	3.3	11.0
Trans-Caucasian	15–18	16.1±0.30	1.9	7.2	8–10	8.9±0.21	2.4	9.4
Variable alfalfa, varietal types								
North Caucasian	13–19	16.1±0.49	3.0	11.8	7–10	8.4±0.23	2.7	10.8
Ukrainian	15–18	16.1±0.27	1.6	6.6	8–10	8.6±0.16	1.8	7.3
North Kazakhstan	15–18	16.3±0.27	1.6	6.4	8–11	9.1±0.23	2.5	10.2
Canadian	15–19	17.1±0.38	2.3	8.8	8–11	9.3±0.22	2.5	9.5
Southeastern	15–22	17.6±0.53	3.0	8.4	8–11	9.4±0.25	2.7	10.5
West Siberian	15–22	18.3±0.53	2.9	11.4	8–12	10.0±0.27	2.7	10.7
Central Russian	18–24	20.3±0.46	2.2	8.8	10–14	11.3±0.30	2.6	9.4
East Siberian	17–25	20.9±0.57	2.7	10.7	9–14	11.7±0.38	2.8	10.9

(Contd.)

Table 19 (*Contd.*)

1	2	3	4	5	6	7	8	9
Varicolored alfalfa	13–20	15.9±0.59	3.7	14.4	7–11	8.6±0.34	4.0	15.7
Semitwisted alfalfa	15–20	17.8±0.38	2.1	8.4	8–11	9.6±0.25	2.6	10.2
Blue alfalfa	15–30	19.2±0.84	4.4	17.7	8–16	10.4±0.45	4.4	17.5
Yellow alfalfa								
Improved varieties of Soviet Union	19–28	22.5±0.55	2.4	9.6	10–16	12.5±0.40	3.2	12.4
Wild populations	27–54	40.1±2.11	5.2	20.4	16–27	20.7±0.81	3.9	15.2

25 days), or in other wild species (27 to 54 days). Duration and variability of the seedling phase of species, groups of varietal types, and individual varietal types of alfalfa in spring and summer sowings are given in Table 19.

Data on the magnitude of variation, given high experimental accuracy (except for spring sowing of wild populations of yellow alfalfa, $R = 5.2\%$), reveals that the time of appearance of seedlings is a genetic and highly heritable character, although it also depends on weather conditions. Early-maturing, multicutting populations from regions of irrigated farming, and improved and local varieties of alfalfa from northern Caucasus, southern Ukraine, Latin American countries, and northern Kazakhstan are characterized by a shorter period of seed germination; in wild species of the Central Asian and Euro-Siberian (without the Crimean region) gene centers the period of seedling emergence is somewhat protracted.

In the steppe regions the seedling phase to budding in alfalfa takes on the average about 50 days and budding to commencement of anthesis another 25 to 30 days. Thus the vegetative period from sowing to cutting maturity varies in different species, varieties, and specimens from 90 to 120 days and more. Given a favorable combination of climatic factors and good soil moisture the periods of seedling–budding and budding–flowering are reduced by more than 30 days.

In western Kazakhstan, under rainfed conditions, high temperatures, and constant soil moisture deficit, the interphase periods of seedling—budding and budding—commencement of flowering in the first year of growth of plants reduce on the average by 25 to 30 days. From the seedling phase to commencement of flowering only 65 to 70 days are needed. On irrigated lands, in the first year of sowing, this period does not reduce.

In the second and subsequent years of plant growth the period from spring sprouting to commencement of flowering requires on the average 55 days in northern Kazakhstan. On rainfed lands in western Kazakhstan it takes about 50 days from spring sprouting to cutting maturity, while under conditions of irrigation in an early and warm spring only 40 days (Table 20).

The period from cutting maturity to seed maturation comprises 65 to 75 days in the steppe zone, but in western Kazakhstan 15 to 20 days less in rainfed crops. On irrigated lands this period does not reduce. The average duration of the vegetative period from spring sprouting to graying of 60 to 80% pods in different species and specimens comprises 120 to 130 days in the steppe regions, 110 to 120 days on irrigated lands of the arid belt, and 100 to 110 days under rainfed conditions in the desert zone (Table 21).

Under conditions of northern Kazakhstan the earliest maturing (vegetative period 100 to 120 days) are varieties and specimens of common

Table 20. Interphase periods (days) of alfalfa in second and subsequent years of growth under conditions of irrigation (Aral Experimental Station of VIR, 1967-1970)

Species, variety, specimens	Origin (country, province, territory, republic)	From spring sprouting to commencement of:			From first cutting to commencement of:	
		Budding	Flowering	Maturation	Budding	Flowering
Common alfalfa						
Tibet (control)	Aktyubin province	29	37	110	24	33
Khebei	China	27	34	100	20	29
Tashkent-721	Tashkent province	28	37	106	23	30
Semirechensk local	Alma-Ata province	29	37	108	23	32
Variable alfalfa						
Vernal	USA	31	41	114	25	36
Rambler	Canada	30	40	115	25	36
Omsk-8893	Omsk province	32	42	115	25	37
Kamalin-930	Krasnoyarsk territory	34	44	118	26	38
Onokhoy-6	Yakutian ASSR	35	46	122	26	39
Yellow alfalfa						
Krasnokutskaya-4009	Saratov province	36	49	128	29	41
Crescentoid alfalfa						
Yellow Kuban	Stavropol' territory	34	45	130	28	40
Trautvetter's alfalfa						
Wild (K-34631)	Aktyubin province	32	46	123	31	41
Blue alfalfa						
Wild (K-29002)	Gur'ev province	35	47	125	32	43

Table 21. Interphase periods (days) of alfalfa in different years of growth under rainfed conditions (Aral Experimental Station of VIR, 1965*)

Species, variety, specimens	Year	Sowing–sprouting	Seedlings (spring sprouting)–commencement of budding	Commencement of budding–commencement of flowering	Commencement of flowering–seed maturation	Seedlings (spring sprouting)–seed maturation
Variable alfalfa						
Tibet (control)	1965	17	51	17	45	130
	1966	—	42	12	56	110
	1968	—	42	7	49	98
Common alfalfa						
Local from India (K-6940)	1965	19	60	8	41	128
	1966	—	43	11	49	103
	1968	—	42	7	47	91
Blue alfalfa						
Wild from Gur'ev province (K-29002)	1965	32	41	14	43	130
	1966	—	42	9	50	101
	1968	—	42	10	55	107
Trautvetter's alfalfa						
Wild from Aktyubin province (K-34626)	1965	28	61	10	39	138
	1966	—	42	17	41	100
	1968	—	42	11	35	88
Yellow alfalfa						
Maikopskaya foothills	1965	22	66	14	43	145
	1966	—	58	18	43	119
	1968	—	57	19	46	112

*Misprint in Russian original; should read "1968".—General Editor.

alfalfa and variable alfalfa from China (K-32860, K-32863, K-32865, K-33741, and K-33743), India (K-6940, K-7397, K-21367, and K-21368), Iraq (K-7221, K-7222, and K-8466), Egypt (K-5143), Sudan (K-7305), Peru (K-11417 and K-21284), Chile (K-5141), Argentina (K-2065), Brazil (K-7227), Ecuador (K-8133), France (Gamma, Omega, Du Puits, Flamande, Provence, Poitou, Marais), Italy (Gigante Cremoneze), as well as local varieties from Bolivia, Uruguay, Panama, Mexico, Morocco, Syria, and Pakistan. Some improved alfalfa varieties of northern Kazakhstan also belong to the group of early-maturing varieties: Shortandinskaya-2, Dolinskaya-2, Karaganda-1, Karabalykskaya, Blue hybrid-1316, and Kokshe. The other group of varieties of Kazakh SSR evolved mainly under irrigation—Tibet, Aralskaya, Irtyshskaya, Semirechensk local, Krasnovodopadskaya-8, and Zaysanskaya—and are medium maturing with a vegetative period of 120 to 130 days.

The medium-maturing group also includes improved and local varieties of common and variable alfalfa from the republics of Central Asia, the Caucasus, the Ukraine, Nechernozem zone of RSFSR, Provolzh'e, Central Chernozem zone of RSFSR, western and eastern Siberia, Ural, Altai, the Far East, and the Baltic republics, as well as improved varieties of Canada and the USA, South Africa, Australia, Oceania, West and central Europe, and also wild populations of varicolored alfalfa.

The late-maturing group (vegetative period 130 to 140 days and more) comprises improved varieties and wild populations of yellow alfalfa (Stepnaya-600, Pavlovskaya-7, Krasnokutskaya-4009, Maikopskaya yellow, Omsk-2251, Kinelskaya-6, K-20044, K-27941, K-28900, K-29208, K-31079, K-31154) and other species of the subgenus *Falcago* which are not used for cultivation.

Statistical analysis has shown that the germination vigor under field conditions (seedling phase) does not correlate well with the duration of vegetative period from seedling to maturation of seeds ($r = 0.38 \pm 0.09$ to 0.44 ± 0.11), although a general tendency toward interrelationship between these two important characters at the level of species or varietal groups is discernible. In controlled experiments the absence of adverse effect of environmental factors on the growth and development of plants increases the interrelationship of these characters ($r = 0.51 \pm 0.10$ to 0.61 ± 0.14).

Under the severe arid conditions in western Kazakhstan seed set is earlier than in the standard (control) not only in specimens from China (K-32860, K-32863, K-32865, K-33741, and K-33743), India (K-6940, K-7397, K-21367, and K-21368), the Near East (K-3368, K-4795, K-6001, and K-7222), Mediterranean (K-5143, K-5677, K-5909, and K-7300), and Latin America (K-2065, K-5141, K-7219, K-8471, K-11416, and K-20894), but also improved and local varieties from northern Kazakhstan, Nechernozem zone of RSFSR, Povolzh'e, Central Chernozem zone of RSFSR, Ukrainian SSR, the Baltic republics, West Europe (Ainsford, English Early, Gamma, Omega, and Du Puits) and the USA (Ladak, Kossak, Ranger, Vernal, Lahontan, and Narragansett). With respect to length of vegetative period these varieties and specimens lag behind the standard (control): from the republics of Central Asia (Tashkent-3192, Fergana-700, Fergana-16, Milyutinskaya-1774, Samarkand local, Mesopotamian-1680, and Iolotanskaya-1763), southern Kazakhstan (Semirechensk local, Kransnovodopadskaya-8, K-6257, K-6294, K-6304, K-6343, and K-26704), western and eastern Siberia (Omsk-8893, Kuzbasskaya variegated hybrid, Onokhoy-6, Kamalin-930, Sretenskaya-66, and Zabaikalka) and wild populations of perennial alfalfa species of the Central Asian gene center, especially the yellow, blue, South Kazakhstan, and Trautvetter's alfalfas and Asiatic subspecies of common alfalfa.

Thus in growing alfalfa under severe rainfed conditions in the arid belt, in contrast to the steppe zone, the group of early-maturing specimens is supplemented by the improved and local varieties of the steppe, forest-steppe, and some taiga (with mild maritime climate—countries of West Europe, Baltic republic of the USSR) ecotypes of different countries and continents, but the medium-maturing group comprises populations that sprout slowly in spring and postharvest from regions with severe continental climate (western and eastern Siberia, Ural, Altai, Buryatian ASSR) or, on the contrary, fast-growing populations from regions of irrigated farming (southern Kazakhstan, Kirgiz SSR, Uzbek SSR, Turkmenian SSR) which are very sensitive to moisture deficit in the soil.

On irrigated lands of the desert belt as well as in the steppe zone or the severe arid zone of western Kazakhstan the specimens from China and India are distinguished by the shortest vegetative period (100 days). Other early-maturing types (100 to 110 days) comprise varieties of common alfalfa in the Trans-Caucasian, Central Asian, Mediterranean, Latin American, West European, and Anatolian varietal groups. Some specimens of variable alfalfa of the USA, Canada, West Europe and the Soviet Union—improved and local varieties of Ukrainian SSR, northern Kazakhstan, Nechernozem zone of RSFSR, western and eastern Siberia—are characterized by a vegetative period of 110 to 120 days. Wild species under irrigation, especially populations of yellow alfalfa belong to the late-maturing group (125 days or more) (Table 22).

Considerable differences were observed in species and varieties of alfalfa in duration of interphase periods, which vary from year to year of plant growth and cutting to cutting. On the average the duration of individual interphase periods in the steppe zone is as follows: year of sowing—seed-

Table 22. Duration (days) from commencement of sprouting to commencement of flowering of alfalfa on irrigated lands of western Kazakhstan (1973–1975)

Species, variety, specimens	Cuttings			
	First	Second	Third	Fourth
Common alfalfa				
Local from India (K-21368)	48	19	19	30
Mesopotamian (K-7221)	49	21	20	30
Peruvian (K-20894)	50	21	23	30
Vakhshskaya-233	54	18	23	33
Local from Iran (K-36596)	51	22	24	32
Tashkent-3192	52	21	24	33
Variable alfalfa				
Khersonskaya-1	53	20	24	33
Polava from CSSR	53	20	24	35
Poltava-256	54	21	25	35
Tibet (control)	55	23	27	36
Omsk-8893	56	24	26	37
Onokhoy-6	57	25	26	37
Blue alfalfa				
Wild, Gur'ev province (K-36051)	51	32	38	—
South Kazakhstan alfalfa				
Wild, Aktyubin province (K-1430)	59	32	37	—
Trautvetter's alfalfa				
Wild, Aktyubin province (K-36761)	57	38	43	—
Yellow alfalfa				
Wild, eastern Kazakhstan province (K-1458)	63	36	41	—

ling to commencement of budding, 50 to 55 days; commencement of budding–commencement of flowering, 20 to 25 days; second year—spring sprouting to commencement of budding, 30 to 35 days; commencement of budding–commencement of flowering, 12 to 15 days; commencement of flowering–maturation of seeds, 70 to 80 days. In western Kazakhstan these periods for the first cutting on irrigated lands are almost the same, but on unirrigated lands vary as follows: year of sowing—seedling to commencement of budding, 50 to 60 days, commencement of budding–commencement of flowering, 10 to 12 days; commencement of flowering–maturation of seeds, 40 to 45 days (in the steppe zone alfalfa seeds do not ripen in the year of sowing); in the second and subsequent years these periods are respectively 30 to 50, 8 to 15, and 45 to 50 days. In the arid belt of the republic the period from commencement of flowering–maturation of seeds is reduced to almost half compared to the steppe zone. This is particularly characteristic for populations of the subtropical belt which are subjected to low temperatures at the beginning of the vegetative growth period (varieties of India, Central America), improved varieties of Siberia, southeast European part of the USSR, and Nechernozem zone of RSFSR, which grow slowly from spring, as well as wild alfalfa species of the Euro-Siberian and Central Asian gene centers, which accelerate in rate of growth and development in the second half of the vegetative period (due to excessive heat). Biometric indexes of the duration for the first cutting under irrigation after spring sprouting, characteristic for cultivated species, are presented in Table 23.

Cultivated species of alfalfa grown on the irrigated lands of western Kazakhstan require 50 to 55 days to become ready for the first cutting, but become ready for the second cutting quickly, within 18 to 20 days; third cutting—within 23 to 25 days, and fourth cutting—within 30 to 35

Table 23. Duration of formation of first cutting (days) in cultivated species of alfalfa on irrigated lands of western Kazakhstan

Species, varietal group, varietal types, groups of varieties	Second year of growth (1973)		Third year of growth (1974)	
	$\bar{x} \pm m$	V	$\bar{x} \pm m$	V
Common alfalfa				
Indian group	47.6 ± 0.24	1.9	46.1 ± 0.22	1.8
Trans-Caucasian group	48.1 ± 0.34	2.1	47.5 ± 0.88	4.7
Varieties of France	49.5 ± 0.24	1.8	48.8 ± 0.32	2.19
Mediterranean group	50.3 ± 0.28	1.9	49.4 ± 0.48	3.8
Central Asian group	51.2 ± 0.29	2.2	50.5 ± 0.37	2.9
Anatolian group	51.7 ± 0.38	2.5	50.6 ± 0.29	2.1
Latin American group	52.4 ± 0.33	2.8	51.2 ± 0.64	3.4
Variable alfalfa				
Varieties of the USA	52.6 ± 0.24	2.3	51.2 ± 0.27	1.6
Varieties of the FRG	53.3 ± 0.37	3.2	53.0 ± 0.11	1.2
Ukrainian varietal type	53.8 ± 0.64	3.6	53.1 ± 0.17	1.1
Varieties of West European countries	54.6 ± 0.53	3.9	53.8 ± 0.54	3.5
North Kazakhstan varietal type	55.3 ± 0.42	2.6	54.0 ± 0.16	1.7
Varieties of western and eastern Siberia	56.8 ± 0.57	2.9	54.7 ± 0.49	2.4

days. Wild species of alfalfa cut in these same periods usually do not achieve the phase of cutting maturity and are less productive. But if cut at the commencement of anthesis, then they, too, like the improved varieties of yellow alfalfa, give one cutting less during the vegetative period than varieties of common and variable alfalfa.

Given summer rains and the adoption of a program of agronomic measures (wide-row sowing, retention of snow, sowing of windbreak rows and border plants, top-dressing of plants with phosphate fertilizers, harrowing, early cutting of grass mixtures, anti-erosion land preparation, strip cropping, etc.) it is sometimes possible to get a second cutting of alfalfa on unirrigated lands in the arid belt of Kazakh SSR. However, under such circumstances the total productivity of the grass mixture is 8.0 to 10.0% that of irrigated lands and rarely exceeds the productivity of hay yield in rainfed crops cut once during the phase of full bloom. The second rainfed cutting is possible 30 to 40 days later, which is 1.5 to 2.0 times longer than on irrigated fields.

Plant Height

Species and varieties of alfalfa vary considerably in rates of growth and plant height. In northern Kazakhstan in nurseries of summer sowing the maximum height (60 to 70 cm) is attained by specimens of common alfalfa from regions of irrigated farming. In varieties of variable alfalfa from the steppe and forest-steppe zones plant height is 50 to 60 cm. Populations of yellow and varicolored alfalfa are not as tall as common and variable alfalfa, but surpass specimens of semitwisted alfalfa (30 to 50 cm), glutinous alfalfa (35 to 49 cm), and blue alfalfa (40 to 48 cm). In spring sowing nurseries varieties of common alfalfa from regions of irrigated farming are equal in height to specimens of variable alfalfa from steppe regions. Under unfavorable weather conditions the maximum height occurs in varieties of variable alfalfa from the southeast European part of the USSR, northern Kazakhstan, and western and eastern Siberia (Table 23a).

Under the severe arid conditions of western Kazakhstan plant height at the commencement of flowering (cutting maturity) is 50% that in the steppe regions and 33 to 40% that on irrigated lands of the arid belt. With the presence of moisture in the soil and a warm and favorable spring, the maximum height (25 to 33 cm) is obtained in improved and local varieties of common alfalfa of Soviet origin from the republics of Central Asia, southern Kazakhstan, and Trans-Caucasus: Fergana-16, Khiva local, Kara-Kalpakian local, Tashkent-721, Mesopotamian-1680, Samarkand local, Krasnovodopadskaya-8, Azerbaydzhanskaya-5, and Kartuli. These are followed by varieties of variable alfalfa (20 to 25 cm) and yellow

Table 23a. Plant height (cm) of alfalfa under summer sowing in different years of growth and different cuttings (Shortandin Auxillary Center of VIR)

| Species, variety, specimens | First year of growth (1961) | | Second year of growth (1962) | | Third year of growth (1963) | |
| | 1st cutting at commencement of flowering | 2nd cutting on 20th day after 1st cutting | 1st cutting at commencement of flowering | 2nd cutting on 20th day after 1st cutting | 1st cutting at commencement of flowering | 2nd cutting on 20th day after 1st cutting |
1	2	3	4	5	6	7
Common alfalfa						
Khiva local	70	51	66	42	52	31
Semirechensk local	66	50	63	35	60	42
Mesopotamian local	63	48	67	36	32	19
Khebei (China)	48	27	51	38	29	16
Variable alfalfa						
Shortandinskaya-2 (control)	56	34	64	46	55	35
Karabalykskaya-18	52	38	69	43	53	39
Poltava-256	52	29	69	49	60	33
Kemlyanskaya-1	50	36	68	46	49	28
Onokhoy-6	49	30	70	34	42	40
Blue hybrid-1316	48	36	68	47	50	36
Flora	44	32	64	47	49	42
Vernal (USA)	43	30	54	42	53	30
Kamalin-930	42	32	66	49	46	41
Rambler (Canada)	42	29	55	37	46	30

(*Contd.*)

Table 23a (*Contd.*)

1	2	3	4	5	6	7
Yellow alfalfa						
Omsk-2251	59	34	56	31	50	45
Yellow Kuban	46	30	56	28	38	35
Krasnokutskaya-4009	31	21	52	29	33	38
Varicolored alfalfa						
Wild (K-29003)	54	31	61	44	56	34
Semitwisted alfalfa						
Wild (K-16691)	52	39	62	47	48	36
Glutinous alfalfa						
Wild (K-2625)	49	32	56	40	48	35
Blue alfalfa						
Wild (K-28645)	48	37	60	47	32	38

alfalfa (20 cm). Under adverse conditions for the growth and development of plants, as in the steppe belt, the tallest (45 to 55 cm) are varieties and specimens of variable alfalfa: Shortandinskaya-2, Kazan-36, Kinel'skaya-2616, Kamyshinskaya-1, Tibet, Slavyanskaya local, Krasnokutskaya-272. However, the tallest plant stand irrespective of weather occurs in wild populations of blue alfalfa (30 to 70 cm), and the shortest (20 to 40 cm) in specimens of glutinous and varicolored alfalfas.

On irrigated lands of western Kazakhstan the tallest plant height is characteristic of varietal specimens of common alfalfa of the Central Asian, Indian, and Trans-Caucasian varietal groups. Improved varieties of the USA, the Federal Republic of Germany, and Ukrainian varietal types are distinctive in height in the collection of variable alfalfa. The least plant height of common alfalfa occurs in the varietal specimens of France and Latin American countries, and in the case of variable alfalfa, in the improved and local varieties of the northern Kazakhstan varietal type, and western and eastern Siberia (Table 24).

The tallest plants (100 cm and more) on irrigated fields of western Kazakhstan are the improved and local alfalfa varieties of the Central Asian gene center: Tashkent-3192, Vakhshskaya-233, Semirechensk local, Krasnovodopadskaya-8, Fergana-700, Samarkand local, Mesopotamian-1680, Tashkent-1, Andizhanskaya-1, Uzgen local, Tokmak local, and others. Varietal specimens of common alfalfa of the Caucasian gene center are shorter than varieties of Central Asia by 5.0 to 7.0 cm: Slavyanskaya local, Nakhichevan local, Azerbaydzhan-1/129, Azerbaydzhanskaya-5, Azerbaydzhan-2/30, ASKhI-1. They are followed by the improved varieties of variable alfalfa of Ukrainian SSR (Khersonskaya-7, Krimskaya local, Poltava Jubilee), West European countries (Alfa—Sweden, Acsai—Hungary, Polava—Poland, Rimnos—the Federal Republic of Germany), the USA (Cayuga, Progress, Brandt) and improved varieties of common alfalfa from France (Cardinal, Fol-100, Gamma, Europe, Omega, Hybride de Crecy, Sochevile F-34), Italy (Maremana, Lucu, Morze, Leonicena), Mexico (Atlixo, Ganverde), whose plant height at the time of first cutting varies from 90 to 100 cm.

Of average height (80 to 90 cm) on irrigated lands of the desert zone are the varietal specimens of common alfalfa from the hilly regions of India, Iran, Chile, China, and the Balkan republics; improved varieties of variable alfalfa from the Soviet Union, Poland, the Federal Republic of Germany, Hungary, England, Rumania, Belgium, Australia, and Oceania; and wild populations of blue alfalfa. Short-statured plants (50 to 80 cm) are characteristic for the majority of the wild species found on irrigated lands (Table 25).

Plant height varies not only from year to year, but also from cutting to

Table 24. Plant height (cm) of alfalfa at first cutting at commencement of anthesis on irrigated lands (Aral Experimental Station of VIR)

Varietal groups, varieties	Second year of growth (1973)				Third year of growth (1974)			
	Range of variability	$\bar{x}\pm m$	P, %	V	Range of variability	$\bar{x}\pm m$	P, %	V
Common alfalfa								
Central Asian group	93–112	103.0±1.24	1.2	5.1	88–108	99.7±1.26	1.3	5.2
Indian group	79–106	101.8±2.36	2.4	7.3	88–105	99.6±2.26	2.2	6.8
Trans-Caucasian group	98–105	100.3±1.17	1.7	3.8	93–106	99.2±1.03	1.2	3.5
Mediterranean group	89–105	99.0±1.28	1.3	4.9	90–107	99.5±1.35	1.3	4.7
Anatolian group	92–109	98.4±2.58	1.9	5.7	86–104	98.3±1.96	1.7	5.6
Varieties of France	90–103	94.9±1.03	1.0	4.6	83–108	98.0±1.56	1.5	6.7
Latin American group	83–104	94.8±1.46	1.5	6.1	76–110	91.1±2.35	2.5	10.3
Variable alfalfa								
Varieties of the USA	95–107	101.0±1.77	1.7	3.4	82–110	93.2±2.02	2.4	6.7
Varieties of the FRG	93–105	99.2±1.93	1.9	4.3	85–100	94.5±3.32	3.5	7.0
Ukrainian varietal type	94–105	99.1±3.01	3.0	5.4	86–91	88.4±1.45	1.6	2.8
Varieties of West European countries	88–103	96.8±1.19	1.2	4.1	83–105	87.9±2.02	2.1	6.5
North Kazakhstan varietal type	75–102	94.2±2.57	2.6	6.2	72–96	84.3±2.69	2.9	7.4
Varieties of West and East Siberia	74–98	91.5±1.96	2.3	6.5	70–93	80.9±1.92	2.4	5.7

Table 25. Plant height (cm) of alfalfa at first cutting at commencement of anthesis on irrigated lands (Aral Experimental Station of VIR)

Species, variety, specimen	1973	1974	1975	Three-year average
Common alfalfa				
Tashkent-3192	112	98	105	105
Vakhshskaya-233	98	102	105	102
Semirechensk local	100	98	102	100
Azerbaydzhanskaya-5	105	94	99	99
Luciole (France)	90	103	101	98
Peruvian (Chile)	98	99	94	97
Rosa (Italy)	89	102	95	95
Local from India (K-21368)	79	75	93	82
Local from Iran (K-36592)	74	78	85	79
Variable alfalfa				
Khersonskaya-7	105	92	97	98
Alfa (Sweden)	105	98	89	96
Progress (USA)	100	98	89	96
Tibet (control)	95	96	94	95
Slavyanskaya local	103	87	93	94
Polava (CSSR)	100	92	85	92
Kazan-64/95	90	90	84	88
Blue alfalfa				
Wild (K-36119)	86	74	85	82
Tian Shan alfalfa				
Wild (K-060234)	76	75	80	77
Trautvetter's alfalfa				
Wild (K-060253)	78	62	72	71
Yellow alfalfa				
Wild (K-062101)	59	61	69	63
South Kazakhstan alfalfa				
Wild (K-063116)	55	53	54	54

cutting. Thus in a given year, especially without irrigation, the plants may be taller or shorter. Variability of plant height in different years of growth vacillates depending on a combination of (favorable or adverse) meteorological factors. A different phenomenon is observed in the change of height of plant stand from cutting to cutting: Plant height gradually reduces from the first to the last cutting. This is true not only of rainfed crops, which are more at the mercy of climatic factors, but also of irrigated crops. The difference in plant height is particularly marked between the first and last cutting. At the time of the last cutting not all species and varieties have reached the stage of commencement of anthesis (Table 26).

Table 26. Plant height (cm) of alfalfa at each cutting at commencement of anthesis on irrigated lands (Aral Experimental Station of VIR, 1973-1975)

Varietal groups, varieties	First cutting	Second cutting	Third cutting	Fourth cutting
	$\bar{x} \pm m$			
Common alfalfa varietal group				
Central Asian	103.0±1.24	78.2±0.92	82.2±1.16	57.5±1.27
Indian	101.8±2.36	74.7±1.75	79.8±1.49	57.4±1.64
Mediterranean	99.0±1.28	73.8±1.11	81.9±1.27	57.4±1.32
Trans-Caucasian	100.3±1.17	73.4±1.61	76.8±1.74	53.1±1.13
Anatolian	98.4±2.58	72.2±1.95	82.2±2.61	62.2±2.60
Varieties of France	94.9±1.03	72.2±0.87	77.9±0.84	54.9±1.04
Variable alfalfa				
Varieties of the USA	101.0±1.77	77.2±1.22	78.5±2.10	58.7±3.61
Varieties of the FRG	99.2±1.93	75.2±1.77	74.8±3.13	51.2±1.46
Ukrainian varietal type	99.1±3.01	71.6±2.02	68.6±5.36	52.3±1.45
Varieties of West European countries	96.8±1.19	74.6±0.97	70.1±1.15	51.1±1.06
North Kazakhstan varietal type	94.2±2.57	70.2±1.95	65.2±1.38	49.6±1.22
Varieties of western and eastern Siberia	91.5±1.96	68.4±2.31	63.7±1.18	45.3±1.57
Wild populations of the Central Asian gene center				
Common alfalfa	76.9±2.61	72.3±2.11	55.4±1.02	32.7±0.54
Variable alfalfa	74.9±2.78	68.7±3.34	53.4±1.14	27.2±0.35
Tian Shan alfalfa	64.0±2.41	57.0±1.38	49.6±1.18	21.6±0.32
Trautvetter's alfalfa	63.6±1.96	62.0±2.18	35.2±0.76	10.9±0.21
Blue alfalfa	59.0±1.69	51.5±1.49	35.9±0.84	10.7±0.34
Yellow alfalfa	58.1±1.58	52.1±1.67	42.2±1.07	10.6±0.20
Steppe alfalfa	56.6±2.14	49.4±1.84	39.7±0.96	9.9±0.18

Variability of plant height of wild alfalfa species, depending on regime of irrigation, is presented in Table 27. In 1974, due to water deficit, the collection nurseries of alfalfa were irrigated only once in the first cutting at the rate of 800 m³/ha. In 1975 the grass stand was irrigated twice for each cutting. The quantity of water used for one cutting was 1,600 m³/ha (800 m³ × 2). The maximum difference in plant height during these three

years was observed in specimens of common alfalfa—23.9 cm, and the
minimum difference in wild populations of variable alfalfa—5.7 cm. In the
rainfed crop, due to severe conditions for growth, variability of plant height
reduced in all alfalfa species in these years of growth. The range of variation for specimens of common alfalfa was 1.8 cm, for variable alfalfa—3.1
cm, Tian Shan alfalfa—5.1 cm, Trautvetter's alfalfa—5.3 cm, blue alfalfa—6.9 cm, South Kazakhstan alfalfa—7.5 cm, and yellow alfalfa—10.1
cm. The difference in plant height of various alfalfa species grown under
irrigated and unirrigated conditions was even greater (see Table 27).

Table 27. Plant height (cm) of wild alfalfa species at anthesis

Species	Year	Irrigated $\bar{x}\pm m$	Unirrigated $\bar{x}\pm m$	Difference	Increase (%) of plant height in irrigated over unirrigated crop
Common alfalfa	1974	60.9±2.75	47.4±2.20		
	1975	84.8±2.56	49.2±2.31		
	Average	72.9	48.3	24.6	51.0
Variable alfalfa	1974	72.0±2.87	53.0±2.17		
	1975	77.7±2.76	49.9±1.70		
	Average	74.9	51.4	23.5	45.7
Trautvetter's alfalfa	1974	54.1±1.77	51.1±1.25		
	1975	73.1±2.60	45.8±1.26		
	Average	63.6	48.4	15.2	31.4
Tian Shan alfalfa	1974	59.2±2.32	52.2±1.83		
	1975	68.8±2.49	47.1±1.24		
	Average	64.0	49.6	14.4	29.1
Blue alfalfa	1974	59.2±1.49	57.7±2.43		
	1975	78.9±1.81	50.8±2.39		
	Average	69.0	54.2	14.8	27.3
Steppe alfalfa	1974	55.7±2.14	50.0±2.27		
	1975	61.6±2.15	42.5±1.96		
	Average	58.6	46.2	12.4	26.8
Yellow alfalfa	1974	57.4±2.52	54.8±2.06		
	1975	68.9±2.62	44.7±1.51		
	Average	63.1	49.8	13.3	26.7

Increase in plant height due to watering, as well as increase in yield of green mass, indicates the responsiveness of species and varieties of alfalfa to irrigation. Studies have shown that to evolve varieties which can yield multiple cuttings under intensive agriculture it is desirable to select varietal specimens of common and variable alfalfa. Responsiveness to irrigation is still higher in improved varieties of cultivated species.

Plant height during browning of the pods is not of particular economic importance. On the average it is 10 to 15 cm greater than at the commencement of anthesis.

Vigor of Spring and Postcutting Growth

Growth of species and varieties of alfalfa is closely related to plant height and depends on genotype, meteorological factors, irrigation regime, and other conditions. Varieties of common alfalfa in regions of irrigated farming of various countries and continents are distinguished by high growth vigor on irrigated lands. The average daily increase in plant height is 2.0 times that of wild species. Under rainfed conditions of the arid belt growth vigor is typical of the more drought-resistant species of blue, Trautvetter's, and yellow alfalfa. In the steppe zone improved varieties of variable alfalfa of northern Kazakhstan, the southeast European part of the USSR, and western and eastern Siberia are known for this particular character: Kamalin-930, Shortandinskaya-2, Karabalykskaya-18, Kokshe, Leninskaya local, Flora, Onokhoy-6, Sretenskaya-77, Karaganda-1, Dolinskaya-2, Blue hybrid-1316, Omsk-8893, Kamalinskaya-530, and Pestraya-57.

Foliage

Leaves comprise about half of the green mass of alfalfa plants and are characterized by a much higher content of crude protein, vitamins, fats, some minerals, and other substances compared to the stems.

In the steppe zone of Kazakhstan high foliage (48 to 52%) is characteristic of varieties of northern Kazakhstan, Khivinsk, Plain Turkestan, and Trans-Caucasian ecogeographic groups. Among specimens of foreign origin the improved varieties of Canada (Rhizoma, Gibride, Beaver, Rambler), the USA (Lahontan, Vernal, Narragansett, Moapa, Zia, Cody), and local populations from Peru (K-5141, K-21284) are known for their foliage (45 to 50%).

On irrigated lands in western Kazakhstan the most profuse foliage is characteristic of varietal specimens of common alfalfa of the Anatolian group of varietal types and varieties of Latin America. Specimens of Trans-Caucasian and Central Asian groups of varietal types yield the lowest foliage (Table 28).

In variable alfalfa the foliage of plants is a more stable character (V=

3.8 to 8.9%*) than in common alfalfa (V = 3.1 to 12.4%). Ranges of variation for cultivated species are: common alfalfa—32 to 53% (difference 21%) and variable alfalfa—41 to 54% (difference 13%). The highest variability in plant foliage among varietal types of common alfalfa is characteristic of varieties from France (V = 7.8 to 12.4%). In variable alfalfa a high coefficient of variation for the given character is observed in improved and local varieties of the Ukrainian groups of varietal types (V = 7.62 to 8.9%). The lowest variation in different years of growth has been recorded for common alfalfa of the Indo-Pakistan (V = 4.0 to 4.0%) [sic] and Central Asian (V = 4.4 to 4.4%) [sic] groups of varietal types. Among specimens of variable alfalfa, stability of this particular character is inherent to improved varieties of the Federal Republic of Germany (V = 3.9 to 4.1%) and the USA (V = 3.8 to 5.1%).

Research has shown that in northern Kazakhstan and irrigated lands of western Kazakhstan significant differences are not observed in plant foliage in different years of growth. On unirrigated lands of the desert zone the foliage of alfalfa in the year of sowing is 3.0 to 12.0% higher than in subsequent years. Plant foliage reduces with aging. It has also been observed that alfalfa foliage in the first cutting, irrespective of zone of cultivation, is usually lower than in second and subsequent cuttings.

Variability of foliage in wild populations of alfalfa in different years of growth depends on water availability (irrigated versus unirrigated) as shown in Table 29. Under rainfed conditions high foliage is characteristic of wild specimens of Tien Shan and variable alfalfas, average foliage of common and yellow alfalfas, and low foliage of Trautvetter's and South Kazakhstan alfalfas. Under irrigation first place in plant foliage is held by wild populations of common and variable alfalfas. As in rainfed conditions, the last place is held under irrigated conditions by Trautvetter's blue, and South Kazakhstan alfalfas. A slight variation of this character in rainfed crops is characteristic of Tian Shan alfalfa, and under irrigation of variable alfalfa. Plant foliage changes significantly on unirrigated lands in the case of blue alfalfa and on irrigated land in common alfalfa.

The foliage of species, varieties, and specimens of alfalfa is largely determined by the size and shape of leaflets. In the improved varieties of common alfalfa and the blue hybrid group of varietal types of variable alfalfa, as well as in many wild populations of glutinous, semitwisted, and Tian Shan alfalfa, the leaflets are large with a well-developed leaf blade that may be oval, elongated-ovate, obovate, or cuneiform; the ratio of length of central leaflet to width varies from 2.4:1.0 to 3.0:1.0. In yellow and

*The figures for variation actually refer to second and third years of growth respectively—General Editor.

Table 28. Biometric indexes of foliage (%) of cultivated varieties and specimens of alfalfa on irrigated lands (Aral Experimental Station of VIR)

Groups of varietal types, varieties	Second year of growth (1973)			Third year of growth (1974)			Average ($\bar{x}$)
	Range of variability	$\bar{x}\pm m$	V	Range of variability	$\bar{x}\pm m$	V	
Common alfalfa							
Anatolian group	40–52	49.4±2.15	9.9	46–51	49.2±0.86	3.9	49.3
Latin American group	32–53	47.3±1.15	9.7	46–51	48.0±0.37	3.1	47.6
Indo-Pakistan group	44–51	47.3±0.64	4.0	44–50	47.4±0.64	4.0	47.3
Varieties of France	37–50	45.8±0.84	7.8	40–70	48.0±1.41	12.4	46.9
Mediterranean group	42–49	45.7±0.65	5.1	42–50	47.1±0.69	5.1	46.4
Trans-Caucasian group	40–50	45.1±1.68	7.7	40–50	45.6±0.94	6.8	45.3
Central-Asian group	41–47	44.8±0.48	4.4	41–47	45.1±0.48	4.4	44.9
Variable alfalfa							
Ukrainian varietal type	42–54	47.3±1.52	8.9	42–49	46.6±2.07	7.6	47.0
Varieties of West European countries	42–50	46.2±0.86	6.1	43–52	46.6±0.84	6.0	46.4
Varieties of the USA	41–49	45.3±0.79	3.8	44–49	46.5±1.19	5.1	45.9
Varieties of the FRG	41–48	44.6±1.04	4.1	42–48	44.5±1.02	3.9	44.5

Table 29. Biometric indexes of foliage (%) of wild alfalfa species of the Central Asian gene center

Species	year	Unirrigated					Irrigated				
		Range of variability	x̄±m	σ	V	P, %	Range of variability	x̄±m	σ	V	P, %
Common alfalfa	1974	38–55	43.4±1.37	5.0	8.5	2.1	33–60	52.4±2.23	5.7	12.1	3.6
	1975	41–55	46.2±1.13	4.3	7.4	2.0	39–50	48.7±1.55	3.0	6.3	3.7
	Average	—	44.8				—	50.5			
Variable alfalfa	1974	37–63	50.0±1.83	6.6	13.1	3.6	38–51	46.8±0.93	3.6	7.1	1.9
	1975	40–53	47.7±1.32	4.7	10.0	2.7	39–50	45.2±1.32	4.7	9.7	2.3
	Average	—	48.9				—	46.0			
Tian Shan alfalfa	1974	47–52	50.4±0.54	1.3	2.8	1.1	32–49	42.8±1.97	4.3	9.5	2.6
	1975	45–52	49.1±0.76	2.4	4.9	1.5	44–52	47.2±1.08	2.4	7.2	2.2
	Average	—	49.7				—	45.0			
Yellow alfalfa	1974	38–52	38.6±2.05	4.5	8.3	1.7	44–62	42.9±1.25	4.8	9.2	2.3
	1975	42–53	47.4±0.94	3.6	7.6	1.9	38–53	46.1±0.90	3.5	7.6	1.9
	Average	—	43.0				—	44.5			
Trautvetter's alfalfa	1974	37–48	39.5±1.29	4.2	10.8	3.2	42–57	47.5±1.15	3.8	8.0	2.4
	1975	37–48	42.0±1.25	4.1	9.8	2.9	33–45	39.1±1.29	4.2	10.9	3.3
	Average	—	40.7				—	43.3			
Blue alfalfa	1974	33–52	46.4±2.27	7.5	14.5	5.0	39–51	40.1±0.77	3.0	6.5	1.6
	1975	30–48	36.1±1.11	3.3	7.0	1.8	39–52	44.5±0.81	3.3	10.9	2.8
	Average	—	41.2				—	42.3			
South Kazakhstan alfalfa	1974	33–44	39.7±0.83	3.2	8.0	2.0	34–52	38.6±2.05	4.5	8.3	1.7
	1975	32–44	38.7±0.83	3.2	8.3	2.1	36–53	43.4±0.94	3.6	7.6	1.9
	Average	—	39.2				—	41.0			

South Kazakhstan alfalfa the leaflets are smaller, often pubescent, bright green, and elongated; the ratio of length to width of leaf blade in these species exceeds 4.0:1.0 and varies in the range of 4.1:1.0 to 4.7:1.0. Populations of the remaining species of alfalfa—varicolored (3.1:1.0), blue (3.1:1.0), and Trautvetter's (3.2–3.6:1.0) occupy an intermediate position with respect to shape and size of leaflets.

Chemical Composition

The quality of coarse, succulent, preserved, dehydrated, and pressed fodders prepared from alfalfa depends greatly on the content of protein, in particular essential amino acids, as well as vitamins, sugars, enzymes, and other biological compounds. A deficiency in the foregoing in an animal's diet leads to marked overconsumption of fodder.

In northern Kazakhstan varieties of western and eastern Siberia, the Ukraine, the southeast and Central Chernozem zone of the European part of the USSR are characterized in the first year of sowing by high protein content: Marusinskaya-425 (22.4%), Blue Ural (21.1%), Zaykevich (20.9%), Omsk-8893 (20.8%), Krasnokutskaya-4009 (20.5%), and others. These, as well as local varieties of alfalfa contain 2.0 to 3.0% more protein in their leaf-stem mass than specimens of other ecogeographic groups and varietal types. Varietal specimens of the central Russian, eastern Siberian, western Siberian, Trans-Caucasian, Ukrainian, and northern Kazakhstan ecogeographic groups are characterized in the second and third years of growth by a high protien content: Kazan-64/95 (23.9%), Zabaikalka (22.5%), Valuyskaya local (21.6%), Aparan local (21.3%), Poltava-256 (21.2%), Sretenskaya-77 (20.9%), local specimen from Turkey, K-3368 (20.4%), and Karabalykskaya-18 (20.1%). Specimens of yellow alfalfa are likewise characterized by a high protein content: wild population (K-28900) from Krasnoyarsk territory (20.5%), Omsk-2251 (21.2%) and yellow Dnepropetrovsk (20.9%), as are specimens of glutinous alfalfa (K-2625, 21.5%), varicolored alfalfa (K-16714, 20.6%), semi-twisted alfalfa (K-16691, 20.6%), and blue alfalfa (K-28645, 19.0%).

Under irrigation in western Kazakhstan the protein content in the aerial mass of species and varieties of alfalfa varies from 21.1% in variety Ainsford (England) to 12.5% in Beaver (Canada). The following varietal specimens were distinguished by high protein content (20% and above) in the first cutting in 1974: Uzgen local (21%), Cayuga from the USA (21%), local (K-36903) from the Federal Republic of Germany (20.9%), and Vakhshskaya-233 (20.4%). An average protein content (18 to 20%) was recorded in these varieties: Kujawska from Poland (19.9%), local (K-36111) from Tadzhik SSR (19.6%), Jubilee from Poltava province (19.6%), local (K-36905) from the Federal Republic of Germany (19.4%), Baska Zms-1

Table 30. Chemical composition (% of dry matter) of alfalfa species and varieties at anthesis on irrigated lands in first cutting of second year of growth (Aral Experimental Station of VIR, 1968)

Species, variety, specimen	Origin	Crude protein	Ether extract	Cellu- lose	Ash	NES*	P	Ca	Na	K
1	2	3	4	5	6	7	8	9	10	11
Common alfalfa										
Peruvian	Peru	19.43	4.5	23.6	8.9	43.57	0.281	1.92	0.120	1.971
Moapa	USA	18.43	3.5	24.7	8.6	44.47	0.246	0.95	0.098	2.102
Mesopotamian	Iraq	16.62	2.4	26.1	7.3	47.58	0.289	1.72	0.200	2.031
Vakhshskaya-233	Tadzhik SSR	16.56	4.1	25.2	8.5	45.64	0.259	2.02	0.098	2.025
Local (K-6940)	India	16.25	3.8	25.8	7.3	46.85	0.269	1.47	0.140	1.689
Kara-Kalpakian	Kara-Kalpak ASSR	15.37	2.3	23.9	8.0	50.43	0.246	1.92	0.098	1.533
Local (K-7219)	Ecuador	15.18	3.3	23.7	8.4	49.42	0.246	1.82	0.120	2.016
Tashkent-3192	Tashkent province	14.68	2.7	24.5	8.1	50.02	0.238	1.67	0.098	1.752
Flamande	France	14.62	3.1	24.7	7.9	49.68	0.233	1.53	0.098	1.887
Khiva local	Uzbek SSR	13.93	2.1	26.1	8.2	49.67	0.258	1.45	0.097	1.841
Iolotanskaya-1763	Turkmenian SSR	13.56	2.5	26.5	8.7	48.74	0.259	1.90	0.120	1.960
Variable alfalfa										
Rambler	Canada	17.68	4.7	24.6	8.5	44.52	0.246	1.38	0.098	1.803
Marusinskaya-81	Tambov province	17.18	3.3	22.2	7.6	49.52	0.280	1.24	0.096	1.916
Severnaya hybrid	Moscow province	16.93	3.5	25.4	8.2	45.97	0.279	1.78	0.066	1.803
Dolinskaya-2	Karaganda province	16.75	2.9	26.1	8.3	45.95	0.264	1.54	0.066	1.861

(Contd.)

Table 30 (*Contd.*)

1	2	3	4	5	6	7	8	9	10	11
Kamalin-930	Krasnoyarsk territory	16.43	3.8	27.3	7.0	45.47	0.339	1.34	0.081	2.372
Valuyskaya local	Volgograd province	16.25	3.8	27.4	8.5	44.05	0.260	1.33	0.098	2.263
Onokhoy-6	Buryatian ASSR	15.94	3.7	22.5	8.4	49.46	0.294	1.53	0.066	2.104
Zaykevich	Poltava province	15.93	3.3	21.1	8.1	51.57	0.262	1.45	0.120	1.866
Vernal	USA	15.81	4.3	24.6	8.3	44.75	0.278	1.29	0.120	2.130
Sretenskaya-77	Chita province	15.56	3.1	25.7	7.8	47.84	0.276	1.49	0.081	1.976
Blue Ural	Ural'sk province	15.25	2.6	26.4	8.2	47.75	0.265	1.61	0.082	1.864
Kamalinskaya-530	Krasnoyarsk territory	14.56	2.4	26.6	9.1	47.34	0.295	1.50	0.098	1.837
Flora	Omsk province	14.50	2.2	26.3	8.3	48.70	0.294	1.39	0.200	1.963
Tibet (control)	Aktyubin province	14.25	3.5	26.6	8.1	47.50	0.297	1.75	0.066	1.738
Karabalykskaya-18	Kustanaisk province	14.06	4.8	25.4	7.8	47.94	0.231	1.49	0.099	1.782
Slavyanskaya local	Krasnodar territory	13.43	2.2	28.6	7.2	48.57	0.246	1.48	0.098	1.638
Beaver	Canada	12.50	2.5	29.4	7.2	48.40	0.257	1.69	0.082	1.636

*NES=nonnitrogenous extracted substances.

from Yugoslavia (19.3%), local (K-36911) from Algeria (19.2%), Azer-
baydzhanskaya-5 (18.9%), local (K-21370) from India (18.8%), local
(K-5909) from Egypt (18.7%), Saranac from the USA (18.6%), Bogarnaya-
2628 from Samarkand province (18.5%), Prima from France (18.4%),
Tibet from Aktyubin province (18.2%), and others. A low protein content
was observed in these varieties: Brand-102 from the USA (17.6%), local
(K-7219) from Ecuador (17.1%), Slavyanskaya local (16.9%), and others.

The chemical composition of some alfalfa species and varieties at the
commencement of flowering on irrigated lands in the Aral Experimental
Station of VIR is given in Table 30. In the second year of growth the maximum content of crude protein (19.4%) was found in variety Peruvian and
the lowest (12.5%) in variety Beaver (Canada). The range of variability
of this character in specimens of common alfalfa (5.87%) and variable
alfalfa (5.18%) was almost identical; so, too, was the range of fat contents
(2.4 and 2.6% respectively) and nonnitrogenous extracted substances
(6.86 and 7.52%). Considerable differences were recorded for populations
of the aforementioned species in content of ash (range of variability 1.6
and 2.1% respectively), phosphorus (0.056 and 0.108%), sodium (0.103
and 0.134%), calcium (1.07 and 0.54%), and potassium (0.569 and
0.736%).

Without irrigation in western Kazakhstan the protein content of all
alfalfa species and varieties is usually reduced by 2.0 to 5.0% and on the
average constitutes 15 to 16%. The content of crude protein reduces notably in rainfed crops of the desert zone in the second and subsequent years
of growth. Above-average protein content has been recorded in different
years for these varieties: English Early, Rhizoma (Canada), Tichantuli
(Hungary), Manych, Onokhoy-6, Kinelskaya-5, Iygeva-17, Flora, Kara-
Kalpakian local, Semirechensk local, Priaralskaya, Karabalykskaya,
Brodskaya local, and Karaganda-1.

The protein content of wild alfalfa species of the Central Asian gene
center under irrigation varies in the following ranges: common alfalfa
19.1 to 21.6%, variable alfalfa 18.3 to 21.2%, blue alfalfa 18.5 to 23.2%,
yellow alfalfa 17.0 to 22.0%, South Kazakhstan alfalfa 15.1 to 21.6%,
Trautvetter's alfalfa 19.2 to 22.4%, and Tian Shan alfalfa 21.4 to 22.2%.
In 1974 the maximum quantity of protein in the first cutting was recorded
in populations of wild species such as blue alfalfa (K-36053) from Gur'ev
province—23.2%, Trautvetter's alfalfa (K-36121) from Ural'sk province—
22.4%, Tian Shan alfalfa (K-34628) from western China—22.2%, yellow
alfalfa (K-37217) from Aktyubin province—22.0%, South Kazakhstan
alfalfa (K-067854) from Karaganda province—21.6%, common alfalfa
(K-30706) from Tadzhik SSR—21.6%, and variable alfalfa (K-067878)
from eastern Kazakhstan province—21.2%.

Research has shown that the worse the conditions of growth and development of plants, the more significant the changes in chemical composition. In the drought year of 1975 the protein content of all specimens of wild species of alfalfa in western Kazakhstan was 3.0 to 8.0% lower than in 1974. On irrigated lands the protein content in the leaf-stem mass increased slightly in the second and subsequent cuttings. This was related to an increase in foliage and much earlier flowering, as well as slender plant stems ($r = 0.56 \pm 0.19$). In the control variety (Tibet), the protein content in different cuttings changed as follows: first cutting—17.7%, second cutting—18.7%, third cutting—20.2%. In the varieties Brand-102 and Saranac from the USA the per cutting change in protein content in the aerial mass was in the same order: first cutting—17.6 and 18.6%, second cutting—17.9 and 19.2%, and third cutting—19.6 and 19.6%. A similar phenomenon was observed in varieties Slavyanskaya local (17.2, 19.6, and 19.6%), Jubilee (19.5, 20.7, and 22.0%), Baska Zms-1 (17.2, 19.6, and 19.6%), Harmignies (18.2, 19.4, and 19.6%), and others.

Statistical analysis of the variability of characters of chemical composition of administrative-geographic groups and varietal types of alfalfa revealed that the maximum amount of protein in the leaf-stem mass is found in varieties of North America ($16.47 \pm 0.64\%$) and the equatorial belt ($16.13 \pm 0.48\%$). The lowest protein content under conditions in western Kazakhstan is characteristic of plants of populations of variety Tibet ($13.44 \pm 0.17\%$) and varieties of Central Asia ($14.94 \pm 0.40\%$). The maximum quantity of fat is inherent in varieties of Kazakh SSR (3.68 $\pm 0.20\%$). Varieties of western and eastern Siberia are rich in phosphorus ($0.29 \pm 0.01\%$) and potassium ($2.08 \pm 0.08\%$). Specimens from the republics of Central Asia contain the highest amount of calcium ($1.77 \pm 0.07\%$). A large quantity of sodium ($0.24 \pm 0.05\%$) was found in varieties of West European countries.

Statistical analysis has also shown that the stable characters of chemical composition are: protein ($V = 5.85$ to 12.08%), cellulose ($V = 5.25$ to 8.85%), ash ($V = 3.13$ to 9.34%), NES ($V = 2.84$ to 5.20%), phosphorus ($V = 3.82$ to 9.42%), and potassium ($V = 7.38$ to 12.12%). Average variability is characteristic for the calcium content of plants ($V = 5.66$ to 18.76%), while the fat content of plants is above average in variability ($V = 15.28$ to 28.16%). The most unstable character of chemical composition of alfalfa is the sodium content of the leaf-stem mass ($V = 21.76$ to 70.86%).

Coefficients of correlation were calculated for content of crude protein and other chemical substances and showed that crude protein in different degrees correlates well with fat content ($r = 0.51$), ash ($r = 0.23$) and potash ($r = 0.29$) in plants, and negatively with cellulose content ($r = -0.39$) and

NES (r= −0.57). There is almost no relationship between content of crude protein and sodium (r=0.05), crude protein and calcium (r=0.10), and crude protein and phosphorus (r=0.17).

A high correlation was established in varieties of western and eastern Siberia between content of crude protein and other chemical substances in plants: fat (r=0.98 ± 0.01), potash (r=0.89 ± 0.08), sodium (r= −0.69 ± 0.23) [sic], and ash (r=0.61 ± 0.27). Varieties of North America exhibit a close inverse relationship between content of crude protein and cellulose (r= −0.89 ± 0.09), crude protein and NES (r= −0.82 ± 0.04). In varieties of the North American continent high and direct correlation was seen between content of crude protein and potassium (r=0.79 ± 0.19) and crude protein and fat (r=0.61 ± 0.28). A negative correlation was found between content of crude protein and sodium in varieties of West European countries (r= −0.86), Siberia (r= −0.69), and republics of Central Asia (r= −0.24). A positive correlation between these indexes was characteristic of alfalfa varieties of Kazakh SSR (r=0.25).

In calculating coefficients of correlation between indexes of chemical composition it is very important to determine the signal relationships by which indirect selections of high protein plants can be made. The easier the determination of chemical substances in plants, closely following the signal link with protein content, the more effective and simpler the selection for high protein content. In our studies such correlations were found for: NES (r= −0.80 and −0.87 respectively for varieties of Kazakh SSR and the tropical belt), fat (r=0.65 for varieties of Central Asia), fat (r= 0.98) and potassium (r=0.89 for varieties of Siberia), cellulose (r= −0.89 for varieties of North America), and sodium (r= −0.86 for varieties of West Europe).

The content of green and yellow pigments in the leaves of alfalfa varieties in different years of growth is presented in Table 31. The data shows that the presence of chlorophylls "a" and "b" as well as carotene, lutein, and xanthophyll in the leaves depends greatly on climatic factors.

Susceptibility to Diseases and Pests

Among the most prevalent diseases of alfalfa in northern Kazakhstan are brown leaf spots, rust, and root rots. The alfalfa of summer sowing is less affected than that of spring sowing.

High resistance to local races of brown leaf spot and rust is found in variegated hybrid varieties of variable alfalfa from Siberia, Altai, Ural'sk, and the southeast European part of the USSR; improved varieties of yellow alfalfa; and wild populations of glutinous and semitwisted alfalfas. Summer crops after fallow are affected less by brown leaf spot, as recorded for specimens from Canada (K-583 and K-32783), the USA (K-8464,

Table 31. Content of pigments (γ/mg of raw substance) of leaves of various alfalfa varieties in the budding stage

Variety	Total pigments	Chlorophyll			Caro-tene	Lutein	Xantho-phyll
		a	b	a+b			
First year of growth, 1967							
Culver	0.754	0.349	0.285	0.634	0.067	0.036	0.017
Karaganda-1	0.639	0.321	0.195	0.516	0.083	0.028	0.012
Tashkent-3192	0.606	0.284	0.216	0.500	0.052	0.038	0.016
Zaykevich	0.572	0.298	0.172	0.470	0.051	0.035	0.016
Zabaikalka	0.551	0.275	0.153	0.428	0.076	0.034	0.013
Second year of growth, 1968							
Culver	0.983	0.470	0.302	0.772	0.110	—	0.101
Karaganda-1	0.964	0.435	0.332	0.767	0.103	—	0.094
Tashkent-3192	0.942	0.427	0.337	0.764	0.092	—	0.086
Zaykevich	0.810	0.407	0.240	0.647	0.091	—	0.072
Zabaikalka	0.769	0.364	0.238	0.602	0.090	—	0.077
Third year of growth 1969*							
Karaganda-1	0.243	0.162	0.050	0.212	0.017	0.013	0.006
Tashkent-3192	0.230	0.170	0.030	0.200	0.016	0.010	0.004
Culver	0.226	0.127	0.060	0.187	0.030	0.005	0.004
Severnaya hybrid	0.180	0.119	0.034	0.153	0.016	0.007	0.004
Zaykevich	0.165	0.121	0.128	0.149	0.009	0.005	0.002
Zabaikalka	0.145	0.112	0.017	0.129	0.009	0.005	0.002

*Soil and atmospheric drought occurred.

K-33681), Argentina (K-7227), India (K-6910), and Egypt (K-5143). Varieties of common alfalfa from the republics of Central Asia are severely attacked by bacterial and fungal diseases, especially in the third year of growth.

Specimens of yellow and blue alfalfa are highly resistant to viral diseases. If favorable conditions prevail for growth and development of plants in the year of sowing, then during the first two years valuable local and improved varieties of alfalfa from the Central Asian republics are very slightly affected by viral diseases: Khiva local, Semirechensk local, Uzgen local, Tashkent-3192, Tashkent-721, Fergana-700, Vakhshskaya-233, Vakhshskaya-300, Iolotanskaya local, Samarkand local, and Kara-Kalpakian local. In drought years as well as after severe winters the suscep-

Table 32. Susceptibility (%) of alfalfa species to viral disease in different periods of sowing in the steppe zone of northern Kazakhstan, 1961–1964

Species, variety, specimen	Spring sowing				Summer sowing			
	With colonies of larvae of psylla in 1st year of growth	Virus infection in:			With colonies of larvae of psylla in 1st year of growth	Virus infection in:		
		2nd year of growth	3rd year of growth	4th year of growth		2nd year of growth	3rd year of growth	4th year of growth
Common alfalfa Khiva local	99	87	100	100	27	24	69	81
Variable alfalfa Shortandinskaya-2 (control)	87	69	98	100	22	19	47	53
Yellow alfalfa Yellow Kuban	25	18	57	64	2	0	16	23
Glutinous alfalfa Wild (K-2625)	51	30	63	71	7	0	22	27
Blue alfalfa Wild (K-12820)	49	28	72	79	9	2	18	25
Semitwisted alfalfa Wild (K-16650)	17	22	49	52	11	6	34	41
Varicolored alfalfa Wild (K-30094)	91	76	98	100	23	12	43	56

tibility of alfalfa varieties from regions of irrigated farming increases in all continents of the globe. Alfalfa varieties of Kazakh SSR—Shortandinskaya-2, Kokshe, Karabalykskaya, Dolinskaya-2, Blue hybrid-1316, Tibet, Priaralskaya, Irtyshskaya local, Zaysanskaya, Krasnovodopadskaya-8, and others are characterized by average to low resistance to viral diseases (Table 32).

Viral diseases are widespread in northern Kazakhstan. They greatly damage seed production by inducing premature drop of flowers and buds. The disease progresses rapidly after overwintering of plants. The pathogen is transmitted by a specialized pest, namely, the alfalfa psylla. Specimens of common alfalfa susceptible to soil drought are the most severely afflicted. The number of plants infected rises rapidly with crop growth and development.

In northern Kazakhstan the following varieties are characterized by high resistance to root rots, an important character of perennial use of the crop: Marusinskaya-425, Kamalinskaya-530, Kamalin-930, Blue Ural, Kazan-64/95, Stepnaya-600, Krasnokutskaya-4009, Sretenskaya-77, Biiskaya, Zabaikalka, and Onokhoy-6 (Table 33).

Studies conducted by us jointly with Academician V.P. Kuz'min (1964) showed that alfalfa varieties of the same ecological group differ in resistance to root rots. For example, in the fifth year of its growth in 1963 the

Table 33. Resistance of alfalfa to root rots in the third year of growth (Shortandin Substation of VIR, 1963)

Species, variety	Spring sowing			Summer sowing		
	Average grade	Suscepti-bility, %	Survi-val, %	Average grade	Suscepti-bility, %	Survi-val, %
Common alfalfa						
Semirechensk local	3.71	94	40	3.19	88	58
Khiva local	3.43	83	51	3.01	68	63
Variable alfalfa						
Zaykevich	3.64	77	68	3.04	75	43
Shortandinskaya-2	3.46	89	46	2.81	63	54
Omsk-8893	2.52	67	74	2.16	50	79
Kazan-64/95	3.03	61	71	2.34	41	81
Kamalinskaya-530	2.48	54	78	2.07	44	85
Marusinskaya-425	2.07	59	81	2.00	40	86
Yellow alfalfa						
Stepnaya-600	2.21	52	84	1.75	31	90
Krasnokutskaya-4009	1.92	51	87	1.47	34	93

extent of infection in variety Gul'kevichskaya of the northern Caucasian blue hybrid varietal type was 91% and the average infection grade 3.28 points; the extent of infection in variety Novokuban of this same varietal type was 73% and the average infection grade 2.0 points. The first variety is not resistant to root rots while the second variety possesses average resistance. Within a species the variability of varieties belonging to different ecogeographic groups is still higher (Table 34).

Resistance of species and varieties of alfalfa to root rots varies not only in different years of growth and times of sowing, but also within a single vegetative period. Maximum plant mortality in an infected nursery in 1962 was recorded in July when the average monthly soil temperature at a depth of 10 cm was 24.6°C.

In the second year of growth plant mortality among common alfalfa was: May—0.3%, June—4.3%, July—13.0%, August—5.1%, and September—1.2%. In yellow alfalfa thinning of the plant stand in these same months was: 0, 2.4, 3.1, 2.7 and 0.4% respectively.

The following varieties are characterized by compound resistance to diseases in northern Kazakhstan: Omsk-8893, Chishminskaya-130, Sretenskaya-77, Flora, Kamalinskaya-530, Kamalin-930, Krasnokutskaya-4009, Stepnaya-600, Zabaikalka, Onokhoy-6, Brodskaya local, Valuyskaya local, Karaganda-1, Kazan-64/95, Blue Ural, Marusinskaya-81, Poltava-256, Marusinskaya-425, Buzulukskaya local, Abakanskaya-1, yellow hybrid, Biiskaya, and Kuzbasskaya. These varieties were developed, barring few exceptions, in Siberia, Altai, Kazakhstan, Ural'sk, and the southeast European part of the USSR, i.e., in regions of severe climate.

Among diseases of alfalfa crops in northern Aral, brown leaf spot has been detected, and among pests, the sweet clover weevil, corn earworm or

Table 34. Distribution of plants of variable alfalfa varieties of different ecogeographic groups according to degree of resistance to root rots in the fourth year of growth, 1962

Variety, ecogeographic group	Number of plants	Infection, grade						Infection, average grade
		0	1	2	3	4	5	
Marusinskaya-81 (Middle Russian blue hybrid)	150	1	77	45	7	2	0	1.31
Shortandinskaya-2 (northern Kazakhstan blue variegated hybrid)	167	1	16	77	54	17	3	2.49
Gul'kevichskaya (northern Caucasian blue (hybrid)	103	0	5	12	35	38	12	3.41

bollworm, and aphids. Significant infections have not been observed in severe drought years. Among pests, aphids are the most prevalent at the time of cutting maturity. Periodically, once in 10 to 15 years, irrigated crops of alfalfa are severely damaged by larvae of the cotton bollworm, with insect density as high as 300 to 400 larvae per square meter. There are no varieties in the collection which are absolutely resistant to pests and diseases. In old crops, especially in irrigated fields, severe infection of plants with root rots is not uncommon.

Under irrigated conditions in 1969 in the sixth year of plant growth the following varieties were characterized by high resistance to root rots: Kuzbasskaya variegated hybrid, Kamalin-930, Flora, Zabaikalka, Barnaul's-kaya-17, Omsk-8893, and Ranger (USA). The grade point of infection of these varieties did not exceed 1.0. Moderate resistance was characteristic of varieties of Kazakh SSR: Blue Ural, Aralskaya, Dolinskaya-1, Dolinskaya-2, Karabalykskaya-18, Semirechonsk local, Karaganda-1, Tibet, Irtyshskaya local, Krasnovodopadskaya-8, and Zaysanskaya.

The average grade of infection of the above varieties of variable alfalfa ranged from 1.09 to 1.72 (Figure 34). Varieties from regions of irrigated farming susceptible to root rots were: Allahabad local (India), Mesopotamian local (Iraq), Azerbaydzhan local, Iolotanskaya-1763, ancient populations of alfalfa from Ecuador, Bolivia, Argentina, Panama, Mexico, Algeria, Egypt, Libya, Pakistan, and Turkey. The average grade of infection ranged from 2.01 to 2.56.

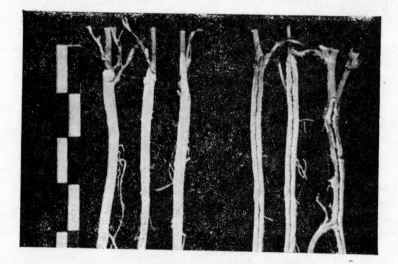

Figure 34. Roots of variable alfalfa in second year of growth (1977).
Left—healthy; right—infected with root rot.

It has been mentioned above that irrigation in the arid belt not only increases plant productivity, but also simultaneously becomes a good medium for the development of diseases and pests. In 1968 in the old crops of alfalfa variety Tibet-6417 plants were analyzed for root rot. In the eighth field, irrigated seven to nine times during the vegetative period, of the 1,476 plants analyzed 260 or 17.6% were healthy. The seventh field was not irrigated regularly, but only in critical periods of plant growth, or merely two to three times throughout the entire season. Under conditions of limited irrigation 520 or 30.9% plants were healthy. In the rainfed field, of the 2,736 plants analyzed only 656 were infected. In this field healthy plants constituted 76.2%. The regime or rate of irrigation affected not only the number of infected plants, but also their quality (average grade of infection under regular irrigation, limited irrigation, and rainfed condition 2.51, 2.37, and 1.48 respectively).

In 1964 at the Aral Experimental Station of VIR at the time of severe infection of alfalfa crops by the corn earworm the average number of larvae on plants and pupae in the upper layer of soil on an area of one square meter was: irrigated fields 421 and rainfed fields 57. The density of larvae and pupae under conditions of irrigations was 7.0 times higher compared with the rainfed field. No difference was seen between varieties of common alfalfa and variable alfalfa with regard to resistance to corn earworm under conditions of mass infection. Wild species of alfalfa, especially those with less foliage and pigmented and pubescent leaves and stems, were infected less.

Under severe moisture stress in the desert zone the process of differentiation of varieties into resistant and susceptible accelerates. This is linked with the fact that plants not resistant to diseases suffer more from the fatal effect of drought and low temperatures and, naturally, die quickly. Alfalfa plants of rainfed crops purify themselves, so to speak, and plants weakened by various factors are rapidly eliminated through natural selection. Therefore in the desert belt, in the context of rainfed crops, it is more correct not to speak of one type of resistance, but rather the compound resistance of plants to diseases and pests, drought and frost. This type of resistance is usually incorporated by plant breeders under the label "plant survival". A high survival rate (70 to 80%) was shown by these varieties in the fifth year of growth in 1968: Khorezmskaya local, Kara-Kalpakian local, Kinelskaya-5, Marusinskaya-425, Abakanskaya-1, Tibet, Onokhoy-6, Dolinskaya-2, Kamyshinskaya-404, Tashauzskaya local, Rambler (Canada), as well as wild specimens of Trautvetter's alfalfa (K-34631, 34633, 34626, and 34629), yellow alfalfa (K-35004), and blue alfalfa (K-29002). Poor survival (0 to 40%) was characteristic of varieties and specimens from Argentina, Chile, Peru, Turkmenian SSR, China,

France, Belgium, England, Sweden, the Federal Republic of Germany, northern Caucasus, Ukrainian SSR, Turkey, Iran, Pakistan, India, northern Africa, and the Middle East.

Specimens with poor plant survival subsequently produce green mass and seeds in which the yield is 10 to 33% that of varieties with compound resistance to adverse environmental factors, diseases, and pests (Table 35).

Winter Hardiness

Productivity of alfalfa species and varieties in the second and subsequent years of growth depends to a considerable extent on their winter hardiness

Table 35. Characteristics of alfalfa varieties under rainfed conditions in the third year of growth (Aral Experimental Station of VIR, 1968)

Variety	Plant height cm	Foliage grade,	Plant survival in third year of growth, %	Average hay yield from 9 m²	
				kg	Percent of adjacent control
Varieties cultivated on irrigated land in republics of Central Asia					
Fergana-700	58	2.0	2	0.26	25
Tashkent-721	48	2.0	45	0.56	49
Tashkent-3192	53	2.6	64	0.67	58
Semirechensk local	56	2.6	71	0.87	66
Varieties of northern and western Kazakhstan					
Blue Ural	64	3.3	97	1.45	89
Karabalykskaya-18	65	3.3	91	1.63	100
Tibet (control)	55	3.3	96	1.23	100
Shortandinskaya-2	60	3.0	90	1.87	114
Varieties of the forest-steppe and steppe regions of the Soviet Union					
Slavyanskaya local	58	3.0	83	2.35	138
Kazan-64/95	67	3.6	93	2.20	145
Brodskaya local	60	3.3	97	2.22	145
Kuzbasskaya	65	3.4	96	2.43	161

(frost resistance), i.e., on the capability of plants to withstand low temperatures and other adverse conditions associated with the winter season.[2]

Local varieties of alfalfa, specimens of Siberian origin, improved varieties of southern Ural'sk, Lower Povolzh'e, Altai, and the steppe region of Ukrainian SSR, and wild populations of yellow, blue, and Trautvetter's alfalfa overwinter well in northern Kazakhstan (85 to 100%). Overwintering in the Kazakhstan steppe is negligible in ancient populations from Ecuador, Venezuela, Paraguay, Colombia, Ethiopia, Panama, Costa Rica, the Honduras, and Guyana. Considerable thinning is observed after the first winter in varieties from Argentina, Australia, India, Algeria, Pakistan, Greece, Italy, Egypt, Chile, Peru, and Mexico. Improved and local varieties from southern regions of the republics of Central Asia and Trans-Caucasus, as well as populations from the hilly regions of Turkey, Italy, Afghanistan, China, India, Chile, Peru, Mexico, and Spain overwinter poorly (30 to 50%). Average winter hardiness (50 to 70%) is characteristic of specimens from West European countries, northern regions of the Nechernozem zone of RSFSR, and the Baltic republics. Above-average winter hardiness (70 to 80%) is found in varieties from the forest-steppe regions of the European part of the USSR, glutinous alfalfa, and semitwisted alfalfa.

In western Kazakhstan varieties of common and variable alfalfa from eastern Siberia, Yakutia ASSR, western Kazakhstan, Kara-Kalpak ASSR, Middle and Lower Volga, steppe part of Trans-Urals, and Canada are characterized by high resistance to low temperatures. Frost resistance among cultivated varieties in the desert zone is usually 20 to 30% lower than that of local wild species. The highest frost resistance during winters from 1965 to 1970 was exhibited by wild specimens of yellow, blue, and Trautvetter's alfalfas and natural hybrids between these species collected in the hills of Mugodzhar, and floodplains of the Ural, Uil, Irgiz, Turgai, and Emba Rivers. In the fifth year of growth, after a particularly severe winter in 1968/1969 when frosts on the soil surface without a snow cover were as severe as − 44°C, plant mortality among wild alfalfa species did not exceed 35%, whereas varietal specimens not resistant to low temperatures perished totally in the first two to three years of growth. This example attests

---

[2]Unlike clover, alfalfa is a frost-resistant crop. Its geographic area of distribution is spread over more arid, less snowy, or snowless regions. Thus the concepts of "winter hardiness" and "frost resistance" are not identical here but nonetheless synonymized. In fact, the survival of alfalfa plants in the area of their cultivation depends almost entirely on frost resistance. Yet under field conditions even in the desert zone where snow is often absent and neither lodging of plants nor their drenching observed but thawing, snowstorms, and high-velocity winds occur, one is confronted with not one, albeit decisive factor, i.e., temperature, but with a number of climatic factors which determine the winter hardiness of plants.

Table 36. Winter hardiness of alfalfa (data of field evaluation of Aral Experimental Station of VIR, 1965-1969)

Species, variety, specimens	Origin	Plant mortality (%) in winter of:				Total
		1965/1966	1966/1967	1967/1968	1968/1969	
Very high winter hardiness						
Yellow alfalfa, wild (K-35004)	Aktyubin province	0	9	0	9	18
Trautvetter's alfalfa, wild (K-34631)	Aktyubin province	0	11	0	12	23
Natural hybrid (yellow alfalfa×Trautvetter's alfalfa) (K-34626)	Aktyubin province	0	15	0	8	23
Variable alfalfa, Nerchinskaya-46	Chita province	0	26	0	7	33
High winter hardiness						
Variable alfalfa, local (K-30106)	Kurgansk province	1	31	0	11	43
Common alfalfa, local (K-8929)	Kara-Kalpak province	0	13	2	29	44
Blue alfalfa, wild (K-29002)	Aktyubin province	4	22	2	16	44
Variable alfalfa, Sretenskaya-77	Chita province	1	40	0	10	50
Yellow alfalfa, Krasnokutskaya-4009	Saratov province	0	34	0	16	50
Variable alfalfa, Nerchinskaya-6	Chita province	0	45	0	5	50
Common alfalfa, Kinelskaya-5	Kuibyshev province	0	51	0	0	51
Variable alfalfa, Onokhoy-6	Yakutia ASSR	0	41	1	12	54
Common alfalfa, local (K-8940)	Kara-Kalpak ASSR	1	26	8	20	55
Variable alfalfa Rambler	Canada	0	35	5	17	57
Tibet	Aktyubin province	0	24	12	22	58

	Province					
Above-average winter hardiness						
Variable alfalfa, Zaykevich	Poltava province	7	13	40	0	60
Common alfalfa						
Local (K-8962)	Khorezmsk province	0	13	31	17	61
Local (K-8951)	Kara-Kalpak ASSR	0	5	30	28	63
Variable alfalfa						
Local (K-3705)	Krasnoyarsk territory	1	1	52	10	64
Kamyshinskaya-404	Volgograd province	0	0	53	13	66
Kamalinskaya-1326	Krasnoyarsk territory	0	5	48	13	66
Abakanskaya-1	Krasnoyarsk territory	2	3	40	23	68
Kazan-36	Tatar ASSR	0	5	56	10	71
Flora	Omsk province	2	4	56	10	72
Average winter hardiness						
Common alfalfa, Semirechensk local	Alma-Ata province	0	10	36	28	74
Variable alfalfa						
Severnaya hybrid	Moscow province	0	2	71	3	76
Vernal	USA	9	3	62	8	82
Poltava-6800	Poltava province	0	6	74	3	83
English Early	England	7	0	74	7	88
Low winter hardiness						
Common alfalfa						
Tashkent-3192	Tashkent province	9	7	67	15	98
Du Puits	France	1	0	76	2	99
Mesopotamian	Asia Minor	1	3	94	2	100
Local (K-6340)	India	56	32	12	—	100
Azerbaydzhan-262	Azerbaidzhan SSR	15	5	80	—	100
Peruvian	Peru	95	—	5	—	100

once again to the fact that wild alfalfa species represent invaluable initial material for breeding for frost resistance (Table 36).

Similar data were obtained at the Aral Experimental Station of VIR from resowing of the collection in 1969, when after the severe winter of 1970/1971 the following varieties were identified for frost resistance: Semirechensk local, Khorezmskaya local, Samarkand local, Tibet, Karaganda-1, Blue Ural, and released varieties of Altai, western and eastern Siberia. Varieties from Italy did not overwinter well: Ascklona, Romagnola, Florida, Gigante Cremoneze, Marchigiana, and Polesana; the plant stand thinned by 47 to 88%. In the fourth year of growth, after the no less severe winter of 1971/1972 when the air temperature at the soil surface dropped to − 35.8°C with complete absence of snow cover, mortality among the alfalfa varieties from Italy due to frost reached 80 to 98%. High winter hardiness was characteristic of alfalfa specimens from Chita province (K-220, K-221, K-222, K-223, and K-224, as well as Irtyshskaya local (Semipalatinsk province) and Samarkand local (K-8919).

Average frost resistance was characteristic of local and improved varieties of Poland—Kleszczewska, Miechowska, Kujawska, Piaskowa, and Pulavska—which were damaged by frost up to 20 to 26%, and varieties of Czechoslovakia—Godoninka, Psherovska, Taborka, Polava, and Nitranka—which suffered a plant mortality of 10 to 20%. Inadequate frost resistance was characteristic of varieties of Bulgaria—Pleven I, Pleven II, Pleven III, and Dunavka—which thinned by 70 to 80%, and varieties of Rumania—Slobodziya, Banat, H-652, and No. 27155—which were destroyed by frosts up to 50 to 80%.

Thinning of alfalfa specimens collected by expeditions of VIR in Afghanistan ranged from 50 to 100%, but specimens introduced into the collection from Iran, Algeria, and Mexico were totally wiped out. Varieties of the USA—Washoe, Dawson, No. 214, No 215, No 303, and No. 305—were damaged by frost up to 80 to 90%, but varieties No. 520 and No. 522 only up to 10 to 20%.

Considerable damage was suffered by crops of improved alfalfa varieties from France and Turkey; after the severe winter of 1971/1972 plant mortality in these varieties was 70 to 95%.

A comparative study of the frost resistance of various alfalfa varieties by the method of freezing the seed sprouts in cold chambers at temperatures of − 8°C, − 10°C, and − 12°C revealed that the given evaluation method is entirely suitable not only for cereal crops for which it was developed, but also for perennial grasses. Results of this methodological experiment are presented in Tables 36a and 37 and show that irrespective of the conditions of freezing and temperature hardening, varieties with a high field winter hardiness are also characterized by a high plant

Table 36a. Comparative frost resistance of alfalfa varieties (field and laboratory evaluation, 1965–1970)

Variety, specimens	Winter hardiness, data of field experiments	Number of plants during freezing of sprouts at:					
		−8°C		−10°C		−12°C	
		Total	After freezing, %	Total	After freezing, %	Total	After freezing, %
		Hardening of sprouts at 2°C					
Kamalin-930	High	150	49	150	35	—	—
Nakhichevan local	Average	150	34	150	23	—	—
Tashkent-721	Low	150	25	75	14	—	—
		Hardening of sprouts at 5°C					
Kamalin-930	High	75	97	75	71	75	68
Krasnokutskaya-4009	High	75	92	75	55	75	53
Nakhichevan local	Average	75	81	75	56	75	39
Slavyanskaya local	Average	85	71	75	44	75	33
Tashkent-721	Average	75	68	75	31	75	29

Table 37. Frost resistance of alfalfa species during freezing in cold chambers, 1971–1972

Species, variety, specimens	Percent of plants surviving at temperature of:		
	−6°C	−9°C	−12°C
Variable alfalfa Kamalin-930	97.2±6.3	97.0±7.1	56.5±21.3
Blue alfalfa Wild (K-36052)	86.3±13.2	76.5±20.4	40.8±13.7
Yellow alfalfa Krasnokutskaya-4009	89.2±13.0	74.2±18.7	31.4±18.9
Common alfalfa Wild (K-35011)	96.5±5.7	69.7±21.2	27.1±20.9
Semitwisted alfalfa Wild (K-35732)	83.7±17.5	75.2±19.4	12.3±13.6
Glutinous alfalfa Wild (K-35729)	63.1±20.6	48.5±21.0	8.3±11.6

survival percentage under the effect of artificial cold on sprouts.

Similar data was obtained by freezing young plants in cold chambers as well. Optimal conditions for quick estimation of alfalfa specimens for frost resistance in this case are: temperature conditions during hardening (2 or 3°C for a period of five to seven days), light (uninterrupted), freezing conditions (− 9°C), and five- to six-leaved stage of plants of medium and late varieties, and four- to five-leaved for very early and early varieties (Table 38).

Comparison of the percentage of plant survival during freezing in cold chambers with data of field experiments revealed that the laboratory method was highly reliable. For example, for specimens of common alfalfa—$r = 0.71 ± 0.11$, yellow alfalfa—$r = 0.84 ± 0.09$, and variable alfalfa—$r = 0.69 ± 0.13$.

We determined the frost resistance of alfalfa species and varieties not only by counting the plants which survived after treatment with low temperatures, but also by evaluating changes in physiological indexes of the water regime. By comparing the results of direct and indirect methods of evaluation of plant resistance to low temperatures, we tried to establish the suitability of physiological methods for identifying resistant varieties at early stages of ontogenesis during the first and second phases of hardening by already mature plants under field conditions.

Field methods of evaluation of plant resistance to low temperatures are extremely laborious and time consuming; they often entail loss of initial

Table 38. Frost resistance of alfalfa varieties (%) (data of field evaluation of Aral Experimental Station of VIR, 1966–1968) and evaluation in cold chambers (Pushkin Laboratories of VIR, 1969–1970)

Species, variety, specimens	Origin (republic, territory, province)	Field evaluation	Laboratory evaluation
Common alfalfa			
Khorezmskaya local	Khorezmsk province	71	84
Semirechensk local	Alma-Ata province	64	70
Fergana local	Fergana province	41	40
Tashkent-3192	Tashkent province	33	26
Aparan local	Armenian SSR	22	18
Azerbaydzhan-262	Azerbaidzhan SSR	20	16
Iolotanskaya	Turkmenian SSR	16	11
Variable alfalfa			
Sretenskaya-77	Irkutsk province	81	88
Pestraya-57	Orenburg province	77	85
Kamalin-930	Krasnoyarsk territory	71	83
Karabalykskaya-18	Kustanaisk province	64	82
Tibet	Aktyubin province	65	81
Local (K-6376)	Issyk-Kul' province	54	78
Irtyshskaya local	Semipalatinsk province	75	74
Kamyshinskaya-404	Volgograd province	47	54
Local (K-32792)	Chuva ASSR	42	53
Chernigovskaya	Chernigov province	25	28
Khersonskaya-1	Kherson province	23	23
Yellow alfalfa			
Krasnokutskaya-4009	Saratov province	66	89
Stepnaya-600	Voronezh province	73	87

material and are not always reliable because in the course of wintering not only plants susceptible to low temperatures are wiped out, but plants weakened by other factors: diseases, pests, drought, trampling, mechanical injuries, excessive grazing by cattle, and so forth. Direct laboratory methods, although rapid compared to field methods, also entail the loss of valuable initial material. A combination of direct and indirect methods of evaluation of plant resistance to low temperatures, according to both Soviet and foreign researchers, ensures the best results.

Now let us examine the data of physiological investigations conducted in autumn 1969 and spring 1970. The autumn analysis of the first and second periods corresponds to the beginning (October 14 to 16) and end (October 30 to November 1) of the first phase of hardening. Observations in the third period (November 17 to 19) were conducted when subzero temperatures had stabilized, corresponding to the second phase of hardening in plants and their entrance into dormancy (period of overwintering).

Research has shown that resistance of plants to low temperatures also depends on low much water is retained in the tissues before and after the effects of low temperatures and also on the qualitative condition of the water contained in the plant cells. High frost-resistant varieties of alfalfa did not differ from average frost-resistant varieties in total water content in the first phase of hardening; in the second phase of hardening they were characterized by a higher water content; during transition from the second phase of hardening to dormancy water loss in resistant specimens was lower (4.0 to 7.0%) compared to varieties considerably inferior in winter hardiness (10 to 15%). Varietal specimens resistant to low temperatures have a much higher water-retention capacity.

Winter-resistant varieties of alfalfa—Kamalin-930, Onokhoy-6, Karaganda-1, Khakasskaya local, Kamalinskaya-530, Biiskaya-3, Omsk variegated hybrid, and Tibet—in the first as well as second phase of hardening contained 50 to 66% so-called free water compared to varietal specimens Urzhumskaya local, Tichantuli (Hungary), Rumania local (K-32479), and English Early which lack high resistance to low temperatures (Table 39). It was established that total water loss in plants is reduced through a reduction of content of less-ordered fractions of water.

A reverse phenomenon was observed regarding the presence of bound water in plants: Resistant varieties are characterized by a higher content of more stable fractions of water in both the first and second phases of hardening. In our experiments during autumn cold-resistant varieties contained 45 to 50% bound water, but average-resistant varieties only 27 to 40%. This same phenomenon was earlier recorded during research conducted by Vasil'ev (1953) and Protsenko (1952), both of whom mention that with the onset of subzero temperatures regrouping of forms of water takes place in dormant plants, leading to an increase in bound water in more winter-resistant varieties. According to these authors this character may be used as an indirect index of frost resistance of plants.

During early spring growth of alfalfa plants after dormancy the total water content of varieties with good resistance to low temperatures did not differ much from those with moderate resistance. However, varieties of moderate resistance contained somewhat more free water and concomitantly less bound water compared to resistant varieties. A higher content of free water in plant cells indicates greater growth and photosynthesis activity in the organism. Naturally, with early resumption of vegetative growth and the recurrence of spring frosts, fast-growing varieties of alfalfa with a higher free-water content in the plant cells lose water faster and suffer more severely from fluctuations in the water temperature.

A high correlation between frost resistance of a given variety and content of bound fractions of water in the aerial organs and roots of the plants (in the first phase of hardening respectively $r = 0.61$ to 0.77 and $r = 0.54$ to 0.70, in the second phase $r = 0.75$ to 0.86 and $r = 0.65$ to 0.81) indicates that the value of the content of firmly bound forms of water in the organism is a reliable diagnostic index of the resistance of that variety.

A study of the variability of cell sap concentration, an index simultaneously characterizing the value of osmotic pressure in plant cells, enabled us to establish that in the first phase of hardening the concentration of cell sap in all alfalfa varieties, irrespective of their resistance to low temperatures, was approximately the same; in the second phase, cold resistant varieties were characterized by a much higher concentration of cell sap. A characteristic property of cold-resistant varieties is that during transition to the second phase of hardening the concentration of cell sap increases notably. During early spring growth of plants after dormancy the cell sap concentration in moderately winter-resistant varieties was 5.0 to 8.0% lower compared to the winter-resistant varieties. With an increase in air temperature and resumption of vegetative growth, a quick reduction in concentration of cell sap is seen in cold-resistant varieties. Later, during vegetative growth, the sap increases once again. D.F. Protsenko, V.N. Remeslo and P.S. Slavnyi observed a similar phenomenon in experiments with winter wheat.

The coefficient of correlation between winter-resistant varieties of alfalfa and concentration of cell sap extracted from the root neck of plants after the first phase of hardening was 0.71 to 0.78, and after the second phase 0.81 to 0.85.

An important index of plant resistance to low temperatures is the degree of protoplasmic permeability. Under the effect of subzero temperatures the permeability of protoplasm increases because the plants strive to eliminate all excess water which has accumulated as a result of inhibition or temporary retardation (during overwintering) of growth processes.

In our experiments, in the first phase of hardening protoplasmic permeability was higher in resistant varieties; in the second phase, with the establishment of a constant regime of subzero temperatures, protoplasmic permeability was higher in moderately winter-resistant varieties. The

Table 39. Fractional composition of water (%) of alfalfa varieties in autumn (1969) and spring (1970)

Varieties, specimens	Total water				Free water				Bound water			
	Autumn		Spring		Autumn		Spring		Autumn		Spring	
	Oct. 30	Nov. 18	March 27	April 3	Oct. 30	Nov. 18	March 27	April 3	Oct. 30	Nov. 18	March 27	April 3
Good resistance to low temperature												
Kamalinskaya-530	72.0	65.3	68.9	71.2	23.0	14.4	23.2	37.8	49.0	50.9	45.7	33.4
Khakasskaya local	70.1	65.3	69.1	71.3	21.3	15.2	25.0	39.5	48.8	50.4	44.1	31.8
Onokhoy-6	71.3	67.7	69.0	71.2	23.1	17.6	24.7	41.0	48.2	50.1	44.3	30.2
Kamalin-930	72.3	65.2	69.2	71.5	23.4	15.5	25.4	40.4	48.9	49.7	44.8	31.1
Karaganda-1	70.1	63.6	—	—	23.9	14.3	—	—	46.2	49.3	—	—
Biiskaya-3	72.6	63.8	—	—	25.2	15.7	—	—	47.0	47.9	—	—
Omsk variegated hybrid	71.8	62.7	—	—	25.2	15.2	—	—	46.6	47.6	—	—
Severnaya hybrid	71.6	66.1	—	—	25.3	18.7	—	—	46.3	47.4	—	—
Tibet	71.9	63.6	67.8	70.9	26.9	17.2	24.6	35.5	45.0	46.4	43.2	35.4
Moderate resistance to low temperatures												
Khorezmskaya local	72.1	61.2	—	—	33.4	21.3	—	—	38.7	39.9	—	—
Mark II (USA)	70.0	59.6	68.5	71.6	32.1	21.4	30.4	41.9	37.9	38.2	38.1	29.7
Urzhumskaya local	71.0	60.4	—	—	34.2	22.9	—	—	36.8	37.5	—	—
Rumanian local	71.3	56.8	67.7	71.2	41.2	24.4	40.9	49.1	30.1	30.4	26.8	22.1
Tichantuli (Hungary)	71.7	56.4	69.7	71.7	42.5	26.6	46.5	49.4	29.2	29.8	23.2	21.7
English Early	71.9	56.4	—	—	44.8	29.2	—	—	27.1	27.2	—	—

common rule is that in both the first phase (r = 0.80) and the second phase (r = 0.79) a close correlation exists between these indexes and resistance of plants to low temperatures. The increase in protoplasmic permeability of plants from the first phase of hardening to the second phase in varieties highly resistant to frosts is insignificant, but in moderately resistant varieties increases markedly (Ivanov, 1970, 1972).

The quick and considerable (2.0 to 3.0 times) increase in protoplasmic permeability observed in moderately winter-resistant varieties indicates severe impairment of the vital functions in plants. In the early spring growth of alfalfa after dormancy, protoplasmic permeability in moderately winter-resistant and highly winter-resistant varieties was almost identical.

Acidity of cell sap affects the survival of plants during the period of their winter dormancy as well as their vital activity. According to S.E. Bresler the spatial organization of proteins of the living cell is dependent on an acid-base equilibrium. Any deviation in this relationship leads to a change in the physico-chemical processes linked with the dynamics of conversion of sugars, coagulation of proteins, water regime, and other functions of the organism directly correlated with frost resistance in plants.

In our experiments varieties with average resistance to low temperatures had a much higher pH value in the first and second phases of hardening compared to highly resistant varieties. The difference in hydrogen ion concentrations in different alfalfa varieties with high and average frost resistance was especially marked at the end of the first phase of hardening. During the second phase of hardening the pH value reduced. During early spring growth of plants after dormancy a change in pH of cell sap (more alkaline) was observed in all varieties of alfalfa. Later the pH value reduced but in resistant varieties remained at a higher (alkaline) level.

A positive correlation between pH of cell sap and degree of frost resistance of alfalfa varieties was established: after the first phase of hardening in overwintering shoots—r = 0.634 ± 0.142 to 0.685 ± 0.184 and in the roots—r = 0.728 ± 0.164 to 0.734 ± 0.171; after the second phase of hardening in the aerial organs—r = 0.648 ± 0.109 to 0.763 ± 0.124 and in the roots—r = 0.795 ± 0.164 to 0.812 ± 0.178.

The most important index of resistance of plants to low temperatures is the content of soluble carbohydrates in the dormant organs. Studies have shown that before hardening disaccharides in the aerial organs of alfalfa are 2.0 to 4.0 times greater than monosaccharides, but in the roots these components are present in almost equal quantities.

During the first phase of hardening the total content of soluble sugars increases considerably: in the roots—2.0 times and in the crown—1.5 times; after the second phase of hardening the content of sugars in the roots continues to increase significantly, but in the aerial parts the increase

Table 40. Sugar content in alfalfa plants (% of dry matter), 1969-1970

Species, variety, specimens	Before hardening			After first phase of hardening			After second phase of hardening			During autumn–winter period		
	Monosaccharide	Disaccharide	Total sugars	Monosaccharide	Disaccharide	Total sugars	Monosaccharide	Disaccharide	Total sugars	Monosaccharide	Disaccharide	Total sugars
						Aerial organs						
Variable alfalfa												
Kamalin-930	1.09	3.86	4.95	0.92	5.30	6.22	1.02	5.25	6.27	1.05	6.05	7.10
Tibet (control)	1.06	3.10	4.16	0.96	4.75	5.71	1.05	4.76	5.81	0.90	5.96	6.86
Slavyanskaya local	1.09	3.50	4.59	1.05	4.26	5.31	1.00	4.85	5.85	1.00	5.40	6.40
Common alfalfa												
Tashkent-721	1.14	3.35	4.49	0.86	4.34	5.20	1.05	4.20	5.25	0.85	5.30	6.15
Zuvandskaya local	1.02	3.20	4.22	1.00	3.30	4.30	0.70	4.35	5.05	0.88	4.87	5.25
Mesopotamian local	1.00	2.90	3.90	1.12	3.24	4.36	0.80	4.20	5.00	0.88	4.16	5.04
Yellow alfalfa												
Krasnokutskaya-4009	1.00	3.10	4.10	1.12	3.34	4.46	—	—	—	1.00	5.92	6.92
Crescentoid alfalfa												
Yellow Kuban	1.10	3.28	4.38	1.05	3.32	4.37	—	—	—	0.93	4.54	5.47

Roots

Variable alfalfa										
Kamalin-930	2.10	2.63	4.73	3.79	7.14	10.93	—	1.72	9.21	10.93
Tibet (control)	2.10	2.54	4.64	3.78	7.08	10.81	—	1.68	9.14	10.82
Slavyanskaya local	2.39	2.52	4.91	3.30	7.24	10.54	—	2.18	8.53	10.71
Common alfalfa										
Tashkent-721	2.33	2.81	5.14	3.42	5.22	8.64	—	2.61	6.32	8.83
Zuvandskaya local	2.31	3.24	5.55	3.13	4.81	7.94	—	2.34	5.81	8.15
Mesopotamian local	2.62	3.62	6.24	4.07	2.74	6.81	—	2.62	4.64	7.26
Yellow alfalfa										
Krasnokutskaya-4009	2.30	2.40	4.70	2.91	5.23	8.14	—	2.23	6.73	8.95
Crescentoid alfalfa										
Yellow Kuban	2.21	2.42	4.68	2.63	5.01	7.64	—	2.24	6.00	8.84

is negligible. The highest content of monosaccharides after the first phase of hardening, and disaccharides after the second phase, is observed in frost-resistant varieties (Table 40).

The correlation between winter hardiness and total sugar content in the aerial organs during the second phase of hardening is expressed by the coefficient—$r = 0.783 \pm 0.126$; between winter hardiness and monosaccharide content in the roots after the first phase of hardening—$r = 0.815 \pm 0.142$; between winter hardiness and disaccharide content in the dormant shoots and roots in the first phase of hardening—$r = 0.773 \pm 0.129$ and $r = 0.822 \pm 0.134$ respectively. The high correlation between winter hardiness and content of mono- and disaccharides and total sugars in the roots and aerial organs at the time of hardening of plants indicates the close correlation between these very important characters, and enables plant breeders in the early stages of the breeding process or under laboratory conditions, i.e., much before hybridization, to identify initial material resistant to low temperatures.

In determining winter hardiness of various species and varieties of alfalfa it is important to take into consideration plant response to photoperiod. Frost-resistant steppe varieties of alfalfa of the European part of the USSR, northern Kazakhstan, and Siberia at the latitude of Leningrad during open freezing of plants in pots, even after prolonged hardening under natural daylight considerably reduced their winter hardiness, which was less than that in treatment with freezing of plants in cold chambers, but under natural conditions inferior to varieties from the Baltic republics. Long day, high humidity, and poor insolation considerably affect the growth processes of alfalfa species and varieties from different geographic regions, reducing or increasing their resistance to cold.

Thus to determine the winter hardiness of alfalfa, in addition to field methods of evaluation, these laboratory methods may be employed: a) method of freezing sprouts in cold chambers; b) method of freezing plants at the stage of five to six leaves in cold chambers; and c) method of determination of resistance of adult plants to low temperatures on the basis of physiological indexes.

Based on field and laboratory evaluation of the alfalfa collection for resistance to low temperatures, these varieties and specimens of common and variable alfalfas have been identified as possessing high winter hardiness (number of VIR catalog): Kazakh SSR (K-25081, K-25782, K-26688, K-28458, K-28909, K-29125, K-29567, K-30102, K-30103, K-31783); Uzbek SSR and Kara-Kalpak ASSR (K-7234, K-7248, K-7250, K-8929, K-8930, K-8940, K-8951, K-8953, K-8958, K-19766, K-19779, K-20132); Middle and Lower Volga region (K-22571, K-23448, K-23449, K-26787, K-26948, K-28178, K-28914, K-18917, K-29570, K-29572, K-31885);

western Siberia (K-20099, K-20131, K-23573, K-23575, K-24988, K-29653, K-29655, K-29660, K-29661, K-30098, K-30106); eastern Siberia (K-23425, K-23426, K-26828, K-26830, K-28901, K-28902, K-29122, K-29657, K-29658, K-29662, K-29664, K-31789, K-31790); as well as varieties and specimens of yellow alfalfa (K-13292, K-20043, K-21351, K-22506, K-22570, K-23447, K-23738, K-23739, K-26683, K-26689, K-26771, K-27941, K-28012, K-28900, K-29208, K-31079); specimens of blue alfalfa, varicolored alfalfa, Trautvetter's alfalfa, glutinous alfalfa, semitwisted alfalfa, and natural hybrids of wild species of alfalfa (K-2625, K-12820, K-15198, K-16650, K-16682, K-16691, K-16720, K-18646, K-28915, K-29002, K-30094, K-33298, K-34626, K-34631, K-35004). The foregoing specimens are valuable initial material for breeding for winter hardiness.

Drought Resistance

Survival of specimens of the alfalfa collection in the steppe and arid zones of the Soviet Union depends to a considerable extent on their drought resistance. Drought resistance can be determined by direct methods (estimating yield, rate of growth, counting live plants or plants which have dried or lodged during drought) and by indirect methods (determining physiological and biochemical indexes signaling disorders in the water regime and metabolic reactions).

Adaptability of plants to drought conditions is manifest in different ways. Some crops develop a strong and deeply penetrating root system that exceeds several times the mass of other vegetative organs. Others reduce the area of transpiration by shedding leaflets and young shoots. Other crops increase the concentration of cell sap, thereby increasing the suction force to maximum value. Some crops have a highly developed cuticular layer or dense network of pubescence on the vegetative organs. There are also crops which complete their life cycle (growth and development) before the onset of drought.

The foregoing adaptive reactions of plants to the effect of drought are characteristic of xerophytes, i.e., plants growing in the arid zone which often experience moisture stress during ontogenesis. As for alfalfa, it combines resistance to high air temperatures (heat resistance) on the one hand, and is characterized by an exceptionally high water requirement on the other. Seedlings die quickly even when the effect of soil and atmospheric drought is of short duration; concomitantly adult plants are capable of withstanding prolonged desiccation.

The contradictory biological properties of alfalfa have prompted researchers to offer different interpretations concerning its drought resistance. Some (Konstantinova, 1960; Poznorikhin, 1961; Makarova, 1965; Fedorov, 1968) relate it to the group of drought-resistant plants; other authors

(Shain, 1964) consider alfalfa a typical mesophyte; a third group (Sinskaya, 1959; Shebalina and Kolikova, 1955) treat alfalfa as a hygrophyte. In our opinion (1968) blue-flowered nonhybrid populations of *sativa* alfalfa should not be related to drought-resistant crops. One can only speak conditionally about the drought resistance of alfalfa because its seed productivity in dry regions is determined almost exclusively by soil moisture (Konstantinov, 1932).

Grossgeim (1945), Kul'tiasov, Smetannikova, Koperzhinskii, Dmitrieva (1958, 1962, 1967),* Kristkalne (1960, 1963, 1964), and Kuznetsov (1967), in evaluating the resistance of alfalfa plants to drought have indicated its duality, by labeling it mesophytic and xerophytic.

Thus the drought resistance of alfalfa is interpreted differently by different researchers: Some affirm it is a mesophyte, others consider it a xerophyte, and still others consider it intermediate between the two—xerophytized mesophyte, xeromesophyte, hemixerophyte, semixerophyte. mexoxerophyte, and so forth.

The main reason for the contradictory interpretations of drought resistance of alfalfa is that the aforementioned authors worked with different species and varieties under different agroclimatic or ecogeographic zones, either using extremely limited initial material or the world assortment of cultivated and wild alfalfas, with results confined to field observations only (comprehensive physiological, anatomical, and morphological methods of investigation were not employed). Such a one-sided approach to the solution of the problem of drought resistance of alfalfa, neither considering the genealogy of the entire genus *Medicago*, nor the agroclimatic conditions of the various regions in which individual species are grown, has understandably yielded no unanimity of opinion regarding its drought resistance.

An analysis of the numerous sources available in literature revealed that in discussing the drought resistance of alfalfa it is necessary to define precisely what initial material is under study. The true resistance of alfalfa to drought can only be established by comparison of experimental specimens with plants of other varieties, species, and populations. Hence true drought or heat resistance is relative, referring to the resistance of one variety or species of plants compared to others.

The physiological nature of drought and temperature resistance of alfalfa plants is closely linked with water-exchange reactions, and has not been studied adequately. Several researchers have paid attention to this aspect but *de facto*, for physiological studies the object is quite difficult.

---

*Separate entries are given for these four authors in the bibliography and the dates given here only partially correspond—General Editor.

Firstly, alfalfa is a perennial plant and thus, without doubt, to establish and regularities in its ontogenetic development is exceedingly difficult, let alone those regularities related to changes in the plant's water regime, which (according to N.A. Maksimov, A.M. Alekseeva, N.G. Vasil'eva, N.S. Petinov, and N.A. Gusev) forms the basis for assessing drought or heat resistance. Secondly, the alfalfa bush consists of numerous qualitatively different young and old shoots, leaves, racemes, flowers, pods, and seeds. Thirdly, the leaflets of alfalfa, the main object of physiological investigations, have a small-sized lamina that differs in shape, pubescence, and anatomical structure which, according to Il'ina (1964, 1966) and Shain (1964), reflect not only seasonal and age changes in the plant as a whole, but the location of the leaflets on the shoots of corresponding internodes of the bush.

Let me add that most of the methods employed for studying the physiological peculiarities of drought resistance of plants have been developed for classical crops: wheat, corn, barley, apple, cotton, tobacco, sugar beet, and soybean. When applied to alfalfa and, that too, in such an exclusively arid zone as northern Aral, related to absolute continental desert by Selyaninov (1966), these methods are either unsuitable or require modifications.

In the Tselinnyi territory during very dry vegetative periods in 1962, 1963, 1968, and 1975 the following varieties and specimens of alfalfa from northern, western, and central Kazakhstan, western and eastern Siberia, southeast European part of the USSR, and Altai easily withstood soil and atmospheric drought: Shortandinskaya-1, Shortandinskaya-2, Karabalyk-skaya, Blue Hybrid-1316, Karaganda-1, Dolinskaya-2, Blue Ural, Kokshe, Irtyshskaya local, Tibet, Omsk-8893, Omsk-2251, Flora, Biiskaya-3, Kuz-basskaya, Barnaulskaya-17, Zabaikalka, Kamalinskaya-530, Kamalin-930, Sretenskaya-77, Nerchinskaya-46, Onokhoy-6, Valuyskaya local, Pestraya-57, and Brodskaya local. In severe drought years these varieties were distinguished not only in productivity, but also in maximum number of green leaflets (70 to 85%) at the commencement of anthesis. Among other ecogeographic groups the following varieties were distinguished for these characters: Kemlyanskaya-1 (88.7%), Maikopskaya yellow (85.2%), Zaykevich (74.6%), Kazan-64/95 (71.3%), as well as wild populations of glutinous alfalfa (70.8%) and blue alfalfa (70.6%). Alfalfa varieties from the tropical and subtropical belts as well as from regions of irrigated farming in the republics of Central Asia and a number of European countries suffered severely from hot, drying winds and soil moisture deficit. At the time of drought plant susceptibility to diseases increases markedly; foliage and productivity decrease and the period of formation of the second harvest (cutting) increases by 25 to 40 days.

The following varieties were highly drought resistant in the arid belt in the fourth year of plant growth, in 1961: Karabalykskaya-18, Karaganda-1, Kuzbasskaya, Milyutinskaya-1774, Shortandinskaya-2, Kazan-64/95, Zabaikalka, Pestraya-57, Onokhoy-6, Marusinskaya-425, Tibet, Poltava-256; improved varieties of yellow alfalfa—Maikopskaya yellow, Yellow Kuban, Stepnaya-600, Krasnokutskaya-4009; and wild populations of the blue, Trautvetter's, South Kazakhstan, and semitwisted alfalfas. Experiencing constant moisture stress the drought-resistant varieties in unirrigated fields of the Aral Experimental Station of VIR yield green mass that is 2.0 to 3.0 times greater in quantity than varieties not resistant to soil drought (Tables 41 and 42).

In the nursery sown in 1965 the following varieties and specimens of variable alfalfa of the northern Kazakhstan varietal type were distinguished for drought resistance: Karaganda-1, Shortandinskaya-2, Karabalykskaya-18, Blue Ural, Kokshe, Blue Hybrid-1316, Dolinskaya-2, Irtyshskaya local, and Tibet. In this group on the average 90.4% leaflets per plant were green. Varieties of Kazakh SSR were also distinguished for productivity and growth rate.

High drought resistance was shown by varieties of the North America varietal type (Progress, Caliverde, Mark, Zia, Cody, Uinta, African, and Lahontan); the quantity of green leaflets per plant was 90.3%. In varieties and specimens of the northern Caucasian varietal type (Slavyanskaya local, Manichskaya, Kizlyarsk, K-23599, K-28462, and K-35012) the quantity of green leaflets in the first cutting was 82.3%.

Soil and atmospheric drought were well tolerated by varieties of common and variable alfalfa from the steppe regions of Ukrainian SSR, southeast European part of the USSR, Ural, western and eastern Siberia, Altai, southern Kazakhstan, northern regions of the republics of Central Asia, Canada, China, Turkey, Iran, and Afghanistan. Poor drought resistance was exhibited by varieties of the middle Russian, Baltic, northern Russian, west European, and southern European varietal types. Specimens from India, Panama, Argentina, Brazil, Colombia, Bolivia, Venezuela, South African Republic, Syria, Iraq, Tunisia, Pakistan, and Egypt proved highly susceptible to soil drought.

Wild populations of alfalfa collected from the territory of Kazakh SSR and the republics of Central Asia were characterized by high drought resistance. In nurseries for long-term study of initial material (crops sown in 1957, 1958, 1965, 1968, 1970, 1972, 1973) the following specimens were distinguished for a series of economically important characters of which, without doubt, drought resistance is the most important: blue alfalfa from Gur'ev province (K-120, K-15198, K-28915, K-29002, K-36118, and K-36119), Ural'sk province (K-35009, K-36501, K-36053, and K-36105),

Table 41. Characteristics of alfalfa varieties under unirrigated conditions in the third year of growth (Aral Experimental Station of VIR, 1960)

Variety	Plant height, cm	Foliage, grade	Plant survival in third year of growth, %	Average seed yield from 9 m² during 1958–1960	
				kg	Percent of control
Tibet (control)	58	3.2	82	1.21	—
Varieties cultivated on irrigated lands of the republics of Central Asia					
Iolotanskaya	65	2.0	1	0.09	5
Fergana-700	58	2.1	12	0.21	24
Tashkent-721	51	2.8	45	0.53	40
Tashkent-3192	53	2.6	59	0.65	58
Semirechensk local	58	3.0	68	0.87	15
Varieties of northern and western Kazakhstan					
Blue Ural	65	3.3	97	1.44	89
Blue hybrid-1316	64	3.2	93	1.30	92
Karabalykskaya-18	66	3.4	91	1.62	103
Priaralskaya	63	3.2	86	1.72	108
Shortandinskaya-2	64	3.3	92	1.87	117
Karaganda-1	62	3.2	94	2.15	124
Varieties of forest-steppe and steppe regions of the Soviet Union					
Poltava-256	61	3.2	91	2.27	129
Marusinskaya-425	58	3.1	83	2.38	132
Kazan-64/95	67	3.5	93	2.20	145
Brodskaya local	61	3.3	95	2.24	146
Pestraya-57	63	3.4	92	2.39	154
Kuzbasskaya	65	3.4	96	2.43	160
Krasnokutskaya-4009	64	3.2	97	2.50	166
Varieties of western and eastern Siberia					
Flora	64	3.4	86	2.41	142
Barnaulskaya-17	63	3.3	88	2.39	149
Sretenskaya-77	67	3.5	89	2.24	161
Kamalin-930	65	3.4	96	2.46	167
Kamalinskaya-530	69	3.6	98	2.59	174

**Table 42. Productivity of better varieties of alfalfa on unirrigated fields
maintained to the fifth year of growth (1958 crop)
(Aral Experimental Station of VIR)**

Species, variety	Yield of green mass, kg from 9 m²				Average per year	Percent of control
	1959	1960	1961	1962		
Common alfalfa						
Khiva local	2.70	0.45	0.63	1.15	1.28	82
Semirechensk local	2.13	0.36	0.48	0.70	0.92	60
Tashkent-3192	1.39	0.33	0.26	0.64	0.66	42
Tashkent-721	1.33	0.24	0.33	0.48	0.60	40
Variable alfalfa						
Kazan-64/95	4.33	1.56	1.0	1.48	2.09	127
Kuzbasskaya	3.42	1.56	0.92	1.37	1.82	117
Shortandinskaya-2	3.70	1.44	0.61	1.35	1.77	113
Zabaikalka	3.76	1.53	0.73	1.05	1.77	113
Karaganda-1	4.05	1.09	0.75	0.82	1.68	108
Tibet (control)	2.32	1.29	1.31	1.33	1.56	100
Karabalykskaya-18	3.12	1.38	0.56	1.09	1.54	99
Marusinskaya-425	2.75	1.80	0.76	0.62	1.48	95
Onokhoy-6	2.63	1.17	0.92	1.04	1.44	92

and Aktyubin province (K-28645); Trautvetter's alfalfa from Aktyubin province (K-114, K-34630, K-34631, K-36759, and K-36761); South Kazakhstan alfalfa from Karaganda province (K-1336, K-063117, K-063123, and K-063124), Semipalatinsk province (K-1364, K-1371, K-1374, and K-063116), and eastern Kazakhstan province (K-1438, K-1446, and K-1447); yellow alfalfa from Ural'sk province (K-179, K-197, K-36751, K-36752, and K-36754) and Aktyubin province (K-1503, K-1534, K-1536, and K-1546); common alfalfa from Dzhambul (K-060239) and Chita provinces (K-35011), Uzbek SSR (K-34638) and Tadzhik SSR (K-30706); variable alfalfa from Karaganda (K-1338 and K-063125) and eastern Kazakhstan provinces (K-1378, K-1410, K-1427, K-1444, and K-1448); Tian Shan alfalfa from China (K-34628), Dzhambul (K-37219), and Chimkent provinces (K-13035 and K-34627).

Physiological analysis of species and varieties of alfalfa for drought resistance revealed that water exchange fluctuates markedly in alfalfa. During adaptation to unusually severe moisture stress alfalfa varieties from different geographic regions show specific peculiarities in water-exchange reactions. These are distinctly apparent in a comparative study of two varieties that differ sharply in degree of drought and heat resistance, namely, varieties Tibet and Augune. The first variety was evolved by the Aral Experimental Station of VIR and the second by the Lithuanian Research Institute of Agriculture.

Pot culture experiments conducted from 1967 to 1969 showed that with drought during the budding stage the variety Augune loses more water than Tibet. The total water content of the resistant variety compared to the susceptible was 5.0 to 6.0% more. In the case of drought of short duration (four days) the water content of the leaf tissues (green mass) of variety Tibet fell by 13.2% and of variety Augune by 17.4%. The water content in the cell tissues of the experimental plants after drought for seven days was 33% and 42.1% less in the resistant and susceptible varieties respectively. After restoration of irrigation the total water content of the leaves was fully restored only in the resistant variety.

The forms of water are redistributed in the case of reduction in total water content of the leaves (Table 43). In the variety Tibet this reduction was accompanied by an increase in content of bound water (34.9%) at the budding stage at an adequately high content of free water (34.3%), which provided high resistance and normal physiological activity. In the less resistant variety Augune, under the same conditions, the content of free water reduced up to 18.4%. A sharp increase in bound water (up to 45.8%) at a low content of free water indicates a serious disruption of the physiological processes, which increases after a seven-day drought.

Water dynamics in control and experimental plants of alfalfa, using sucrose solutions as water-removal forces in a concentration of 30% (34 AT), 45% (72 AT), and 60% (153 AT), revealed that with an increase in water-removal forces the ratio of water fractions in the plant cells also changes: Free water increases and bound water decreases. The difference in content of free and bound fractions of water increased in both alfalfa varieties but was manifest most sharply in plants of the susceptible variety. On the whole, bound water was higher in leaves of the experimental plants than in leaves of the control plants. Even in the case of water-removal forces at 153 AT the water-retention capacity of the leaf tissues remained adequately high.

Plants of the drought-resistant variety were distinguished by a higher content of bound fractions under conditions of extreme dehydration of the organism. The alfalfa variety Augune suffers more severely from the prolonged effect of high atmospheric temperatures and water deficit in the soil.

N.A. Maksimov, Yu.S. Grigor'ev, N.S. Petinov, and P.A. Genkel'

Table 43. Effect of drought on fractional composition of water (% of green mass) in alfalfa leaves at different stages of growth and development (1967–1969)

Type of water	Treatment	4-day drought			7-day drought		
		Vegetative growth	Budding	Commencement of anthesis	Vegetative growth	Budding	Commencement of anthesis
				Variety Tibet			
Total	Control	82.6	80.4	79.0	81.2	82.0	80.6
	Experiment	79.2	69.2	69.8	55.2	43.2	56.5
	Difference	−3.4	−11.2	−9.2	−26.0	−33.8	−24.1
Free	Control	59.5	65.6	52.0	56.2	52.9	53.2
	Experiment	38.8	34.3	30.9	17.9	16.5	18.7
	Difference	−20.7	−31.3	−21.1	−38.3	−36.4	−34.5
Bound	Control	22.6	14.8	27.0	24.0	29.1	27.4
	Experiment	40.4	34.9	38.9	39.3	26.7	37.8
	Difference	17.8	20.1	11.9	13.3	−2.7	10.4
				Variety Augune			
Total	Control	84.4	81.6	80.6	84.2	82.2	80.8
	Experiment	78.2	64.2	62.4	42.8	36.8	51.2
	Difference	−6.2	−17.4	−18.2	−41.4	−45.4	−29.6
Free	Control	58.7	60.6	51.1	56.8	55.0	51.3
	Experiment	31.9	18.4	17.9	11.1	27.3	36.3
	Difference	−26.8	−42.2	−33.2	−45.7	−27.7	−15.0
Bound	Control	25.7	21.0	29.5	27.4	27.2	29.5
	Experiment	46.3	45.8	44.5	31.7	9.5	14.9
	Difference	20.6	24.8	16.0	4.3	−17.7	−14.6

relate increased drought resistance of plants to their high water-retention capacity. Resistance to drought depends on the dissimilar capacity of cells to resist desiccation and hence difference in plant resistance to leaf wilt become evident. Therefore drought resistance of plants can be determined from water loss by incised leaves and shoots. In our experiments, under a seven-day drought, irrespective of the stage of development the control plants lost water 2.0 to 3.0 times faster than the experimental plants. This confirms that the water-retention capacity of plants subjected to drought is higher than that of plants not exposed to drought; in other words, drought increases the water-retention capacity of alfalfa plants.

The maximum discharge of water in the incised shoots occurred during the first hour of wilting. The water-retention capacity of both control and experimental plants changed according to stage of development. Plants of the drought-resistant variety, due to the effect of drought, acquired a high water-retention capacity during the stage of vegetative growth and flowering. Variation in water-retention capacity of both control and experimental plants was sharpest during the budding stage: Control plants of variety Augune during one, two, and three hours of wilting lost water 2.0 times faster than plants of variety Tibet. Plants of the susceptible variety during these same hours lost 7.6, 10.85, and 12.60% water, while those of the resistant variety lost 4.48, 7.91, and 9.10%, i.e., on the average 27 to 41% less.

Determination of the restoration capacity of the incised shoots of alfalfa after keeping them in humidifier for 24 hours revealed that a four-day drought did not cause irreversible injuries to the experimental plants of variety Tibet. The susceptible variety exposed to a seven-day drought also regained its initial mass after four hours of wilting. However, the normal turgor of the plants of this variety was restored very slowly, but the quantity of absorbed water, in the context of initial mass of the experimental plants, did not exceed 30% during the budding stage.

According to L.S. Litvinov, one of the fundamental indexes of the degree of drought resistance of plants is water deficit. He believes that the manifestation in plants of midday water deficit is a normal process widely found in nature. Residual water deficit is an abnormal phenomenon attesting to plant depression due to the effect of drought. It is evident from the data of Table 44 that the control plants at all stages of growth and development, irrespective of drought resistance of the variety, displayed an insignificant residual water deficit: changes in the drought resistant variety were 5.0 to 8.9% and in the susceptible variety 4.2 to 9.6%. Even in the case of short-duration drought (four days) the residual deficit increased sharply. The maximum water deficit (35%) was recorded for

Table 44. Effect of soil drought on residual water deficit (% of total saturation) of alfalfa varieties at different stages of development (1968–1970)

Treatment	Variety Tibet			Variety Augune		
	Vegetative growth	Commencement of budding	Commencement of anthesis	Vegetative growth	Commencement of budding	Commencement of anthesis
Control	5.5	8.9	5.0	4.2	7.4	5.4
Drought for 4 days	13.7	18.7	12.3	13.7	19.4	15.1
Control	5.9	6.9	5.9	4.7	8.7	6.4
Drought for 7 days	18.4	28.7	30.9	22.5	31.4	38.7
Control	6.4	7.1	6.3	4.9	9.6	5.5
Drought for 8 days	22.4	34.3	35.0	26.7	43.1	40.5

variety Tibet at the stage of commencement of flowering and in Augune (43.1%) at the budding stage.

The magnitude of residual water deficit in different varieties of alfalfa was most distinct under conditions of prolonged drought (seven to eight days) during the critical periods of plant growth (budding to commencement of flowering), especially at the budding stage, when the residual water deficit of the experimental plants was 3.0 to 4.0 times higher than in the control plants. At the end of drought the water deficit was not uniformly restored in plants of different varieties: Plants of variety Augune continued to experience water deficit even on the third day after restoration of irrigation; in plants of the resistant variety the water balance was restored completely in this same period and the water deficit that had developed in the drought period eliminated.

Investigations also showed that during drought the concentration of cell sap increases considerably, particularly at the budding stage (up to 27.7%). Ten days after restoration of irrigation the concentration reduces but, nevertheless, in our experiments was 1.0 to 1.5% higher than in control plants. During short-term drought in variety Augune, at the stage of vegetative growth and budding cell sap was 2.0 and 8.8% respectively higher than in plants of variety Tibet.

It was proved that loss of water by plants leads to increased protoplasmic permeability of their cells. Short-term drought (four days) causes reversible dehydration, while prolonged drought (seven to eight days) causes high, irreversible increase of protoplasmic permeability. For example, during the budding stage the specific electrical conductivity of plants of the resistant variety after an eight-day drought increased up to 413.6 units (reciprocal $mho \times 10^{-6}$) versus 22.4 in the control. The degree of protoplasmic permeability of the susceptible variety reached 721.5 units versus 28 in the control.

Drought not only changes the water regime of plants, but also affects other physiological and biochemical processes in the organism. For example, in our studies with an increase in duration of drought the content of vitamin C in alfalfa leaves reduced sharply during the flowering stage. Short-term drought caused an insignificant loss of this vitamin. With severe wilting, the vitamin C content in the leaf tissues reduced (up to 2.9 mg/100 g in variety Augune, and up to 4.8 mg in Tibet), and at the end of the short-term drought attained the control level only in variety Tibet. The effect of drought on vitamin content was manifested more severely in variety Augune. The vitamin C content in the case of plant wilting in all experimental treatments (drought for a period of four, seven, and eight days) was lower in variety Augune than in variety Tibet.

Table 45. Effect of short-term soil and atmospheric drought on content of pigments (γ/mg raw matter) in leaves of alfalfa variety Tibet in different stages of development (1968–1969)

Treatment	Total pigments	Chlorophyll			Carotene	Lutein	Xanthophyll
		$a+b$	a	b			
Vegetative growth							
Control	1.357	1.125	0.667	0.458	0.132	0.066	0.034
Drought for 4 days	1.645	1.284	0.621	0.663	0.192	0.133	0.036
Budding							
Control	1.608	1.354	0.806	0.548	0.139	0.083	0.032
Drought for 7 days	1.826	1.487	0.783	0.704	0.196	0.100	0.043
Flowering							
Control	1.731	1.502	0.837	0.665	0.110	0.078	0.041
Drought for 8 days	1.681	1.439	0.565	0.874	0.180	0.046	0.016

An analysis of pigments in the leaves of control and experimental plants of the alfalfa variety Tibet revealed that during the stages of vegetative growth and budding experimental plants contained a maximum quantity of yellow pigments and chlorophyll b (Table 45). At the commencement of flowering experimental plants after short-term drought lagged behind control plants in content of pigments; their physiological activity was reduced at this stage. In the case of short-term drought in all experimental treatments the content of chlorophyll b increased and the content of chlorophyll a reduced. In the control plants the maximum quantity of pigment was found at the commencement of flowering, and in the experimental plants during the budding stage. The maximum content of lutein occurred at the stage of vegetative growth in the experimental plants and that of carotene at the budding stage.

Thus pot culture experiments revealed that stoppage of irrigation considerably changes the water regime of alfalfa: Total water content reduces, while water deficit, concentration of cell sap, and permeability of protoplasm increase. Drought leads to the redistribution of the forms of water: The content of highly ordered fractions increases, while the content of less-ordered fractions reduces.

Short-term soil and atmospheric drought do not cause irreversible disruptions in the water balance of plants. They cause an insignificant dehydration of the organism, stimulate growth processes of resistant varieties, and increase their resistance to wilting. The variety Tibet after a four-day drought underwent hardening which increased its drought and heat resistance.

Susceptible varieties react more actively to short-term drought; they dehydrate more, the content of bound water increases notably in them, and the concentration of cell sap and protoplasmic permeability to electrolytes likewise increase markedly.

Notable restructuring of the water regime takes place in alfalfa plants in the case of prolonged drought. Resistant to short-term drought, resistant varieties do not utilize their potential capabilities for overcoming adverse environmental factors and, therefore, compared to susceptible varieties have a certain "reserve strength" to counter a critical level of dehydration up to some extent, after which plant tissues die.

A prolonged drought (seven, eight, and ten days) causes deep disruptions in the water regime and leads to irreversible changes in the intracellular structure (plants in experiments with 30% of the total soil moisture capacity of the field dried without reaching the budding stage). The life cycle (equilibrium) of the plants is disturbed: Further intensification of drought results in gradual death of cells and individual organs, the organism's resistance to drought falls sharply, and intensification of dehydration enhances the destructive process. But alfalfa plants are characterized by an exceptionally high restoration capability. Their well-developed root and vascular systems, the distinctive function of the stomatal apparatus, and the presence of other adaptive reactions enable alfalfa plants to withstand desiccation and to quickly restore turgor even with a loss of 35 to 40% of their water.

Susceptible varieties suffer more severely from prolonged drought. After resumption of irrigation their previous water content is not restored. The more protracted the drought, the greater the water loss at all stages of ontogenesis (21 to 41% more than in drought-resistant varieties), the more severe the deep midday and residual water deficit (up to 40 to 43%), and the greater the concentration of cell sap and dehydration, which threaten the plant's further existence. In cells of drought-susceptible plants under conditions of critical dehydration the content of firmly bound water fractions reduces 5.0 to 6.0 times, the concentration of cell sap reduces 2.0 to 3.0 times, and protoplasmic permeability increases 10 to 20 times.

Maximum variability of all indexes of the water regime is observed in alfalfa in the period of intense vegetative growth to sporadic flowering. Obviously, in the case of an inadequate water supply this period of ontogenesis is also a critical period for the vital activity of plants because, especially in the period of intense vegetative growth of the aerial organs (branching–budding–stem elongation–budding), the sensitivity of plants to water deficit is much greater, which affects their yield and other important agrobiological indexes (Table 46).

A comparison of indexes of the water regime of species and varieties of alfalfa grown on irrigated and unirrigated lands in northern Aral revealed that the total water content of plants on unirrigated fields was 7 to 15% lower than on irrigated fields. During the stage of vegetative growth (spring sprouting) if the soil has an adequate reserve of productive moisture, then the difference in total water content of plants on irrigated and on unirrigated plots reduces to minimum. At the budding stage and during flowering it increases, but toward the browning stage of pods (maturity) reduces again. Differentiation of varieties on the basis of their ability to withstand prolonged dehydration with minimum losses for the organism takes place in the period when moisture reserves in the soil reduce to the level of permanent wilting moisture. In northern Aral this usually occurs in the summer months (June to August), although in certain years, with the absence of autumn–winter precipitation, it may also occur in April–May. The more severe the growth conditions for plants, the more intense the process of differentiation of varieties on the basis of their resistance to drought.

Table 46. Agrobiological characteristics of alfalfa variety Tibet on irrigated and unirrigated lands (Aral Experimental Station of VIR, 1961–1965)

Index	Year of cultivation			
	Second	Third	Fourth	Fifth
Irrigated				
Yield of green mass, kg/m^2	3.38	8.50	7.62	5.0
Yield of seeds, g/m^2	54.3	32.1	11.6	—
Survival rate of plants, %	100	80	76	65
Duration up to first cutting, days	57	46	47	55
Plant height at first cutting, cm	82	95	100	93
Susceptibility to diseases, grade	1	1	1	4
Susceptibility to root rots, %	—	—	—	82.4
Number of cuttings in vegetative period	3	4	4	3
Unirrigated				
Yield of green mass, kg/m^2	5.52	0.35	0.45	0.40
Yield of seeds, g/m^2	3	1	—	—
Survival rate of plants, %	99	95	92	76
Duration up to first cutting, days	42	40	45	5
Plant height at first cutting, cm	69	58	52	60
Susceptibility to diseases, grade	0	0	0	1
Susceptibility to root rots, %	0	0	0	23.8
Number of cuttings in vegetative period	1	1	1	1

Drought-resistant varieties during the period of intense growth (bud-ding–flowering) are characterized by a high content of bound water, lower moisture deficit, high water-retention capacity of tissues, active functioning of the transpiration apparatus, and low magnitude of proto-plasmic permeability (Tables 47 and 48). Varieties not resistant to drought reorganize the functioning of organs which control water exchange more slowly.

With a sharp deterioration in growth conditions, in some varieties (Tashkent-3192, Azerbaydzhan-262, Vakhshskaya-233, Indiiskaya local, and Mesopotamian) the growth processes stop quickly, but in others (Iygeva-12, Onokhoy-6, and Severnaya hybrid) the rate of transpiration increases significantly initially, but later curling of leaflets sets in. In varieties of the forest-steppe zone the concentration of cell sap in leaves of the upper tier of the bush increases up to maximum value (22 to 27%), while leaflets of the lower and middle tiers are concomitantly shed. In

Table 47. Water regime of plants and chemical composition of leaves of alfalfa variety Tibet in the second year (first cutting) of growth (1965–1968)

Index	Irrigated			Unirrigated		
	Vegetative growth	Budding	Flowering	Vegetative growth	Budding	Flowering
Total water content, %	76.5	73.4	62.8	74.5	64.3	52.7
Free water content, %	51.6	43.8	24.5	36.4	11.9	11.5
Bound water content, %	24.9	29.6	38.3	38.1	52.4	41.2
Concentration of cell sap, %	10.3	12.8	14.4	13.4	17.9	19.9
Rate of transpiration (mg/g raw matter/hr)	1,680	2,180	2,350	2,840	940	395
Protoplasmic permeability to electrolytes (mho$\times 10^{-6}$)	25.9	44.7	85.4	64.8	159.3	284.8
Moisture deficit, % :						
Morning	17.8	22.2	21.8	23.7	39.7	40.4
Midday	23.1	35.1	28.8	29.5	55.6	61.2
Diurnal	16.5	21.6	20.1	23.6	43.0	45.8
Content of vitamin C (mg/100 g raw matter)	99.9	112.5	101.8	62.8	49.9	32.5
Content of crude (N$\times$6.25) protein, % of dry matter	24.6	25.2	23.7	19.4	16.8	14.9
Total pigments (γ/mg raw matter)	0.652	0.905	1.129	0.285	0.352	0.124

Table 48. Water regime of species of alfalfa in the second year (first cutting) at anthesis (1969)

Species, variety, specimens	Concentration of cell sap, %	Specific electrical conductivity (mho×10^{-6})	Water loss during 6 hrs of wilting	Water absorption during 24 hrs of saturation	Water deficit, % of total saturation			Acidity of cell sap, %
					Morning	Midday	Diurnal	
			percent					
Common alfalfa Tashkent-3192	18.3	40.6	40.3	80.3	21.9	24.9	23.9	5.30
Variable alfalfa Karaganda-1	17.6	38.2	17.1	112.2	21.8	24.8	20.1	5.70
Yellow alfalfa Krasnokutskaya-4009	15.8	17.9	16.9	114.3	20.0	22.3	16.1	5.64
Blue alfalfa Wild (Dagestan ASSR)	17.0	32.1	20.6	105.1	23.2	24.2	22.8	5.50
Varicolored alfalfa Wild (Stavropol' territory)	16.9	26.3	15.5	100.1	23.6	25.1	19.2	5.62
Tian Shan alfalfa Wild (Chimkent province)	17.6	25.8	24.1	108.9	23.4	23.9	20.2	5.58
Semitwisted alfalfa Wild (Armenian SSR)	16.4	23.5	22.7	122.9	20.6	29.9	21.8	5.55

drought-resistant varieties the adaptive reactions of plants to the effect of drought associated with death of individual organs, function at a slower rate, i.e., other conditions remaining the same, drought-resistant varieties under moisture stress exhibit a more flexible water exchange, which imparts to them the plasticity and vitality so essential under such conditions.

Alfalfa varieties of the Nechernozem zone of RSFSR suffer more from soil moisture deficit when drought occurs in early spring. In the second and third year of growth the strong and deeply penetrating root system and high resistance to drought of varieties of Kazakh SSR, Kara-Kalpak ASSR, and western and eastern Siberia, and southern varieties which have been cultivated a long time under irrigation, exhibit a high drought resistance in the first year of plant growth; varieties from Kara-Kalpak and wild specimens of alfalfa from western Kazakhstan display drought resistance during the stage of development of green pods. With age, crops of varieties from regions of irrigated farming thin rapidly due to poor winter hardiness. Very early maturing specimens from China, India, Bolivia, Chile, Peru, and Tadzhik SSR suffer less from drought, but after their first winter also thin notably.

Agriculture in the arid zone of Kazakhstan requires varieties with compound resistance: drought resistance, heat resistance, winter hardiness, salt tolerance, and resistance to diseases and pests. To include in one variety compound resistance together with high plant productivity is an exceptionally difficult task; nevertheless such a variety is urgently needed at the present stage of breeding.

A study of the dynamics of protoplasmic permeability of rainfed alfalfa crops revealed that during flowering, when water supply to plants deteriorates sharply, high protoplasmic permeability is found in varieties from the republics of Central Asia, especially the drought-resistant ancient specimens of Kara-Kalpak ASSR and wild alfalfa species of the desert regions of Kazakhstan. This is associated with the fact that the southern varieties and wild species of the arid zone of Kazakhstan are characterized by high heat resistance, which is manifested during the stage of flowering. These very varieties are distinguished by high yield of green mass, good water content of tissues, moderate moisture deficit, and high protein and vitamin C content.

On the basis of many years of agrobiological, physiological, and biochemical study of the alfalfa collection from rainfed lands of northern Aral we have identified specimens with high drought resistance. These are: wild populations of yellow, blue, and Trautvetter's alfalfas collected by expeditions to Ural'sk, Gur'ev, Aktyubin, Turgai, Karaganda, Semipalatinsk, Taldy-Kurgan, eastern Kazakhstan, Dzhezkazgan, and Kyzyl-Orda provinces; improved and local varieties of alfalfa from Kara-Kalpak

ASSR, western and central Kazakhstan, Lower Povolzh'e and Kalmyk ASSR; some ancient populations from the northern regions of Uzbek SSR; alfalfa varieties developed at the Krasnokutsk breeding station; ancient local varieties of steppe regions of Ukrainian SSR, and Khakass autonomous province. Among the foreign material, varieties of the USA and wild specimens from the foothills of central and western China were distinguished for their drought and temperature resistance.

Effect of Physiologically Active Substances on Water Exchange

Biologists and chemists have discovered many diverse substances with high physiological activity. Their effect on the organism is determined by the dose and duration of plant treatment. In small doses the growth substances act as stimulants of vital processes and exert a multifaceted effect on plant metabolism. Their application in higher concentrations, however, produces just the opposite effect: arrestation of growth, reduction in rate of metabolism, and weakening of all vital functions.

When growth regulators produce a favorable combination of positive symptoms, the process of plant vitality improves and their productivity increases.

Since the problems of the effect of growth regulators, especially retardants, on augmenting heat and drought resistance in alfalfa have not been adequately studied, we conducted field and pot culture experiments at the Aral Experimental Station of VIR (1966 to 1969) and in the Pushkin laboratories of VIR (1970 to 1973). In the experiments we used chlorocholine chloride (gran. CCC), heteroauxin (indoleacetic acid), and gibberellin. The granular preparation (CCC) was used at the rate of 4.0, 6.0, and 8.0 kg/ha through irrigation and foliar sprays; for seed soaking a 1.0% solution was used. Growth stimulants were used in a concentration of 0.01% for spraying the leaf-stem mass of plants. The crops were treated in different stages of growth and development.

The studies revealed that in treatment of variety Tibet with the CCC and IAA preparations during vegetative growth, irrespective of soil water supply (irrigated, rainfed), reduction of total water content of the plants was negligible (Table 49).

Under strictly rainfed conditions in treatment of alfalfa crops with CCC the total water content of plants was less than in IAA spraying. On increasing the concentration of the solution from 4.0 to 8.0 kg/ha, the level of total water content of the plants reduced, but the content of bound water increased by 10 to 13%. In spraying plants with CCC the total water content was more than in soil application of the preparation. Potentially, under drought conditions, in the presence of a large quan-

Table 49. Effect of growth regulators on water regime of alfalfa variety Tibet (second year of growth, 1968)

Treatment	Irrigated						Rainfed					
	Total water, %	Specific electrical conductivity (mho×10^{-6})	Water loss during 5 hrs of wilting	Water deficit, % of total saturation			Water loss during 5 hrs of wilting	Specific electrical conductivity (mho×10^{-6})	Total water, %	Water deficit, % of total saturation		
				Morning	Mid-day	Diurnal				Morning	Mid-day	Diurnal
Control	74.6	55.4	24.1	23.7	25.6	26.1	24.4	21.1	67.7	39.8	49.2	45.1
Soil application of CCC, kg/ha:												
4	73.0	58.4	21.9	17.0	22.6	17.9	19.1	57.0	61.1	37.5	42.7	39.8
6	71.8	67.9	22.2	19.7	21.0	21.1	16.3	46.3	60.1	29.9	34.9	30.2
8	71.5	58.8	20.7	18.3	23.6	19.2	13.1	38.6	57.0	30.4	38.8	32.5
Spraying with CCC, kg/ha:												
4	73.8	69.1	20.2	17.2	23.8	18.0	13.4	77.2	60.1	35.9	42.3	40.8
6	72.4	66.0	19.3	20.0	22.7	20.6	12.3	47.3	58.3	38.6	42.6	39.0
8	72.3	65.2	19.6	21.1	23.8	21.5	9.8	45.3	58.9	32.1	38.3	35.1
Spraying with 0.01% IAA	72.6	54.6	21.4	21.9	26.4	22.7	24.1	34.7	62.2	38.1	48.6	43.9

tity of colloidly bound water plants treated with growth regulators, especially with CCC, will have a higher water content in the tissues. That this is so will be confirmed by their growth and development and eventually their productivity.

Plants treated with CCC were noted for lower values of midday and residual water deficit and, contrarily, an increased water-retention capacity. Alfalfa crops treated with growth regulators had dark green leaves, increased foliage, and shed fewer buds and ovaries. All these indexes indicate the much higher temperature and drought resistance of the experimental crops treated with growth regulators, especially CCC. In rainfed crops IAA exerted almost no effect on the water regime of alfalfa.

In experiments with variety Priaralskaya the water content was reduced only on irrigated lands. Under dry farming conditions the total water content in the experimental plants was 3 to 11% more than in the control plants. Under conditions of constantly effective soil and atmospheric drought the control plants and those sprayed with gibberellin lagged behind plants treated with CCC and IAA in content of total and bound water.

Thus under conditions of adequate water supply as well as under conditions of constant natural or artificial (in pot culture experiments) drought, the water content of the tissues of plants sprayed with CCC was higher. Indoleacetic acid (IAA) produced an effect only in irrigated fields. Treatment of plants with gibberellin produced a negative effect under drought conditions.

Growth regulators change not only the water regime of the plants but also the chemical composition. Plants grown under irrigation contain 5 to 10% more protein and 20 to 60 mg/100 g more vitamin C than plants from unirrigated fields. CCC and IAA increase the content of crude protein and vitamin C. Spraying alfalfa with CCC effects a greater increment in content of protein and ascorbic acid than soil application does. CCC is more effective than IAA. With an increase in dose of application of CCC the content of vitamin C increases: on irrigated fields by 13 to 15% and on rainfed fields with soil application from 4.0 to 7.0%, and with spraying from 10 to 26%. The content of crude protein, however, does not change significantly with an increase in dose of growth regulators.

Growth regulators favorably affect the content of green and yellow pigments in plants. In treatment with CCC the content of pigments increased at both early and late stages of plant growth. In contrast to the retardant, IAA produced an effect only during the budding stage (Table 50).

The content of chlorophyll b and carotene, and in the budding stage of lutein and xanthophyll increased significantly due to the effect of growth regulators. Plants treated with CCC in the budding stage contained less

Table 50. Effect of growth regulators on content of pigments (γ/mg of raw matter) in leaves of alfalfa variety Tibet in second year of growth (irrigated, 1968)

Treatment	Vegetative growth						Flowering						
	Total pigments	Chlorophyll			Carotene	Lutein	Total pigments	Chlorophyll			Carotene	Lutein	Xantho-phyll
		$a+b$	a	b				$a+b$	a	b			
Control	0.491	0.446	0.243	0.203	0.019	0.026	0.996	0.820	0.522	0.298	0.081	0.068	0.027
Soil application of CCC, kg/ha:													
4	0.515	0.463	0.314	0.024	0.149	0.028	1.168	0.936	0.450	0.486	0.113	0.084	0.035
6	0.547	0.482	0.268	0.214	0.032	0.033	1.209	0.948	0.449	0.120	0.100	0.100	0.041
8	0.597	0.522	0.261	0.261	0.035	0.040	1.170	0.935	0.449	0.486	0.102	0.089	0.044
Spraying with CCC, kg/ha:													
4	0.651	0.580	0.289	0.291	0.040	0.031	1.059	0.840	0.429	0.411	0.091	0.088	0.040
6	0.646	0.562	0.265	0.297	0.044	0.040	1.108	0.886	0.420	0.466	0.100	0.083	0.039
8	0.779	0.688	0.374	0.314	0.049	0.042	1.015	0.784	0.410	0.375	0.105	0.083	0.043
Spraying with 0.01% IAA	0.504	0.448	0.261	0.187	0.028	0.028	1.198	0.957	0.527	0.430	0.135	0.084	0.052

chlorophyll *a* than the control plants even though the sum of chlorophylls *a* and *b* and the total sum of all pigments was considerably higher than in the control plants.

A study of the effect of chlorocholine chloride (CCC) on the chlorophyll content in varieties of different ecological groups revealed that the alfalfa variety Tibet, released for cultivation in the province, when treated with this preparation contained more green pigments than variety Peruvian from another region. However, the content of chlorophyll *a* was greater in the latter variety than in variety Tibet: In variety Tibet the maximum chlorophyll content was found under conditions of irrigation with a 1.0% solution of chlorocholine chloride, and in variety Peruvian after three sprayings. The chlorophyll content of variety Tibet increased by 27 to 29% and of variety Peruvian by 8 to 12%. Here varietal differences arising from difference in origin were distinctly expressed.

The quantity of green mass from 3.0 m² in control irrigated fields was 6.14 ± 0.015 kg, and seeds from one square meter 198.9 g. With soil application of CCC, the quantity of green mass varied from 6.20 ± 0.019 to 6.93 ± 0.084 kg and seeds from 204.6 to 223.3 g. In spray treatment the productivity was 5 to 25% higher than in control. Indoleacetic acid also augmented productivity of the crop. Growth regulators also stimulated to some extent such indexes as foliation, pod filling, and mass of 1,000 seeds.

By improving the water regime and augmenting the content of protein and pigments the CCC preparation (to a lesser extent IAA also) in irrigated fields ensured a much higher level of plant activity which, no doubt, led to an increase in temperature resistance and productivity.

The increased content of protein, ascorbic acid, and carotene in the treated plants ensured an improvement in their fodder values, which is no less important in desert zones.

Under rainfed conditions the yield of green mass in control was 0.61 ± 0.032 kg, which varied from 0.66 ± 0.38 to 0.71 ± 0.029 kg with soil application of CCC; in the case of sprays (except for the dose 4.0 kg/ha) productivity was lower than in control. Treatment of alfalfa with CCC in doses of 6.0 and 8.0 kg/ha during high summer atmospheric temperatures (up to 44°C) and low relative humidity (10 to 7%) caused heliosis of the leaflets.

Under the arid conditions of the desert zone of northern Aral as well as in pot culture experiments with soil moisture constituting 30 and 50% of the total field moisture capacity, IAA and gibberellin proved less effective than CCC. The growth stimulants considerably improved growth processes and augmented yield of green mass only in fields with regular irrigation. Contrarily, the physiological activity of chlorocholine chloride becomes evident when plants are subjected to soil or atmospheric drought.

according to the methods of the Department of Fodder Crops of VIR, Department of Biochemistry, and Department of Physiology.

Data from the experiments conducted in Leningrad province revealed that not a single variety subjected for a period of 40 days from the seedling stage to short 8-hour illumination changed over to reproductive development in the year of sowing. Under long days many varieties reached the budding stage, while the most early maturing among them (Peruvian, Tashkent-3192, Zaykevich, Poltava-256) even began to flower (Table 51).

Long days stimulate growth processes. Plants grown under an 18-hour day have an erect bush, elongated internodes, slender stems, and small leaflets. Plants grown under an 8-hour day have a creeping or semi-erect bush, several shortened internodes, and very large leaf blades (Figures 35 and 36).

Figure 35. External appearance of alfalfa plants.
a—common (Peruvian); b and c—variable (Zaykevich and Marusinskaya-81); d—blue (wild specimen); e—yellow (Krasnokutskaya-4009) grown under long, 18-hour (above) and short, 8-hour day (below).

Figure 36. External appearance of plants of blue alfalfa (K-36118) grown under: continuous illumination (1); long, 18-hour day (2); short, 8-hour day for a period of 40 days from seedling stage (3); constant, short, 8-hour day (4). Stages of growth and development of plants in pots: 1—flowering; 2—seed maturity; 3—commencement of budding; 4—vegetative growth.

The varieties studied could be divided into two groups on the basis of their response to daylength. The first group included taller specimens with faster growth in both treatments. They comprised mostly the early- and medium-maturing varieties. The second group included late-maturing varieties characterized by slow growth rate, especially under an 8-hour day. In the 40 days of vegetative growth their stem measured only 2.0 to 8.0 cm in length versus 18 cm for the early-maturing variety Peruvian. In the second group only one late-maturing variety, Kamalin-930, was distinguished for plant height, which did not lag behind the medium-maturing varieties in terms of growth rate, especially under long days.

The different photoperiodic treatments exerted great influence on the metabolism of pigments in the leaves of the alfalfa varieties. After 40 days of vegetative growth the content of pigments in most of the varieties grown under long days increased compared to short days. Chromatographic analysis revealed that the quantity of both chlorophyll *a* and *b* reduced in leaves under short days. Individual varieties differed insignificantly in content of pigments under conditions of different photoperiods (Severnaya hybrid, Rambler, Yellow Kuban). The most early-maturing alfalfa variety, Peruvian, was distinguished by increased pigments under short days, which was possibly related to internal plant readiness for transition to reproductive development. Finally, the hypothesis of Academician **P.M.** Zhukovskii that the Chilean alfalfas are characterized by a neutral reaction to photoperiod was confirmed.

A high level of green and yellow pigments was observed in these varieties in both treatments: Karaganda-1, Zaykevich, Severnaya hybrid, and Yellow Kuban. The lowest pigment content was recorded for varieties Zabaikalka, Rambler, and blue alfalfa. In late-maturing varieties the content of carotenoids increased under short days.

Metabolism of pigments under conditions of different photoperiods also depends on the physiological condition of the plant and peculiarities of the variety.

Analysis before cutting, 15 days after the transfer of plants from short to long days, revealed that only three early-maturing varieties—Peruvian, Zaykevich, and Rambler—reached the budding stage; the others remained at the stage of branching. The control plants had already flowered and formed pods by this time, remaining as before much taller and more productive than plants subjected to the effect of short day during the first 40 days of vegetative growth.

Control plants of the early-maturing varieties—Peruvian, Zaykevich, and Rambler—yielded less stem growth 15 days after their transition from short to long day. In the medium-maturing varieties—Severnaya hybrid, Poltava-256, and Marusinskaya-81—in this same period stem growth was quite similar. Late-maturing varieties, remaining the most short-statured under both conditions of illumination, were characterized by much greater stem growth, i.e., they exhibited the aftereffect of short day on main stem growth (Figures 37 and 38).

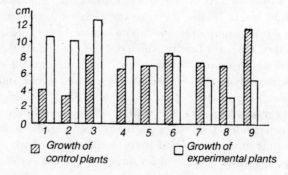

Figure 37. Stem growth of varieties of different maturation periods 15 days after restoration of plants (55 days old) to uniform light regime.
Early-maturing varieties: 1—Peruvian; 2—Rambler; 3—Vernal. Medium-maturing varieties: 4—Severnaya hybrid; 5—Poltava-256; 6—Marusinskaya-81. Late-maturing varieties; 7—Kamalin-930; 8—Saarema Kollane; 9—Taiga.

Figure 38. External appearance of yellow alfalfa plants (K-21267) grown under: continuous illumination (1); long, 18-hour day (2); short, 8-hour day for a period of 40 days from seedling stage (3); constant, short, 8-hour day (4).

Stages of growth and development of plants in pots: 1—commencement of seed maturity; 2—fully mature seeds; 3—budding; 4—vegetative growth.

The aftereffect of light conditions in the first year of growth was more evident in the second year. The aftereffect of photoperiod was particularly significant in the survival of varieties of alfalfa and productivity. Plants subjected to short days were much more winter hardy, bushier, and stronger, with more profuse foliage in the second year of growth. The control plants after overwintering generally lagged behind in growth and development. Such a lag was most pronounced in plants which entered the winter period uncut, which was obviously linked with additional consumption of nutrients for their vegetative and reproductive growth in the first year. The aftereffect of light conditions was quite conspicuously manifested in varieties Flora and Iygeva-18 in both control and experimental plants cut in the first year; these plants were much taller, bushier, and more productive compared to other varieties (Table 52).

In the desert zone of western Kazakhstan in varieties of the northern part of the geographic area of the crop—Severnaya hybrid and Kamalin-930—growth processes were more severely retarded in short days than in varieties of Central Asian origin—Tashkent-721 and Tashkent-3192. Different photoperiods caused changes in the developmental stage, content of vitamin C, length of stem, expansion of roots, and in shoot mass, as well as in length of vegetative period.

Commencement of flowering after short days was delayed on the

Table 52. Effect of light conditions of previous year on winter hardiness, growth processes, and yield of green mass of alfalfa in second year

Variety	Day length in 1st year, hrs	Overwintering, grade points	Height, cm	Indexes of first cutting		Stage
				No. of shoots	Yield of green mass from one plant, g	
Karaganda	18	3	60.0	8	20.0	Budding
	8	4	90.0	39	300.0	Commencement of anthesis
Severnaya hybrid	18	1	50.0	6	70.0	Budding
	8	4	112.0	37	210.0	Budding
Rambler	18	2	80.0	18	140.0	Budding
	8	4	83.0	42	240.0	Sporadic flowering
Iygeva-118	18	2	80.0	23	180.0	Budding
	8	4	80.0	58	310.0	Commencement of anthesis
Flora	18	1	50.0	6	70.0	Budding
	8	5	110.0	40	350.0	Sporadic flowering
Iygeva-18*	18	1	115.0	44	300.0	Flowering
	8	5	110.0	57	650.0	Flowering

Flora*	18	1	90.0	8	Budding	160.0
	8	5	110.0	54	Sporadic flowering	500.0
Zaykevich*	18	1	76.0	18	Flowering	100.0
	8	1	120.0	43	Flowering	300.0
Poltava-256*	18	3	100.0	20	Sporadic flowering	150.0
	8	1	110.0	38	Flowering	200.0
Marusinskaya-81*	18	1	105.0	32	Budding	200.0
	8	2	90.0	82	Sporadic flowering	440.0

*Plants cut in first year of growth.

average by 40 to 45 days. The alfalfa variety Tibet flowered 61 days later than under continuous illumination. Under a 24-hour day flowering was profuse and uniform, but under short days sparse and prolonged.

The aftereffect of photoperiodism in the year of sowing was evident in all varieties, and expressed in the intensification of growth processes after the transfer of plants from short to long days. Medium-maturing varieties Kamalin-930 and Severnaya hybrid in this case were more short-statured compared to variety Poltava-256 and the Central Asian populations, which were less repressed by a short photoperiod. The aftereffect of photoperiodism continued even into the second year of growth, when the control plants were characterized by higher water content of tissues, greater vitamin C content in the leaf-stem mass, faster growth, and increased winter hardiness.

Our study of the response of alfalfa species to photoperiodism revealed that all of them are long-day plants. However, some specimens develop faster under continuous illumination: common alfalfa (K-34638 and K-35011), yellow alfalfa (K-36122), blue alfalfa (K-29002), Trautvetter's alfalfa (K-36711), Tian Shan alfalfa (K-30706), and varicolored alfalfa (K-34625). Other specimens such as blue alfalfa (K-36118), Trautvetter's alfalfa (K-34626), common alfalfa (K-34638 and K-35011) flowered earlier under an 18-hour natural day. The third group comprised populations that were neutral in terms of daylength: common alfalfa (K-28458 and K-29125), yellow alfalfa (K-21267, see Figure 39), and Tian Shan (K-34629). With a reduction in daylength in the early period of plant life seed productivity reduces because the reproductive organs fall off. Continuous short-day exposure generally prevents the transition of plants to the reproductive stage (Table 53).

Under long days plants are tall with an erect bush, slender stems, small leaf blades, and elongated internodes; under short days growth is retarded, the number of internodes reduces, the shape of the bush changes (to prostrate type), the size of the leaf blades increases, and their content of green and yellow pigments is less.

Later, after countering the effect of different light conditions, when the plants had reached the flowering stage under continuous illumination, the content of chlorophyll and carotenoids reduced. Contrarily, the rate of growth processes induced by a short photoperiod over a period of 40 days quickly increased under natural day conditions. Evidently, this was linked with high photosynthetic activity due to the increased size of the leaf blades and the content of green and yellow pigments in them, which increases rapidly under natural-day conditions.

Table 53. Agrobiological characteristics of species of alfalfa under different photoperiods, 1972

Species	Photoperiod, hours	Number of days from seedling stage to:			Plant height after 40 days, cm	Number of internodes after 40 days	Size of leaflet, mm		Leaf stem mass from one pot, g	
		Budding	Flowering	Commencement of maturation			Length	Width	Fresh	Dried
1	2	3	4	5	6	7	8	9	10	11
Common alfalfa (K-28458)	24	37	46	51	13	10	—	—	—	—
	18	37	46	51	21	12	7	3	12.6	5.0
	8 (40 days)	74	105	—	6	9	15	9	9.1	4.1
	8	—	—	—	6	6	12	8	7.0	1.5
Common alfalfa (K-34638)	24	37	46	65	22	11	—	—	—	—
	18	43	59	86	21	11	12	3	19.6	6.3
	8 (40 days)	104	—	—	11	9	14	7	17.3	5.7
	8	—	—	—	6	7	8	5	11.0	3.6
Yellow alfalfa (K-21267)	24	46	49	65	26	10	—	—	—	—
	18	46	49	64	32	14	12	4	40.5	15.0
	8 (40 days)	71	85	—	16	11	15	10	29.3	12.2
	8	—	—	—	10	6	12	8	15.0	4.3
Yellow alfalfa (K-36122)	24	47	61	—	25	10	—	—	—	—
	18	60	70	—	19	10	11	5	17.0	5.9
	8 (40 days)	76	—	—	8	9	15	10	14.0	5.0
	8	—	—	—	9	8	10	7	8.5	2.5

(*Contd.*)

Table 53 (*Contd.*)

1	2	3	4	5	6	7	8	9	10	11
Blue alfalfa	24	47	63	69	16	8	—	—	—	—
(K-29002)	18	48	63	73	29	13	10	2	31.8	12.5
	8 (40 days)	—	—	—	11	13	18	10	15.0	4.5
	8	—	—	—	6	6	10	6	3.5	1.4
Blue alfalfa	24	48	64	85	21	10	—	—	—	—
(K-36118)	18	42	51	58	25	12	11	4	16.0	4.2
	8 (40 days)	84	—	—	3	8	17	9	12.8	4.2
	8	—	—	—	1	—	9	6	4.5	0.9
Trautvetter's alfalfa	24	48	65	86	21	11	—	—	—	—
(K-34636)	18	46	51	59	18	11	12	3	21.5	8.6
	8 (40 days)	92	—	—	8	8	23	11	12.9	4.2
	8	—	—	—	1	6	12	5	2.0	0.2
Trautvetter's alfalfa	24	41	57	63	22	12	—	—	—	—
(K-36761)	18	51	86	—	19	13	12	5	24.7	9.8
	8 (40 days)	84	103	—	7	10	20	9	15.6	4.6
	8	—	—	—	5	7	9	4	4.9	1.2
Tian Shan alfalfa	24	43	49	51	20	11	—	—	—	—
(K-34629)	18	43	49	51	24	13	10	3	23.5	6.8
	8 (40 days)	—	—	—	12	9	15	6	13.8	4.5
	8	—	—	—	8	7	15	11	2.0	0.8

Variety	Days									
Tian Shan alfalfa (K-30706)	24	43	49	51	19	10	—	—	—	—
	18	46	51	74	23	12	13	5	26.7	7.2
	8 (40 days)	—	—	—	10	8	17	10	12.1	3.9
	8	—	—	—	6	6	11	6	7.8	2.6
Variable alfalfa (K-36117)	24	57	63	—	9	8	—	—	—	—
	18	58	—	—	8	9	12	7	19.8	7.2
	8 (40 days)	—	—	—	3	6	15	11	11.7	3.8
	8	—	—	—	1	—	11	6	8.2	2.4
Variable alfalfa (K-36763)	24	59	65	—	11	9	—	—	—	—
	18	61	—	—	8	7	10	5	29.3	18.7
	8 (40 days)	—	—	—	4	6	14	10	15.6	4.9
	8	—	—	—	2	4	12	8	9.8	4.0
South Kazakhstan alfalfa (K-063116)	24	51	59	—	12	9	—	—	—	—
	18	58	64	—	11	9	11	4	17.9	5.6
	8 (40 days)	79	98	2	7	7	23	7	12.5	4.2
	8	—	—	—	2	5	15	4	3.7	1.1
South Kazakhstan alfalfa (K-063102)	24	68	98	—	9	8	—	—	—	—
	18	79	—	—	9	9	17	3	19.7	5.8
	8 (40 days)	—	—	—	5	6	25	7	16.4	4.9
	8	—	—	—	2	4	14	5	4.1	1.3
Varicolored alfalfa (K-34625)	24	46	59	65	28	11	—	—	—	—
	18	58	74	86	24	12	11	5	21.0	6.4
	8 (40 days)	85	—	—	13	11	22	10	16.3	5.7
	8	—	—	—	9	12	10	10	8.1	2.7

Pollination and Pollinators

The most important condition for increasing the seed productivity of alfalfa is finding a solution to these agronomic and organizational tasks: Determination and wider application of scientifically based recommendations for augmenting rate of anthesis, identification of important pollinators and study of their biology, artificial rearing of the most active solitary bees, and creation of back-up reserves of pollinators in order to increase the density of bees in seed plots during the optimal time for collection of pollen (and pollination).

Based on the nature of flowering and pollination alfalfa belongs to the category of cross-pollinated entomophilous plants. The pollen is transferred from one flower to another mainly by different species of wild bees and bumblebees. The structure of the alfalfa flower precludes self-pollination and pollination by wind. The structure of the flower, nature of its pollination, process of fertilization, seed formation, conditions of growth, and preservation of pollen viability have been described at length by many authors. According to the classification of E.N. Gerasimova-Navashina, fertilization in alfalfa is of the promitotic type.*

According to the data of V.V. Popov, in the Soviet Union alfalfa is pollinated by 161 species of bees. The specific and numerical composition of pollinators changes from one climatic zone to another. Differences are also observed in one and the same field and depend on cutting, time and method of sowing, level of agronomic practices, and other factors. However, irrespective of the region of cultivation the pollination of flowers is mainly the work of five to eight species of bees. Other species of pollinators are represented by solitary specimens in the crops.

The most important and numerically large species of bees actively frequenting alfalfa flowers are: *Andrena flavipes* Pz., *A. labialis* Kby., *A. ovatula* Kby., *Melitturga clavicornis* Latr., *Halictus eurygnathus* Bluthg., *H. quadricinitus* F., *H. rubicundus* Christ., *Nomia diversipes* Latr., *Rofitoides canus* Ev., *Melitta leporina* Pz., *Anthidium florentinum* F., *Megachile argentata* F., *M. pilidens* Alfk., *Eucera clypeata* Erichs., *Bombus laesus* F. Mor, and *B. terrestris* L. These species are widespread in the Soviet Union.

In Kazakhstan, in addition to the aforementioned pollinators, alfalfa flowers are actively visited by these bees: *Andrena wilkella* Kby., *Eucera longicornus* L., *Megachile analis* Myl., *M. centuncularis* L., and *M. leucomalla* Gerst.

Wild solitary bees collect pollen and nectar from flowers and do not store honey in their hives. Most of them nest in the soil, preferring virgin lands or plots where the plant canopy is rarely disturbed. Species of

*Misprint in Russian original; should read "primitotic type"—General Editor.

Andrena and *Halictus* settle in the soil in large and small colonies and live in the exact same place for a number of years; *Melitta* and *Nomis* build solitary hives in the soil. *Megachile rotundata,* like members of the genera *Anthidium* and *Osmia,* prefers to build its hive in clay walls, under stones, in hollow reed roofs, and so forth. Species of the genus *Anthophora* usually make their nest from clay.

Wild solitary bees feed their offspring pollen which they have moistened with nectar. They thrust the proboscis into the mouth of the corolla, support themselves on the keel, and with the head under the standard force both head and proboscis into the corolla tube to collect the nectar from its base. Removing the standard from the keel by use of their wings, wild bees open the closed floral apparatus which holds the stamens and pistil inside. When the styles are tripped, the anthers and stigma strike against one of the thick and chitinized jaws of the bee, its thorax, or the base of its throat. Due to the impact of the anthers on the lower side of the bee's head pollen is deposited at the base of the maxilla. When the deposit of pollen has reached a certain size, using its forelegs the bee transfers it to the abdominal brush or brush of the hind legs. Bees of other genera (*Anthidium, Eucera, Halictus, Megachile, Osmia, Melitturga, Andrena* and *Rhophites*) collect pollen and nectar in the same way except that the pollen is deposited in a different place on their body.

When the flower is opened the stigma rubs against the loose deposit of pollen collected by the bee from several plants. This ensures cross-pollination. The common honeybee (*Apis mellifera* L.) collects nectar from alfalfa flowers not through the mouth of the corolla but from the side of the flower through a slit between the alae and standard. In such cases only solitary flowers are opened, in which the staminal column rubs against the base of the bee's throat. The pollinator experiences discomfort since the proboscis is pressed tightly by the column toward the standard. Consequently honeybees are rather reluctant to visit seed nurseries of alfalfa and when they do, tend to collect nectar from flowers that are already open. Hence the role of the common honeybee in pollination of alfalfa is insignificant.

In experiments conducted at the Fergana Experimental Station, M.I. Tishchenko established that the maximum number of bees visit during the first cutting. The density of all species of bees in one hectare in the first cutting was, on the average, 7,384, of which wild bees constituted 93.2%, wasps and bumblebees 5.7%, and honeybees 1.1%. In the second cutting the number of bees was 3,979 of which 83.7%, 1.5%, and 0.8% belonged to the aforementioned species respectively. In the third cutting 3,618 bees were counted, of which solitary bees comprised 37.7%, wasps and bumblebees 61.2%, and honeybees 1.1%.

Table 54. Opening of flowers of perennial species of alfalfa
(August 28, 1961)

Species	No. of flowers observed	Percent of opened flowers			Day's total	
		Up to 11:00 a.m.	11:00 to 5:00 p.m.	5:00 to 8:00 p.m.	Absolute	%
Common alfalfa	271	6.6	61.6	31.8	91	33.7
Yellow alfalfa	364	7.4	64.8	27.8	108	29.7
Semitwisted alfalfa	261	8.9	82.2	8.9	45	17.3
Varicolored alfalfa	243	12.5	66.7	20.9	48	19.6

In Kazakhstan the highest activity of bees was recorded during the warmest hours of the day. In our experiments the density of all bees in one hectare in the first cutting was as follows: morning (from 7:00 to 11:00)—900 bees, midday (1:00 to 4:00)—4,300 bees, and evening (5:00 to 8:00)—1,750 bees. The process of opening of flowers, i.e., the course of pollination of seed alfalfa, depends on the flight activity of the pollinators. In these same experiments in 1961 to 1963 it was established that up to 10:00 a.m. 4,010 flowers were opened; from 10:00 to 1:00—16,600 flowers; 1:00 to 5:00 (the period of highest activity)—54,620; 5:00 to 7:00—17,150; and 7:00 to 9:00—6,720 flowers. The number of flowers opened, on the average, in one hour was: morning (7:00 to 8:00)—300; midday (12:00 to 1:00)—7,720; afternoon (2:00 to 3:00)—15,360; and evening (8:00 to 9:00)—2,350. Bee activity was not uniform on different species of alfalfa (Table 54).

The intensity of opening of flowers by solitary bees, wasps, and bumblebees also differed, and clearly depended on temperature, wind velocity, relative atmospheric humidity, and other factors (Table 55; Figure 39).

The most active species of solitary bees opened 25 to 30 flowers in one minute, and bees of average activity, 18 to 20 flowers. In the northern regions of the Soviet Union the activity of bees is lower than in the south. During the hot hours of the day, when the air temperature in the shade exceeds 30°C, according to the data of A.N. Ponomarev (1950), flight activity reduces; the diurnal course of pollination then yields a curve with two peaks or one with several peaks, although some researchers dispute these findings (see Table 56).

In recent years because of extensive reclamation of virgin and wasteland, active ameliorative works, reclamation of slopes, limans, and saline soils, and expansion of agriculture to desert, semidesert, and high altitude hilly regions, the number of wild bees pollinating alfalfa has

Table 55. Diurnal course of opening of alfalfa flowers and meteorological indexes

Date	Index	Time of day													
		7:00	8:00	9:00	10:00	11:00	12:00	1:00	2:00	3:00	4:00	5:00	6:00	7:00	8:00
August 29, 1961	Opening of flowers, %	0.4	2.0	2.2	3.7	3.8	7.0	18.2	13.1	9.2	7.1	8.5	3.3	2.2	0.3
	r	76	74	62	58	53	46	40	42	44	43	45	47	48	59
	t	15.8	16.2	18.2	20.0	21.9	22.0	22.8	21.9	21.0	21.0	19.8	18.1	15.3	14.0
	v	2	3	4	3	4	6	7	5	4	3	3	3	2	1
August 30, 1961	Opening of flowers, %	—	—	0.4	2.5	5.9	6.6	12.2	18.3	15.2	9.2	16.4	5.0	4.8	3.5
	r	79	73	69	63	55	49	40	40	38	43	48	49	49	53
	t	9.6	11.9	15.6	18.0	20.0	21.2	22.7	23.1	22.7	22.1	25.1	23.4	21.2	19.1
	v	—	—	1	2	3	5	5	4	4	3	3	2	2	2
July 7, 1962	Opening of flowers, %	0.5	2.7	4.5	10.0	13.3	15.0	15.0	11.4	8.7	6.7	5.8	2.7	1.7	1.2
	r	60	53	48	42	39	36	37	29	24	26	30	34	40	48
	t	15.2	18.1	24.1	26.2	28.3	30.0	32.2	32.1	33.0	30.8	27.4	25.2	16.1	13.6
	v	2	3	4	3	5	6	4	5	2	3	4	1	1	1

Note : r—relative humidity of air (%); t—temperature of air (°C); v—wind velocity (m/sec).

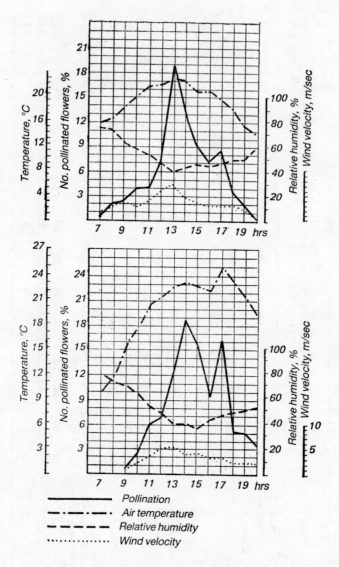

Figure 39. Diurnal course of alfalfa pollination.
Top—August 29; bottom—August 30.

reduced sharply. With the increase in plowed area and elimination of nesting places for bees, their number will further reduce, leading inevitably to a reduction in seed yield.

Several researchers have suggested that the biology of pollinators be

Table 56. Diurnal course of opening of alfalfa flowers in northern Kazakhstan (1961)

Date	No. of racemes	Number of flowers opened, time of day														Day's total
		7:00	8:00	9:00	10:00	11:00	12:00	1:00	2:00	3:00	4:00	5:0	6:00	7:00	8:00	
August 10	100	2	7	10	22	53	66	73	105	62	82	54	33	26	18	613
12	108	6	18	21	39	11	54	96	139	103	63	59	47	22	12	695
13	264	2	11	29	43	63	79	36	108	172	241	154	85	37	22	1,082
14	141	10	16	14	29	41	59	77	101	83	80	92	24	47	13	686
15	113	7	24	39	49	87	91	90	123	73	92	53	75	54	26	883
25	259	—	—	14	27	18	59	115	99	91	147	119	63	85	35	872
26	278	—	9	21	18	35	64	182	201	102	83	54	77	35	13	894
27	362	—	2	42	27	61	78	154	217	153	117	92	101	60	19	1,183
28	274	—	11	25	38	19	35	79	75	132	59	104	72	21	45	715
29	121	3	13	17	29	30	55	143	103	72	56	67	24	16	2	630
30	272	—	3	3	18	42	47	87	130	108	66	117	36	34	25	713
31	350	—	—	25	41	48	85	115	135	170	212	98	15	—	25	944
Absolute %	—	0.3	1.1	2.6	3.8	5.1	7.8	12.6	15.5	13.1	13.7	11.0	6.6	4.4	2.4	100
Total	2,642	30	111	260	380	508	772	1,247	1,536	1,321	1,358	1,063	652	437	235	9,910

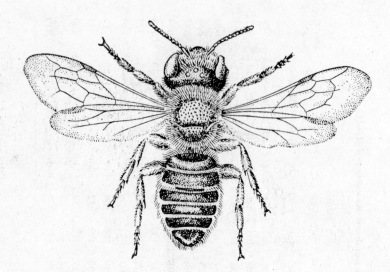

Figure 40. External appearance of *Megachile rotundata,* the solitary leaf-cutting bee of alfalfa.

studied for the purpose of artificial rearing and the creation of favorable conditions for their concentration near alfalfa crops.

American specialists (W.P. Stephen, G.E. Bohart, and G.A. Hobbs) have developed a method for artificial rearing of the solitary leaf-cutting bee of alfalfa (*Megachile rotundata*) (Figure 40). On the basis of their research an entire field of "entomological industry" has been developed in the USA. The pupae of solitary Palearctic bees, brought incidentally to North America in the 1930's from Europe and now fairly widespread, have become a commercial object. These pupae are bought by England, Belgium, France, the Netherlands, Denmark, Hungary, Rumania, Czechoslovakia, and other countries. Using wild bees it is possible to increase seed yields of alfalfa from 1.0 to 2.0 to 20 quintals/ha.

Development of Root Mass

The fact that the root system of alfalfa enriches the soil has long attracted the attention of specialists. It has been established that in two to three years from the sowing of alfalfa the content of nitrogen, phosphorus, potash, calcium, and other macro- and microelements increases in the arable soil layer. The more vigorously developed the root system, the more the enrichment of the soil with organic residues and minerals. Experiments have shown that the concentration of alfalfa root mass depends on the time and methods of sowing, system of land preparation, appli-

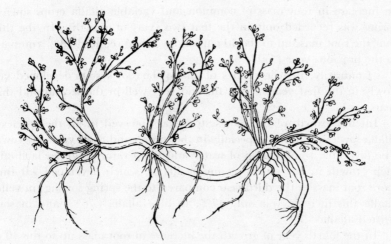

Figure 41. South Kazakhstan alfalfa (*M. difalcata* Sinsk.). Rhizomatous form growing on meadows of hillocks briefly flooded intermittently. Semipalatinsk province, Abaisk region, "Kainarskii" state farm.

cation of fertilizers and so forth. Alfalfa varieties of the meadow-pasture type, with a rhizomatous root system, are quite promising (Figure 41).

Lubenets (1956) of the Kuban Experimental Station of VIR established that species and varieties of alfalfa vary considerably in concentration of root mass and consequently potential for restoration of soil structure and improvement of its fertility.

The nature of development of the root system and concentration of root mass up to the 40 cm soil layer were studied in a special nursery at the Shortandin Substation of VIR. The study comprised 20 varieties and specimens of common, variable, yellow, blue, and semitwisted alfalfas. Every year two monoliths (50 cm × 50 cm × 40 cm) were cut in the plot and divided into layers for analysis: 0 to 10 cm, 10 to 20 cm, 20 to 30 cm, and 30 to 40 cm. The soil monoliths were washed in the river using a sieve with a 1.0 mm mesh. The washed roots were air-dried and weighed. Productivity of root mass was also studied in 34 varietal specimens of alfalfa after five years of growth.

The study of root systems in northern Kazakhstan did not comprise a large assortment of varieties from different species and wild forms. By and large the investigations were limited to one or two of the most promising varieties of alfalfa or grass mixtures with cereal components.

As mentioned earlier the spring nurseries suffered from a poor water supply throughout the period of alfalfa investigations and the plants of common alfalfa sown in spring considerably infected with diseases. Hence an increase in root mass of common and variable alfalfa crops sown in spring was recorded only in the first two years of growth. In the third year the root mass up to the 40 cm soil layer had reduced 28% compared to the previous year (Table 57).

Contrarily, in wild species of alfalfa the root system developed very slowly in the first year of growth, and very well in the second and third years.

Intense growth of the root system was observed in all the species of alfalfa sown in summer, especially in the second and third years of growth. The favorable combination of water and temperature regimes facilitated such growth in varieties of common alfalfa, which developed 2.0 times more root mass in the third year compared to the spring sowing; in yellow alfalfa this increase was only 47%, in blue alfalfa—76%, and in semi-twisted alfalfa—52%.

In the fourth year of growth the increase in root mass up to the 40 cm soil layer in the summer sowing was quite high in semitwisted and blue alfalfas (22 and 27% respectively); in common alfalfa the root mass reduced by 12%, and in yellow alfalfa increased only 4.5%. The increase in roots in the third and fourth years, compared to the second year, under favorable conditions for growth and development was poor (3 to 12%) in the cultivated varieties, but very significant (up to 200%) in the wild forms of alfalfa.

The root mass of the alfalfa species studied was not uniformly distributed in different layers of the soil. In general over 60% of the roots spread up to the 40 cm soil layer were concentrated in the arable layer (0 to 20 cm). With an adequate water supply (summer sowing) the root

Table 57. Mass of air-dried roots (g/m^2) of alfalfa up to the 40 cm soil layer at different times of sowing and years of growth (1961–1964)

Sowing	Alfalfa species	Year of growth				Average mass, percent of control
		First	Second	Third	Fourth	
Spring	Common	260	475	344	—	100
	Yellow	185	460	450	—	131
	Semitwisted	110	280	312	—	91
	Blue	60	110	240	—	70
Summer	Common	320	680	700	620	100
	Yellow	260	530	660	690	111
	Semitwisted	78	375	476	585	94
	Blue	24	225	424	540	87

mass in the upper soil layer (0 to 10 cm) increased by 8 to 15%, and in the tilled horizon by 10 to 20%. The yellow and blue alfalfas, and in the spring sowing semitwisted alfalfa as well, maintained 20 to 30% of their root mass in the layer below the tilled stratum (20 to 40 cm).

In summer sowing 13% of the root mass of blue alfalfa occurred in the upper layer of the soil (0 to 10 cm) and the diameter of the roots was no more than 1.0 mm; in semitwisted alfalfa only 1.0% of the roots were found in this soil layer. In variable and semitwisted alfalfa 24 to 32% of the roots occurred in the 10 to 30 cm soil layer but in yellow and blue alfalfas 11 to 20%, i.e., about 10% less. In the 30 to 40 cm soil layer the mass of finer roots in all alfalfa species was greatly reduced; however, in variable alfalfa finer roots in this layer still comprised 23% of the total root mass.

Among varieties of variable alfalfa the most productive with respect to root mass up to the 40 cm soil layer were Kamalinskaya-530, Omsk-8893, Blue Ural, Shortandinskaya-2, Marusinskaya-425, Kazan-64/95, Slavyanskaya local, and Uzgen local. Among the yellow alfalfas variety Krasnokutskaya-4009 was distinguished.

In the third year of growth maximum development of root mass was seen in varieties of variable alfalfa from western and eastern Siberia. However, if development of the root system based on the average annual index is compared, then first place goes to local varieties—Shortandinskaya-2 and Blue Ural—which develop their root system rapidly, in the first two years of growth. In the Siberian varieties and yellow alfalfa intense root growth occurs only from the second year. In varieties of cultivated species no increase in root mass occurs in the fourth year.

In the fifth year of growth the maximum root mass up to the 40 cm soil layer was found in varieties of variable alfalfa (Marusinskaya-81, Flora, Karaganda-1, Shortandinskaya-2) and yellow alfalfa (Pavlovskaya-7). These varieties also proved the most resistant to root rots, and hence were the most productive in yield of hay and seeds. Improved and local varieties of common alfalfa had disappeared from the collection by this time.

Not all alfalfa varieties characterized by faster accumulation of root mass are high yielding under prolonged use. The varieties Tibet, Slavyanskaya local, and Gulkevichskaya are highly productive in accumulation of root mass in the first two years. However, their susceptibility to root rots resulted in a poor crop stand by the fifth year (Table 58).

Yield of Green Mass and Hay

In northern Kazakhstan under conditions of plentiful moisture the most productive alfalfa varieties in yield of green mass in the year of sowing are

Table 58. Characteristics of some alfalfa varieties in the fifth year of growth (1958-1962)

Species, variety	Yield of green mass per m²		Root mass per m² in 0–40 cm soil layer		Average grade of infection	Infection of roots, %
	r	%	r	%		
Variable alfalfa						
Marusinskaya-81	1,610	127	590	116	1.81	54
Flora	1,440	113	540	106	1.99	46
Novokuban	1,400	110	545	107	2.00	73
Karaganda-1	1,320	104	515	101	2.24	72
Poltava-256	1,275	100	545	107	2.43	44
Shortandinskaya-2	1,270	100	510	100	2.62	78
Priaralskaya	945	74	480	94	2.62	80
Blue Ural	635	50	425	83	2.75	81
Gulkevichskaya	480	38	300	59	3.28	91
Slavyanskaya local	360	28	250	49	3.01	87
Poltava-6800	350	27	210	41	3.43	92
Tibet	210	17	200	39	4.51	100
Yellow alfalfa						
Pavlovskaya-7	1,540	121	575	113	2.21	66
Yellow hybrid	1,115	88	480	94	2.40	72
Yellow Kuban	680	54	280	55	2.64	80

those cultivated in irrigated lands in the southern regions of the Soviet Union as well as other countries. They are very responsive to moisture and effectively utilize summer rains for the formation of the second crop, which often exceeds the first harvest in terms of yield.

After overwintering in the second, third, and fourth years of growth, particularly under unusual drought conditions, first place in terms of yield of green mass is usually occupied by varieties cultivated in the regions of western and eastern Siberia, southeast European part of the USSR, northern Kazakhstan, and a negligible number of specimens from other regions of the Soviet Union, among which the best in the nursery in the 1961 sowing were: Omsk-8893, Sretenskaya-77, Flora, Kuzbasskaya, variegated hybrid, Barnaulskaya-17, Zabaikalka, Kamalinskaya-530, Omsk-2251, Pestraya-57, Valyuskaya local, Leninskaya local, Karaganda-1, Blue Ural, Shortandinskaya-2, Kurskaya-1, Kazan-64/95,

Poltava-256, Marusinskaya-425, Tibet, Stepnaya-600, Krasnokutskaya-4009, Yellow hybrid (K-29119), and Bazulukskaya local.

In the nursery sown in 1965 the following varieties considerably surpassed the control in total yield of green mass during the six-year study: Kurskaya-1 (45.2%), Barnaulskaya-17 (29.2%), Karabalykskaya (27.5%), Kuzbasskaya (26.3%), Nerchinskaya-46 (26.2%), Flora (22.8%), Severnaya hybrid (18.9%), and Rambler from Canada (18.5%). The varieties Karabalykskaya, Kuzbasskaya, Flora, Nerchinskaya-46, Severnaya hybrid, and Chernigovskaya surpassed the control every year in yield of green mass. A good vigorous plant stand was retained in the aforementioned varieties in the sixth year and they surpassed the control in plant height; they were also distinguished by high winter hardiness.

In the collection nursery sown in 1972, 17 specimens were selected for yield of green mass. As in the previous years, these were mostly varietal specimens of Siberian origin—Kamalin-930 (135.5% of the control), Kuzbasskaya (131.6%), Zabaikalka (129.5%), Chernigovskaya (122.6%), and Kazan-64/95 (122.6%).

In the collection nursery sown in 1973 the following varieties exhibited considerable superiority over the control in total yield of green mass for three years: Karabalykskaya (138.6% of the control), Blue Ural (125.8%), Fravois (128.1%), and Cayuga (111.8%) from the USA, Blue hybrid-1316 (120.3%), Kamalinskaya-1341 (120.0%), Semirechensk local (K-6267, K-6257, and K-6323 by 117.4, 114.5, and 113.8% respectively), local variety (K-1738) from Saratov province (111.0%), and Kazan-64/95 (105.0%).

Based on many years of evaluation of the collection of variable alfalfa sown in the nurseries from 1961 to 1965, 1965 to 1970, 1972 to 1975, and 1973 to 1975, ten varieties have been identified which are promising for breeding work and distinguished not only by high yield of green mass, but also by high winter hardiness, intense growth, and resistance to drought, diseases, and pests (Table 59).

Evaluation of the alfalfa collection from the desert zone under severe arid conditions revealed that the following varieties from regions of irrigated farming of the republics of Central Asia, the Caucasus, and countries abroad yielded 34 to 75% less hay than the control variety Tibet released for cultivation in this region: Fergana-700, Tashkent-721, Tashkent-3192, Semirechensk local, Vekhshskaya-233, Iolotanskaya, Frunzenskaya, Azerbaydzhan-262, Mesopotamian, Peruvian, Chilean, and Argentine. The following specimens from the steppe and forest-steppe regions of the Soviet Union surpassed the control by 38 to 61% in hay yield from 1958 to 1960: Kuzbasskaya, Brodskaya-17, Valuyskaya local, Poltava-256, Kinelskaya-1, Krasnokutskaya-4009, Leninskaya local,

Table 59. Varieties of variable alfalfa promising for breeding in northern Kazakhstan identified for yield of green mass (kg/m²) and other characters during a multiyear study under conditions of Tselinograd province (1961-1975)

Variety	Origin (republic, territory, region)	Yield of green mass			Average annual yield of green mass			
		1965–1970	1972–1975	1973–1975	1965–1970	1972–1975	1973–1975	Average for 1965–1975
Shortandinskaya-2 (control)	Tselinograd province	6.92	1.24	2.05	1.15	0.31	0.68	0.71
Karabalykskaya-18	Kustanaisk province	8.82	—	2.83	1.47	—	0.94	1.25
Nerchinskaya-46	Chita province	8.73	1.67	2.44	1.46	0.42	0.81	0.90
Chernigovskaya	Novosibirsk province	8.18	1.48	2.91	1.36	0.37	0.97	0.90
Kuzbasskaya	Kurgansk province	8.74	1.62	2.75	1.46	0.41	0.69	0.86
Onokhoy-6	Buryatia ASSR	8.14	1.58	2.30	1.36	0.40	0.77	0.85
Kurskaya-1	Kursk province	8.18	1.36	2.28	1.37	0.34	0.76	0.82
Variegated hybrid-192	Omsk province	8.20	1.26	2.06	1.37	0.32	0.69	0.79
Kainskaya-4146	Novosibirsk territory	7.60	1.38	2.17	1.27	0.35	0.72	0.78
Kamlin-930	Krasnoyarsk territory	7.65	1.72	1.92	1.28	0.43	0.64	0.78
Kazan-64/95	Tatar ASSR	7.42	1.56	2.14	1.24	0.39	0.71	0.78

Pestraya-57, Kurskaya-1, and Kuibishevskaya. Varieties of northern Kazakhstan were almost equal to control in terms of productivity: Karabalykskaya-18, Shortandinskaya-2, Blue Ural, Karaganda-1, Dolinskaya-2, Blue hybrid-1316, and Zaysanskaya. With regard to other economically important characters (plant height, winter hardiness, foliage, survival rate, protein content), alfalfa varieties of the northern and western regions of Kazakh SSR did not lag behind the most productive specimens from the forest-steppe and steppe regions of our country (Table 60).

Table 60. Agrobiological characteristics of alfalfa in rainfed crop (Aral Experimental Station VIR, 1958-1960)

Variety	Plant height, cm	Foliage, grade	Plant survival in third year of life, %	Average hay yield from 9 m²	
				kg	Percent of control
Varieties cultivated under irrigation					
Fergana-700	58	2.0	2	0.26	25
Peruvian (K-11417)	56	2.1	11	0.31	26
Tashkent-721	48	2.0	45	0.56	49
Chilean (K-5141)	55	2.4	53	0.58	50
Tashkent-3192	53	2.6	64	0.67	58
Argentine (K-7226)	54	2.5	64	0.69	59
Semirechensk local	56	2.6	71	0.87	66
Varieties of northern and western Kazakhstan					
Blue Ural	64	3.3	97	1.45	89
Blue hybrid-1316	66	3.2	93	1.39	94
Karabalykskaya-18	65	3.3	91	1.63	100
Tibet (control)	55	3.3	96	1.23	100
Karaganda-1	64	3.2	92	1.91	113
Shortandinskaya-2	60	3.0	90	1.87	114
Varieties of forest-steppe and steppe regions of the Soviet Union					
Slavyanskaya local	58	3.0	83	2.35	138
Kuibishevskaya	62	3.2	85	2.18	139
Kazan-64/95	67	3.6	93	2.20	145
Valuyskaya local	65	3.3	94	2.25	145
Brodskaya	60	3.3	97	2.22	145
Barnaulskaya	63	3.4	98	2.37	157
Kuzbasskaya	65	3.4	96	2.43	161

In the nursery sown in 1965, after five years of study (1965 to 1969), the following varieties and specimens were identified for yield of green mass: Ladak (K-19883, K-22377, K-23217) from Tibet (123.4%, 110.2%, and 102.0% of the control), ancient local population (K-6348) from Kirgiz SSR (123.1%), Ozarenetskaya local (109.2%), Dolinskaya-2 (107.3%), ancient local populations (K-8940, K-8941) from Kara-Kalpak ASSR (105.8% and 104.9%), Kinelskaya-5 (105.8%), Stepnaya-600 (101.6%), and Trautvetter's (100.8%).

Specimens of variable, blue, and Tian Shan alfalfas were distinguished for yield of green mass in nurseries of wild populations sown in 1971, 1972, and 1973. The lowest yield was obtained from wild populations of South Kazakhstan, yellow, and Trautvetter's alfalfas (Tables 61 and 62).

Under irrigation in the year of sowing as well as after mild winters alfalfa varieties from the regions of irrigated farming of the Soviet Union and foreign countries were the most productive followed by varieties from the steppe and forest-steppe regions of the European part of the USSR. Low yields in the first year of growth were recorded for varieties

Table 61. Yield of green mass (kg/m^2) of alfalfa in different agronomic backgrounds (Aral Experimental Station VIR)

Species	1974	1975	Average	Ratio of irrigated : unirrigated
	Unirrigated ($\bar{x}\pm m$)			
Common	0.49±0.07	0.35±0.04	0.42±0.06	
South Kazakhstan	0.28±0.02	0.20±0.01	0.24±0.02	
Yellow	0.38±0.03	0.30±0.03	0.34±0.02	
Trautvetter's	0.41±0.04	0.37±0.03	0.39±0.03	
Blue	0.61±0.09	0.55±0.09	0.58±0.07	
Variable	0.79±0.10	0.57±0.06	0.68±0.07	
Tian Shan	0.61±0.08	0.42±0.02	0.51±0.05	
	Irrigated ($\bar{x}\pm m$)			
Common	5.72±0.47	5.26±0.41	5.49±0.39	13.0
South Kazakhstan	1.90±0.21	2.45±0.23	2.18±0.18	9.1
Yellow	2.56±0.37	3.17±0.34	2.87±0.27	8.4
Trautvetters	3.14±0.43	3.29±0.29	3.22±0.31	8.3
Blue	4.09±0.23	4.14±0.15	4.12±0.18	7.1
Variable	5.27±0.51	4.63±0.42	4.45±0.42	6.5
Tian Shan	3.48±0.45	2.59±0.24	3.03±0.36	5.9

Table 62. Hay yield (kg/m²) of specimens of wild species of alfalfa from rainfed crops
(Aral Experimental Station VIR)

VIR catalog number	Species, origin (province)	1972	1973	1974	1975	Average for four years	Percent of control
1	2	3	4	5	6	7	8
	Common alfalfa						
K-060249	Chimkent province	0.32	0.87	0.37	0.27	0.46	131
K-060239	Dzhambul province	0.26	0.88	0.31	0.16	0.40	114
K-060238	Dzhambul province	0.11	0.45	0.16	0.07	0.19	54
	Variable alfalfa						
K-063125	Karaganda province	0.33	0.89	0.38	0.24	0.46	131
	Tibet (control)	0.21	0.68	0.25	0.27	0.35	100
K-063098	Taldy-Kurgan province	0.08	0.53	0.13	0.14	0.23	66
	Blue alfalfa						
K-36119	Gur'ev province	0.22	0.44	0.27	0.38	0.33	94
K-36105	Ural'sk province	0.17	0.41	0.22	0.42	0.31	89
K-36121	Ural'sk province	0.10	0.27	0.13	0.23	0.18	52
	Yellow alfalfa						
K-063121	Karaganda province	0.07	0.42	0.08	0.10	0.18	52
K-063114	Alma-Ata province	0.06	0.19	0.07	0.17	0.12	34
K-062101	Aktyubin province	0.04	0.14	0.06	0.15	0.10	29

(Contd.)

Table 62 (*Contd.*)

1	2	3	4	5	6	7	8
	Trautvetter's alfalfa						
K-063122	Karaganda province	0.08	0.36	0.11	0.22	0.19	54
K-060253	Aktyubin province	0.04	0.23	0.06	0.10	0.11	31
K-060251	Aktyubin province	0.01	0.15	0.01	0.06	0.06	17
	Tian Shan alfalfa						
K-060234	Dzhambul province	0.10	0.18	0.12	0.10	0.12	34
	South Kazakhstan alfalfa						
K-063116	Semipalatinsk province	0.07	0.18	0.08	0.14	0.12	34
K-063112	Alma-Ata province	0.05	0.19	0.06	0.07	0.09	26
K-063103	Taldy-Kurgan province	0.01	0.01	0.01	0.08	0.03	9

developed in the research institutions of western and eastern Siberia. Responsiveness to irrigation and postharvest sprouting were slow in varieties of Siberian origin (Table 63).

With age, the plant stand of specimens of southern origin thinned faster. In the nursery sown in 1961 in the third year of growth the hay yield of varieties from regions of irrigated farming were lower by 41 to 79%

Table 63. Hay yield of alfalfa (kg/m²) on irrigated field sown in 1961 (Aral Experimental Station VIR)

Variety, specimen	Agro-ecological group	Hay yield in different years of growth			Average percent of control
		First	Second	Third	
1	2	3	4	5	6
Tibet (control)	Northern Kazakhstan	0.47	2.50	1.25	100
Varieties cultivated in regions of irrigated farming					
Local (Peru, prov. Lima)	Chile-Peruvian	0.69	0.56	0.24	21
Local (prov. Saladina)	Argentinian	0.64	0.70	0.27	24
Local (Chile, prov. Santiago)	Chile-Peruvian	0.61	0.88	0.51	36
Semirechensk local	Semirechian	0.58	1.10	0.53	39
Local (Ecuador)	South American	0.60	1.20	0.60	32
Local (Paraguay)	Chile-Peruvian	0.61	1.23	0.60	57
Local (Argentina, prov. Buenos Aires)	Argentinian	0.75	1.25	0.63	59
Varieties of steppe and forest-steppe regions of the Soviet Union					
Kazan-64/95	Middle Russian blue hybrid	0.50	1.70	0.76	64
Penzenskaya hybrid	Middle Russian blue hybrid	0.67	1.20	0.78	64
Bolshevyaskaya	Middle Russian blue hybrid	0.62	2.80	0.78	67
Chimshinskaya-130	Middle Russian blue hybrid	0.76	1.60	0.79	68
Brodskaya local	Southeastern blue hybrid	0.39	1.75	0.79	68
Baluiskaya local	Southeastern blue hybrid	0.14	1.50	0.80	70

(Contd.)

Table 63 (*Contd.*)

1	2	3	4	5	6
	Varieties of western and eastern Siberia				
Flora	West Siberian blue hybrid	0.12	0.86	0.79	66
Barnaulskaya-17	West Siberian blue hybrid	0.26	1.35	0.97	81
Sretenskaya-77	West Siberian blue hybrid	0.42	1.52	1.15	96
	Varieties of northern and western Kazakhstan				
Irtyshskaya local	Northern Kazakhstan	0.40	1.35	0.72	58
Blue Ural	Northern Kazakhstan	0.24	1.20	0.73	58
Blue hybrid-1316	Northern Kazakhstan	0.37	1.80	0.98	78
Shortandinskaya-2	Northern Kazakhstan	0.41	1.54	1.03	82
Karabalykskaya-18	Northern Kazakhstan	0.62	1.90	1.15	92

compared to varieties of Kazakh SSR. The average hay yield of varieties from the steppe and forest-steppe regions was 80% of that of northern and western Kazakhstan, while specimens of Siberian origin were equal in yield to varieties from Kazakh SSR. In spite of the fact that in the third year of growth the improved alfalfa varieties of northern and western Kazakhstan proved better in productivity, their yield of hay from the first to the third year reduced by 42.8%; for varieties of western and eastern Siberia this reduction was only 28%. Specimens of Siberian origin, with a much higher plant survival rate possessed a certain "reserve of strength" for high yields in subsequent generations. After severe winters the highest yields of green mass and hay were obtained from the most winter-hardy varieties, irrespective of moisture conditions and age of crop.

A study of the initial material of foreign origin revealed that on irrigated lands in western Kazakhstan the most promising varieties and specimens of alfalfa for breeding are: from Peru (K-11416, K-12194, and K-21287), Ecuador (K-7219), Syria (K-4764), Sudan (K-7302 and 7305), Kenya (K-33677), South African Republic (P-58/327), India (K-6940, K-21366, K-21367, K-21369, and K-21370), Egypt (K-5909, K-7300, and K-7301), Algeria (K-36911), Iraq (Mesopotamia), Pakistan (K-33685), Chile (Liguen), France (Boreal), Yugoslavia (Baska Zms-1), Hungary (Acsai), and the USA (Progress, Saranac, Cayuga). In certain years these varieties were highly productive: Sweden (Alfa, Tuna),

France (Luciole, Prima, Hybride de Millefeuille, Etoile du Nord), Mexico (Tanverde), Italy (S. Luce, Leonicena), the Federal Republic of Germany (Wehrdaer Hildebrand, Rimpaus Mittel), Czechoslovakia (Polava), and Poland (Mehowska). However, by the third year all these varieties of foreign origin lagged behind the improved and local varieties of the Soviet Union in yield of green mass.

In the collection nursery sown in 1972, based on a three-year study (1972 to 1974) and the absence of severe winters, the following varieties and specimens were identified as most promising in productivity, foliage, plant height, and sprouting vigor: Uzgen local (yield of green mass 126% of the control), local (K-7305) from Sudan (126%), Krasnovodopadskaya-8 (125%), local specimens (K-21367, K-6940, K-21369) from India (123, 114, and 107% respectively), Vakhshskaya-233 (122%), Tokmak (122%), local (K-7275) from Turkmenian SSR (119%), local (K-36111) from Tadzhik SSR (117%), P-58/327 from the South African Republic (116%), Slavyanskaya (113%), local specimens (K-5909, K-7300) from Egypt (112 and 105%), Tashkent-3192 (111%), Cayuga from the USA (111%), Semirechensk (110%), local (K-4764) from Syria (110%), and Bogarnaya-2628 (105%). All constitute invaluable initial material for developing varieties for intensive agriculture.

Evaluation of wild populations of alfalfa under irrigated and rainfed conditions revealed that specimens of common alfalfa are the most responsive to irrigation. Their yield of green mass on unirrigated fields was 8.0% that on irrigated fields (0.42 ± 0.06 and 5.49 ± 0.39 kg/m^2). A high responsiveness to irrigation was also characteristic of wild populations of South Kazakhstan alfalfa (0.24 ± 0.02 and 2.18 ± 0.18), yellow alfalfa (0.34 ± 0.02 and 2.87 ± 0.27), and Trautvetter's alfalfa (0.39 ± 0.03 and 3.22 ± 0.31). Yield of green mass increased in these species respectively 9.1, 8.4, and 8.3 times under irrigation versus nonirrigation. Populations of blue alfalfa are less responsive to irrigation (0.58 ± 0.07 and 4.12 ± 0.18) with an increase in yield under irrigation of 7.1 times; variable alfalfa (0.68 ± 0.07 and 4.45 ± 0.42)—6.5 times; and Tian Shan alfalfa (0.51 ± 0.05 and 3.03 ± 0.36)—5.9 times.

Seed Yield

In the steppe zone evaluation of the collection from 1961 to 1965 for seed yield identified these varieties as most productive: Marusinskaya-81, Kemlyanskaya-1, Saranskaya local, Kazan-64/95, Iygeva-2, Kuzbasskaya, Milyutinskaya-1774, Poltava-256, local from China (K-32863), variety Narragansett from the USA, and Mesopotamian (K-7221) from Iraq. Alfalfa varieties of northern and western Kazakhstan were average in yield of seed. Improved varieties of yellow alfalfa and wild populations

Figure 42. External appearance of early-maturing specimen of common alfalfa
(K-132860) from China.

of varicolored, blue, glutinous, and semitwisted alfalfas produced a seed
yield 36.2 to 62.8% below the improved varieties of common and variable
alfalfas (Figure 42).

In nurseries sown in 1965, 1972, and 1973 the most productive in
terms of seed yield were these varieties and specimens: Semirechensk
local—217% of the control, Krasnokutsk-3125 (194%), blue alfalfa from
Gur'ev province (K-36118) (191%), Karabalykskaya-18 (146%), Krasno-
kutskaya-3990 (143%), Blue hybrid-1316 (136%), Brodskaya (131%),
blue alfalfa from Gur'ev province (K-36053) (131%), Ferax from Canada
(127%), Kainskaya-4146 (110%), Amur-33 (107%), and Kamalinskaya-
1341 (102%).

Under severe unirrigated conditions in western Kazakhstan in the nursery sown in 1965 the maximum yield of seed from 1965 to 1969 was given
by ancient populations of alfalfa from Kirgiz SSR (K-6348) (209% of the
control), Kara-Kalpak ASSR (K-8932) (195%), Uzbek SSR (K-8930,

K-8962, K-7251) (181%, 168%, and 165% respectively), Chuvash ASSR (K-32792) (175%), Kirov province (K-32097, K-32096) (168 and 167% respectively), Armenian SSR (K-5092) (146%), Turkmenian SSR (K-6455) (139%), as well as individual specimens from Italy (K-5677) (156%), Turkey (K-6001) (153%), Czechoslovakia (Brnenskaya) (147%), India (K-23209) (128%), and the USA (Grimm) (112%). Among the improved and released local varieties the following were distinguished for seed yield: Semirechensk local (K-26704 and K-6257) (193 and 170%), Uzgen local (163%), Samarkand local (163%), Slavyanskaya local (156%) Manichskaya local (156%), Azerbaydzhan-2/30 (151%), Krasnokutsk-3125 (147%), East Kazakhstan-5057 (144%), Lyulinetskaya (135%), and Kamalinskaya-530 (125%). Thus, unlike northern Kazakhstan in rainfed crops of the desert zone, the most productive in seed yield, well adapted to local hot climate, plastic, and moderately tolerant to soil drought and low temperatures are the ancient alfalfa varieties developed by the people and wild populations from the southern regions of Kazakhstan, and the republics of Central Asia adjacent to Aral, as well as the more tolerant varieties and specimens of Siberia, Altai, and other regions of the country.

Among wild species populations of blue alfalfa were distinguished by high seed yield (82 to 126% of the control). Wild specimens of Tian Shan alfalfa gave a seed yield at par with the control (95%). Wild specimens of variable (16 to 51%), yellow (4 to 43%), common (27 to 38%), Trautvetter's (6 to 32%), and South Kazakhstan alfalfa (4 to 16%) gave a seed yield lower than the control on unirrigated lands in the Aral Experimental Station of VIR.

Under irrigation the maximum seed yield in western Kazakhstan was obtained from improved varieties of variable alfalfa of the Ukrainian blue hybrid group of varietal types (33.1 ± 2.81 g/m^2); next came the improved varieties of common alfalfa of the Central Asian (28.2 ± 1.99) and Trans-Caucasian groups of varietal types (23.7 ± 2.08) and variable alfalfa of the eastern European countries (27.4 ± 2.52). High seed yields under irrigation were also produced by improved varieties of variable alfalfa of West European countries (21.9 ± 1.58) and common alfalfa from France (21.3 ± 1.02).

Low yields of alfalfa seeds on irrigated lands in western Kazakhstan were produced by improved varieties from the USA (18.5 ± 0.89), local varieties of the Latin American countries (17.4 ± 2.08), and specimens of common alfalfa of the Indian (16.5 ± 1.26) and Mediterranean (14.2 ± 1.68) groups of varietal types. Ancient populations of common alfalfa of the Anatolian group of varietal types produce almost no seeds on the irrigated lands of western Kazakhstan (5.92 ± 0.48).

In the nurseries sown in 1966, 1968, 1972, and 1973 the following alfalfa varieties and specimens were identified for seed yield: Krimskaya local (241% of the control), Azerbaydzhanskaya-5 (235%), Mesopotamian-1680 (216%), local from Tadzhik SSR (K-8862) (216%), Polava from Czechoslovakia (208%), Slavyanskaya local (202%), Miechowska from Poland (200%), Tokmak local (184%), Tashkent-1 (183%), Vakhshskaya-233 (166%), Alfa from Sweden (164%), local from the Federal Republic of Germany (K-36903) (162%), Milyutinskaya-1774 (162%), local varieties of India (K-6940, Puna) (159% and 132%), Khersonskaya-7 (157%); improved varieties of France: Warote (157%), Boreal (156%), F-34 (139%), Hybride de Millefeuille (123%); Semirechensk local (153%), Uzgen local (152%), Peruvian (135%), and Acsai from Hungary (132%).

The average yield of the widely cultivated alfalfa variety Tibet during this same period was 18.5 g/m^2 or 1.85 q/ha. The maximum seed yield from seed fields under irrigated conditions in western Kazakhstan was 5.6 to 6.0 q/ha. Under rainfed conditions, especially in favorable years, the maximum seed yield from commercial crops did not exceed 0.5 to 0.8 q/ha.

Variability of Important Characters

Success in breeding of alfalfa, as in any other crop, greatly depends on in-depth study of the laws of variability and heritability of economically important characters and properties of plants. Scientists are inclined to think that the magnitude of phenotypic variability of important characters of alfalfa involved in the formation of hay and seed yield, is determined by the genotypic nature of the variety and the conditions of its cultivation. Norms for reaction and magnitude of variability of characters make it possible to judge the efficacy of a given selection, its propriety, and continuity, and to influence the breeding process accordingly.

In our experiments phenotypic variability was determined on the basis of the following characters: plant height, diameter of stem at level of seventh to eighth internode, number of shoots in bush, foliage, degree of fungal infection, postharvest sprouting vigor, period from spring sprouting to commencement of flowering, period from postharvest sprouting to commencement of flowering, number of cuttings during vegetative period, number of internodes, length and width of leaflet, shape and color of leaflet, shape of rosette of spring sprouting and shape of bush, fresh and dry weight of plants (in grams), number of racemes, flowers, buds, and seeds per plant, seed set of pods, weight of seeds per plant, number of seeds per pod, weight of 1,000 seeds, number of flowers, pods, and seeds in one raceme, winter hardiness of plants, content of crude protein, fat, cellulose, NES, ash and other elements in the leaf-stem mass, yield of green mass, and yield of hay and seeds.

Morphological characters were considered for each cutting for a number of years in a large assortment of varieties and wild populations in nurseries sown in rows and in individual plants (Figure 43). Very comprehensive research was undertaken in the irrigated crop rotation of the Aral Experimental Station of VIR with variety Tibet and wild species from the Central Asian gene center (Table 64). Data on the variability of chemical composition of plants, plant height, foliage, vegetative period, winter hardiness, drought resistance, resistance to diseases and pests, and other characters has already been presented in corresponding sections of this monograph while characterizing the initial material. Hence here, using variety Tibet as an example, only a brief summary is given of the results of some investigations of the variability of important characters of alfalfa in

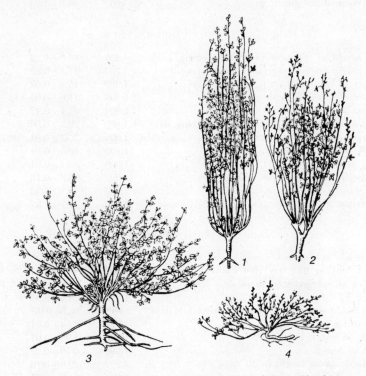

Figure 43. Shape of bush of alfalfa species used for cultivation.

1—*M. sativa* L. (specimen from Mesopotamia); 2—*M. varia* Mart. (Marusinskaya-81); 3—*M. falcata* L. (Pavlovskaya-7); 4—*M. borealis* Grossh. (Saarema Kollane).

Table 64. Variability of characters of alfalfa variety Tibet in different cuttings (1967–1968)

Index	No. of plants analyzed	$\bar{x} \pm m$	V
First cutting			
Plant height at commencement of flowering, cm	5,182	75.9±0.26	19.3
Number of internodes on main stem	5,182	18.0±0.03	6.3
Number of shoots in bush	5,182	13.3±0.04	17.5
Foliage, %	1,989	47.0±0.37	14.2
Period from spring sprouting to flowering, days	2,000	52.8±0.05	4.6
Diameter of main stem, mm	2,000	3.59±0.01	17.0
Length of leaflet, cm	2,000	2.99±0.01	12.5
Width of leaflet, cm	2,000	1.46±0.01	25.4
Fresh weight of one plant, g	5,032	159.7±4.69	42.6
Dry weight of one plant, g	5,032	46.8±1.24	32.9
Second cutting			
Plant height at commencement of flowering, cm	5,182	68.9±0.22	16.5
Plant height on 20th day after cutting, cm	5,182	47.4±0.22	23.4
Number of internodes on main stem	1,999	15.3±0.03	8.3
Number of shoots in bush	1,999	11.6±0.05	20.0
Foliage, %	1,999	47.4±0.42	16.7
Period from postharvest sprouting to flowering, days	1,999	28.5±0.06	8.9
Diameter of main stem, mm	1,999	2.72±0.01	19.5
Length of leaflet, cm	1,999	2.85±0.01	16.2
Width of leaflet, cm	1,999	1.17±0.01	31.6
Increase in plant height in 20 days, cm	1,999	33.8±0.18	24.0
Fresh weight of one plant, g	2,153	144.5±5.32	44.1
Dry weight of one plant, g	2,153	40.7±0.87	29.2
Third cutting			
Plant height at commencement of flowering, cm	1,992	51.9±0.28	24.2
Plant height on 20th day after cutting, cm	1,992	30.2±0.21	30.6
Number of internodes on main stem	1,992	14.0±0.05	14.9
Foliage, %	1,992	55.5±0.96	17.9
Period from postharvest sprouting to flowering, days	1,992	19.7±0.07	16.9
Diameter of main stem, mm	1,992	2.64±0.01	14.8
Length of leaflet, cm	1,992	1.98±0.01	21.7
Width of leaflet, cm	1,992	0.79±0.01	29.1
Increase in plant height in 20 days, cm	1,992	29.0±0.16	31.0
Fresh weight of one plant, g	1,901	115.9±6.71	47.8
Dry weight of one plant, g	1,901	32.3±1.69	44.1

different cuttings and between structural groups (morphobiological types) within a single population. In this summary maximum attention has been given to the variability of characters of wild species.

A comparison of coefficients of variation revealed that in alfalfa the least variable characters are: duration of formation of first and subsequent cuttings, length and width of pod, number of internodes on main stem, weight of 1,000 seeds, length of leaflet, foliage, diameter of stem, plant height, and number of shoots in bush. The most variable are: number of racemes, pods, and seeds in one plant or an area of 1.0 m^2, fresh weight of seeds from one plant, dry weight of one plant, sprouting vigor, plant height on 20th day after cutting, and width of leaflet. Under favorable weather conditions in the nursery, on the whole the variability of characters in the first cutting was less than in the last cutting. This was particularly true of the fresh weight of plants (in grams), height, number of internodes, and length of leaflet.

Variability of morphobiological types of alfalfa variety Tibet, identified on the basis of the form of rosette in spring sprouting and form of bush, is presented in Table 65. Characters of the morphobiological types are briefly summarized below:

Type I: rosette not well developed, small, loose; bush tall, erect, compact; stems soft, with profuse foliage; flowering early, uniform.

Type II: rosette small or medium, loose; bush erect, not compact; stems soft, not pigmented, with good foliage; racemes mainly located in upper fourth of bush; flowering early, uniform, spring as well as postharvest sprouting vigorous.

Type III: rosette large, well developed; bush vigorous, semiprostrate; stems woody at base, pigmented, sometimes pubescent, with scant foliage; foliage profuse in upper half of bush; racemes mainly located in upper third of bush; flowering protracted; productivity of plants high.

Type IV: rosette large, with profuse foliage; bush vigorous, prostrate; yield of green mass and hay high; spring sprouting slow, postharvest sprouting vigorous.

Type V: rosette very large, compact, with large number of reduced shoots and dark green leaflets; bush semi-erect; stems pigmented; sprouting slow.

Type VI: rosette very large, compactly pressed; bush creeping; flowering protracted; postharvest sprouting slow.

Table 65 reveals high polymorphism of characters and high variability of coefficients of variation in morphobiological types of alfalfa within one cutting as well as in different cuttings within one vegetative period. For example, in the third cutting a wide range of variability was observed in the foliage of plants—from 8.0% (type V) to 48% (type IV), and number

Table 65. Variability of morphobiological characters of structural groups

Index	Structural groups according			
	I		II	
	$\bar{x}\pm m$	V	$\bar{x}\pm m$	V
First				
Plant height, cm	95.6±0.24	10.3	94.7±0.37	12.0
Number of internodes on main stem	16.4±0.07	5.6	16.4±0.03	5.6
Foliage, %	40.8±0.67	20.3	42.8±0.29	19.6
Period from spring sprouting to cutting, days	54.0±0.18	4.6	54.0±0.08	4.5
Diameter of main stem, mm	3.69±0.04	16.7	3.59±0.02	17.0
Length of leaflet, cm	3.14±0.04	14.7	3.07±0.02	14.7
Width of leaflet, cm	1.57±0.33	28.6	1.48±0.01	25.0
Fresh weight of plants, kg	0.99±0.03	34.6	0.97±0.01	35.0
Second				
Plant height, cm	75.2±0.88	15.5	74.9±0.38	15.5
Plant height on 20th day after cutting, cm	39.7±0.76	25.5	42.8±0.38	23.6
Increase in plant height in 20 days, cm	34.2±0.57	22.0	34.1±0.25	22.4
Number of internodes on main stem	14.8±0.07	6.7	14.9±0.04	8.7
Foliage, %	36.1±2.20	20.3	38.6±0.98	17.5
Period from postharvest sprouting to commencement of flowering, days	28.0±0.18	8.5	28.2±0.08	8.1
Number of shoots in bush	91.2±3.06	44.7	79.8±1.01	38.4
Diameter of main stem, mm	2.48±0.04	21.0	2.71±0.02	18.8
Length of leaflet, cm	2.91±0.03	14.4	2.87±0.02	16.2
Width of leaflet, cm	1.15±0.02	28.7	1.16±0.01	31.0
Fresh weight of plants, kg	0.52±0.01	34.0	0.47±0.01	42.6
Third				
Plant height, cm	52.6±0.95	24.0	51.6±0.40	24.1
Plant height on 20th day after cutting, cm	32.0±0.72	29.0	31.6±0.29	28.0
Increase in plant height in 20 days, cm	22.4±0.52	30.8	22.0±0.22	29.8
Number of internodes on main stem	14.5±0.15	14.0	14.2±0.66	12.8
Foliage, %	39.0±1.82	19.6	54.1±1.42	16.8
Period from postharvest sprouting to commencement of flowering, days	19.5±0.24	16.5	19.7±0.10	15.1
Number of shoots in bush	50.7±1.37	35.8	57.8±0.63	33.4
Diameter of main stem, mm	2.66±0.03	15.8	2.63±0.02	16.7
Length of leaflet, cm	2.02±0.03	19.3	1.99±0.01	21.6
Width of leaflet, cm	0.79±0.02	32.9	0.79±0.01	29.2
Fresh weight of plants, kg	0.18±0.01	44.3	0.18±0.01	55.6

*Late-maturing types (V and VI) with an early and favorable spring in 1968 began alfalfa were cut simultaneously. Hence, their early maturation is "imaginary".

of alfalfa variety Tibet in nurseries in the second year of growth (sown 1967)

to shape of bush (type)

III		IV		V		VI	
$\bar{x}\pm m$	V	$\bar{x}\pm m$	V	$\bar{x}\pm m$	V	$\bar{x}\pm m$	V
cutting							
92.6±0.47	13.6	92.8±1.74	13.3	91.2±1.06	12.6	83.4±3.43	13.0
16.4±0.03	5.6	16.5±0.15	6.5	16.7±0.08	4.8	16.0±0.02	13.5
43.1±0.32	19.9	39.6±1.54	25.2	42.7±0.96	23.6	46.2±6.34	30.8
52.6±0.08	4.2	52.3±0.40	5.3	51.4±0.23*	4.6	51.0±0.87	4.0
3.55±0.02	16.6	3.52±0.09	17.6	3.42±0.05	17.0	2.80±0.07	7.0
2.97±0.02	13.8	2.85±0.06	16.2	2.89±0.04	16.6	2.60±0.22	21.2
1.44±0.01	25.0	1.34±0.04	23.1	1.33±0.04	27.8	0.70±0.09	29.6
1.02±0.02	44.1	0.82±0.06	50.0	0.90±0.04	42.3	—	—
cutting							
72.8±0.51	17.6	70.4±1.91	19.2	71.0±1.07	15.6	66.4±3.41	12.6
43.6±0.43	27.0	39.0±1.57	28.5	40.4±0.92	22.7	29.2±3.83	32.4
33.6±0.31	25.3	32.4±1.07	23.4	28.6±0.74	27.1	21.6±5.48	18.9
15.7±0.04	6.9	15.7±0.17	7.7	16.1±0.11	7.0	14.0±0.49	7.9
38.8±0.93	13.3	—	—	—	—	—	—
28.8±0.09	8.9	29.2±0.40	9.7	29.7±0.25	8.9	27.0±1.86	16.9
66.3±1.34	60.6	73.0±6.79	65.7	64.0±3.02	49.0	45.6±6.02	29.6
2.18±0.02	26.6	2.66±0.08	19.9	2.62±0.05	17.7	2.05±0.03	24.2
2.76±0.02	16.3	2.82±0.07	17.7	2.72±0.05	18.7	2.30±0.14	20.1
1.15±0.01	26.0	1.17±0.05	30.8	1.10±0.03	28.2	0.70±0.04	15.1
0.48±0.01	42.5	0.51±0.03	47.1	0.45±0.02	49.0	—	—
cutting							
50.3±0.46	24.2	46.4±1.70	25.9	45.8±1.15	25.1	45.0±4.75	23.7
27.2±0.33	32.9	23.4±1.16	35.1	20.6±0.81	35.6	18.4±1.87	31.3
20.1±0.27	29.9	19.8±1.27	39.2	16.0±0.78	31.2	14.6±5.48	38.9
14.0±0.07	13.8	13.3±0.31	16.4	12.7±0.24	19.9	14.0±0.49	7.9
42.8±1.18	27.7	53.4±3.60	48.0	56.1±2.02	8.0	—	—
19.9±0.13	17.6	19.2±0.60	22.0	19.7±0.37	19.7	18.5±1.74	23.0
56.2±0.81	39.4	49.9±3.09	43.8	46.9±1.76	39.0	43.0±1.90	9.9
2.59±0.02	16.6	2.58±0.06	15.7	2.45±0.04	18.8	2.30±0.07	7.0
1.98±0.02	21.8	1.82±0.06	23.8	2.01±0.04	21.9	1.50±0.09	13.3
0.79±0.01	32.9	0.73±0.03	27.4	0.76±0.02	29.0	0.70±0.09	28.6
0.18±0.01	54.0	0.17±0.01	41.2	0.17±0.01	53.0	—	—

to sprout three to four days later than the early types (I and II), but all the types of of shoots in bush—from 9.9 to 29.6% (type VI) to 43.8 to 65.7% (type IV). The magnitude of variability of characters determining the genetic affinity of populations is more stable irrespective of cutting; in a cultivated variety such characters are: period from spring sprouting to commencement of flowering, diameter of stem, length of leaflet, weight of 1,000 seeds, number of seeds in pod, number of internodes, postharvest sprouting vigor, plant height, and length and width of pod.

Characters distinguished by high variability depend greatly on weather conditions (e.g., quantity of green mass, mass of hay, weight of seeds, number of racemes, pods, and seeds on one plant, and so forth). Changes in climatic factors (especially day length temperature, and water regime, degree of insolation) cause reciprocal reactions in plants of all morpho-biological types and lead to a change in characters. Coefficients of variation under conditions nonspecific for the crop (for example, the last cutting) increase. However, the degree of adaptation of characters to new growth conditions differs from one variety and morphobiological type of alfalfa to another. This permits a differential approach to the selection of initial material, taking into consideration soil and climatic conditions of the region of cultivation of the future variety and its genotype.

Calculations of correlation variability of characters within the variety Tibet revealed that in all the morphobiological types distinct correlations are few.

In the erect (type I), early maturing biotypes plant height is directly correlated with fresh weight of plants (0.61 to 0.77) and inversely with foliage (-0.57 to -0.65); in the prostrate forms (types III and IV) close correlations were observed between fresh weight of plants and tillering in the first cutting (0.51 to 0.82), degree of plant disease and tillering (0.55 to 0.75), fresh weight of plants and diameter of stem (0.68 to 0.89), length of leaflet and foliage (0.40 to 0.85) in the first and second cutting; and in creeping biotypes (types V and VI)—between degree of plant disease and diameter of stem (0.31 to 0.69). Positive correlations exist between yield of green mass and plant height. The average value of coefficient of correlation between these characters for all types was 0.50 in the first cutting and 0.66 in the second. The coefficients of correlation in the first cutting were 0.36 to 0.61, and in the second—0.56 to 0.77.

In the morphobiological types of alfalfa comprising the population Tibet direct correlations were observed between yield of green mass and sprouting vigor ($r = 0.28$ to 0.49), number of shoots in bush ($r = 0.22$ to 0.52), length ($r = 0.14$ to 0.34) and width of leaflet ($r = 0.12$ to 0.24), diameter of stem ($r = 0.18$ to 0.89), and between tillering and degree of plant disease ($r = 0.11$ to 0.75), tillering and foliage ($r = 0.46$ to 0.35)

Table 66. Coefficients of correlation (r) between total yield of green mass and other economically important characters of wild species of alfalfa (1973)

Character	Cutting	Species						
		Common	Variable	Yellow	Blue	Trautvetter's	Tian Shan	South Kazakhstan
Days from sprouting to flowering	1st	0.02	0.18	0.23	0.18	0.18	0.08	0.10
	2nd	-0.12	-0.12	0.52	0.22	0.12	-0.78	0.34
	3rd	0.38	0.23	0.40	0.14	0.29	0.47	0.01
Plant height, cm	1st	0.45	0.41	0.66	0.10	0.41	0.18	0.36
	2nd	0.51	0.47	0.72	0.39	0.47	0.82	0.43
	3rd	0.34	0.29	0.40	0.38	0.29	0.91	0.08
	4th	0.55	0.45	0.27	0.18	0.45	0.68	0.28
Foliage, %	1st	0.93	0.91	0.90	0.84	0.91	0.93	0.84
Yield of green mass, g/m²	1st	0.87	0.80	0.87	0.70	0.80	0.85	0.83
	2nd	0.81	0.91	0.92	0.78	0.91	0.95	0.85
	3rd	0.80	0.85	0.68	0.53	0.85	0.80	0.50
	4th	0.58	0.34	0.66	0.07	0.34	-0.74	0.35
Yield of hay from four cuttings, g/m²		0.85	0.80	0.88	0.53	0.80	0.78	0.91

[*sic*], length of leaflet and foliage (r=0.15 to 0.85), and width of leaflet and foliage (r=0.13 to 0.61).

Negative correlations change considerably from type to type and cutting to cutting and were found between degree of plant disease and fresh weight of plants (r= −0.02 to 0.59), plant height (r= −0.07 to 0.75), foliage (r= −0.01 to 0.44), postharvest sprouting vigor (r= −0.10 to 0.71), number of internodes (r= −0.13 to 0.92), and diameter of stem (r= −0.02 to 0.49); and between foliage and fresh weight of plants (r= −0.06 to 0.68), plant height (r= −0.08 to 0.77), and diameter of stem (r= −0.06 to 0.50).

Correlations between the structural groups of one population were not always evident in much larger taxonomic units. In our case this pertained to foliage. If in the morphobiological types of alfalfa variety Tibet and the entire population per se there was a negative correlation between foliage and plant height, then at the level of species this correlation disappeared. Moreover, the value of the coefficient of correlation between these characters depended greatly on cultural practices. For example, in the case of irregular irrigation in wide-row crops for which a negative correlation was established between foliage and fresh weight of plants, a weak positive correlation of these characters was obtained for wild populations of variable and Tian Shan alfalfas (r=0.04 to 0.29).

Under conditions of optimal water supply all wild populations of perennial alfalfa species were characterized by a high positive correlation between foliage and fresh weight of plants (r=0.84 to 0.93). This fact indicates that in the course of breeding and subsequent use of released varieties, through appropriate treatment of the breeding material and implementation of high agronomic practices in growing commercial crops, correlations between foliage and fresh weight of plants can be increased and thus the quality of green, dry, and ground feeds prepared from alfalfa likewise enhanced.

Correlations calculated between vegetative period, plant height, foliage, and yield of green mass and hay of different alfalfa species grown in Kazkh SSR and the republics of Central Asia revealed that for all species there is a definite close dependence between general productivity of plants and height at commencement of flowering (r=0.42 ± 0.15 to 0.76 ± 0.07), and yield of green mass and hay (r=0.89 ± 0.04 to 0.98 ± 0.06).

Taking into consideration the biological peculiarities of the crop it is easy to explain other more or less close correlations indicating the interrelationship of characters in different cuttings and at different stages of ontogenetic development of plants. For example, plant height in the first cutting correlates well with that in the second cutting (r=0.41 ± 0.17 to 0.69 ± 0.10), yield of green mass in the first cutting (r=0.45 ± 0.16 to 0.74 ± 0.08), yield of green mass from two cuttings (r=0.51 ± 0.15 to 0.76 ±

0.07). It is easy to explain this fact as well: Early-maturing, vigorous sprouting populations attaining maximum plant height in the first cutting, retain high rates of growth in subsequent cuttings. The same can be said for the interaction between cuttingwise productivity of populations and total yield of green mass ($r = 0.78 \pm 0.07$ to 0.98 ± 0.01) and hay ($r = 0.85 \pm 0.05$ to 0.98 ± 0.07) obtained during the vegetative period.

The interactions between important characters contributing to yield and their effect on each other during development of first and subsequent cuttings in one vegetative period are shown in Table 66. All these alfalfa species are characterized by indistinct, weak, negative correlations between the period of formation of cuttings and hay yield, i.e., in the case of multicuttings the yield of hay, although insignificant, is determined by early maturation of the species, and postharvest sprouting vigor. A negative correlation was also found between duration of development of every cutting and plant height in the first cutting. Positive correlations were obtained for such characters as duration of development of the first and third cuttings ($r = 0.70$ to 0.90), plant height in third and fourth cuttings ($r = 0.65$ to 0.88), plant height in first three cuttings and yield of green mass in these cuttings ($r = 0.50$ to 0.75; 0.58 to 0.66; 0.50 to 0.73). In wild alfalfa species (*M. difalcata* Sinsk.) of the arid belt, which are highly xerophilous, all these correlations were weak.

In tetraploid wild populations of common, variable, and Tian Shan alfalfas, which are most productive under irrigated conditions and distinguished by vigorous postharvest growth, negative correlations occurred between the duration of formation of the second cutting and all other characters except duration from second cutting to commencement of flowering in the third cutting. The second cutting forms very quickly—within 18 to 25 days. The longer the duration of its development in early-maturing, vigorous-sprouting tetraploid populations, the less the yield, foliage, and plant height at the time of harvesting (Table 67).

In the drought-resistant diploid wild populations of Trautvetter's and South Kazakhstan alfalfas growing in the low-lying desert belt, as well as in wild populations of yellow alfalfa characterized by moderate rates of growth, negative correlations were not obtained between the period of formation of the second cutting, plant height, and yield of green mass. In the floodplain ecotypes of blue alfalfa correlations between these characters and responsiveness to irrigation were not distinct.

Under conditions of regular irrigation positive correlations of different levels were observed in all the species of alfalfa between total productivity of plants and duration of development of the first, third, and fourth cuttings, plant height in all cuttings, foliage, and yield of green mass in the first three cuttings (the last cutting is not always complete). Hay yield

Table 67. Variability of coefficients of correlation (r)
alfalfa on irrigated lands (Aral

Character	Cutting	Commencement of sprouting to commencement of flowering in different cuttings		Plant height at each		
		2nd	3rd	1st	2nd	3rd
Period from commencement	1st	0.18	0.04	−0.82	0.05	0.05
of sprouting to commence-	2nd	—	0.21	−0.01	−0.62	−0.63
ment of flowering	3rd		—	−0.01	0.58	0.31
Plant height	1st			—	0.01	0.16
	2nd				—	0.87
	3rd					—
	4th					
Foliage	1st					
Yield of green mass	1st					
	2nd					
	3rd					
	4th					
	Total					

coefficients of correlation between duration of development of cuttings and productivity were weak (r = 0.15 to 0.25), between plant height in different cuttings and productivity, medium (r = 0.40 to 0.60), and between foliage yield of green mass, yield of hay, and total productivity of plants, high (r = 0.80 to 0.90).

Use of the World Collection of Alfalfa in Breeding

Plant resources in the collection of the VIR are the pride of our country, its national wealth. They are beneficially used in breeding work and in solving many theoretical problems of crop husbandry. At present it is almost impossible to develop a good intensive variety for such important agricultural crops as wheat, cotton, corn, rice, alfalfa, potato, sugar beet, clover, soyabean, and sorghum. This has been repeatedly pointed out by eminent scientists of the Soviet Union and other countries. The demand for plant resources of fodder crops is ever increasing. During the eighth Five-Year Plan the Department of Fodder Crops of VIR sent 7,100 to 8,200 specimens every year to plant-breeding institutions at their request;

per cutting in wild populations of Tian Shan
Experimental Station VIR, 1973)

cutting	Foliage in first cutting	Yield of green mass per cutting					Hay yield of four cuttings
4th		1st	2nd	3rd	4th	Total	
1.17	0.13	−0.53	0.14	0.35	0.03	0.08	−0.62
−0.46	−0.66	−0.69	−0.72	−0.78	−0.55	−0.78	−0.68
0.35	0.47	−0.30	0.52	0.30	−0.42	0.47	−0.30
0.24	0.04	0.56	0.02	0.25	−0.48	0.18	0.57
0.76	0.81	0.56	0.81	0.77	−0.76	0.82	0.56
0.78	0.89	0.74	0.83	0.76	−0.83	0.91	0.66
—	0.65	0.39	0.71	0.69	−0.75	0.68	0.43
	—	0.68	0.90	0.62	−0.79	0.93	0.53
		—	0.70	0.74	−0.59	0.85	0.95
			—	0.69	−0.63	0.95	0.65
				—	−0.62	0.80	0.82
					—	−0.74	−0.47
						—	0.78

thereafter, in 1971—11,559 specimens; 1972—9,874; 1973—11,446; 1974—11,706; 1975—13,231; 1976—17,263; and 1977—13,252. The volume of initial material of fodder crops despatched by the VIR has thus increased 2.0 to 2.5 times.

In the past ten years 98 varieties of fodder crops, including 19 varieties of alfalfa, have been developed in the Soviet Union with the use of the world collection of fodder crops. At present 129 specimens of fodder crops have been released for cultivation, which were evolved with the use of the world collection of the VIR and have been recommended for an area of about 1,000,000 hectares. Of the 82 released varieties of alfalfa, two have been evolved under the system of VIR (Tibet and Yellow Kuban), 28 varieties developed by breeding institutions of the Soviet Union with the use of the world collection (ASKhI-1, Azerbaydzhanskaya-5, Azerbaydzhan-262, Vakhshskaya-233, Vakhshskaya-300, Veselopodolyanskaya-11, Kazan-36, Kazan-64/95, Kamalinskaya-530, Kamalin-930, Krasnodarskaya Early, Krasnokutskaya-4009, Krasnokutskaya variegated hybrid, Kuibishevskaya, Karakalpakian-1, Milyutinskaya-1774, Omsk-8893, Onokhoy-6, Pavlovskaya-7, Raduga, Severnaya hybrid, Stepnaya-600, Tashkent-3192, Flora, Chishminskaya-130, Chernigovskaya, Khersonskaya-7, and Shortandinskaya-2); 13 are derivatives of improved varieties evolved from the collection material (Barnaulskaya-17, Belorusskaya, Yellow hybrid-191, Iolotanskaya, Kurskaya-1, Kokshe, Kievskaya variegated hybrid, Krasnoufimskaya-6, Mezhotnenskaya, Pestraya-57, Taiga, Khersonskaya-1, and Khersonskaya-9).

If in estimating the economic efficiency of the released varieties of fodder crops we assign 3.0% weightage to the initial material, then the average annual profit from the utilization of specimens of the world collection, from which different varieties have been evolved, amounts to 1,000,000 rubles.

In addition to the collection, specialists of the Department of Fodder Crops of VIR sent plant breeders sources of CMS, interspecific hybrids, methodological instructions, and catalogs. The Department also extends direct assistance to all breeding institutions on theoretical problems of breeding fodder crops and the effective utilization of initial material.

Taking into consideration the fact that at the centers of origin of cultivated plants many species and forms are disappearing, more and more countries are looking to the world collection of the VIR.

Conclusions

Alfalfa was brought under cultivation about 6,000 to 7,000 years ago. Its introduction for cultivation was polyphyletic through several independent channels at different historical times in the Eurasian and Central Asian gene centers.

The greatest botanical diversity of perennial species of alfalfa of the subgenus *Falcago* (Reichb.) Grossh. is found in three gene centers identified by N.I. Vavilov and P.M. Zhukovskii, which are directly associated with the Soviet Union: Eurasian (VI), Central Asian (V), and Euro-Siberian (IX). Most of the perennial species of alfalfa found in the hills of the Caucasus are diploids. Six of them (crescentoid, Dagestan, Dzhavakhet, villous, glutinous, and checkered) are strictly endemic to Eurasia.

Phylogenetically much younger tetraploid species (*M. sativa* L., *M. falcata* L., *M. varia* Mart., and *M. tianschanica* Vass.) are concentrated in the hilly regions of the Central Asian gene center. The areas of diploid species (*M. trautvetteri* Sumn., *M. coerulea* Less., and *M. difalcata* Sinsk.) are situated far in the north in the intermediate desert-steppe belt located between gene centers V and IX and connected with gene center VI through the Caspian lowland. Varietal types known throughout the world for their valuable biological properties have evolved in the Central Asian center of origin: Plain Turkestan, Turkmenian, Semirechensk, Khiva, Kashgar, Kandhar, Gerat-Khorasan, and others.

The Euro-Siberian gene center is secondary for the subgenus *Falcago*. Here the diploid *M. borealis* Grossh. evolved while the tetraploid *M. varia* Mart. achieved maximum spread and development.

The Crimean region of the Euro-Siberian center of origin, whose flora spreads over to the Mediterranean and Eurasian centers, occupies a special position in the evolution of perennial and especially annual species. Among species of the genus *Medicago* growing here are: diploids—*M. marina* L., *M. prostrata* Yaeq., *M. glandulosa* David, and *M. rupestris* Bieb.; tetraploids—*M. varia* Mart. and *M. falcata* L.; and the hexaploid *M. saxatillis* Bieb.

The general course of evolution of the genus *Medicago* proceeded from diploid to tetraploid and hexaploid species through polyploidy and hybridization. Species evolved in two ways: either without change in the chromosome set or with doubling of the chromosome number. In the first case gradual variability was observed with multiple intermediate forms in the transitional zones (*M. quasifalcata, M. difalcata, M. glandulosa,* and *M. borealis*); in the second case transitional forms were few (*M. sativa, M. falcata, M. saxatilis,* and *M. cancellata*) or altogether absent. The second method of species evolution associated with auto- and allopolyploidy is more progressive.

The oldest blue-flowered species of alfalfa is *M. coerulea* Less., from which the genealogy of *M. sativa* L. is traced. The phylogeny of cultivated species is as follows: *M. praecoerulea—M. coerulea—M. praesativa—M. sativa* L. subsp. *caucasica—M. sativa* L. subsp. *transoxana—M. sativa* L. subsp. *sativa.* The leading role in the evolution of cultivated alfalfa at the diploid level is attributed to the Eurasian gene center, and that at the tetraploid level to the Central Asian gene center.

Evolution of the yellow-flowered species began with the primitive forms of *M. quasifalcata,* the endemic mesophytic species of the Eurasian gene center, from which evolved the xerophytic species *M. difalcata* and *M. glandulosa* and the hydrophytic species *M. borealis.* The area of *M. quasifalcata* is the hilly valleys and riverine floodplains of northern Caucasus, that of *M. difalcata* the arid belt of central Kazakhstan, of *M. glandulosa* the steppe regions of the European part of the USSR, and of *M. borealis* the Nechernozem zone of RSFSR.

Data from an immunochemical analysis of seed proteins of wild yellow-flowered alfalfa species does not exclude the possibility of considering the xerophytic *M. difalcata* Sinsk. the most primitive species of the yellow-flowered series. Species of hybrid origin are: diploids—*M. hemicycla* and *M. trautvetteri*; tetraploids—*M. glutinosa, M. polychroa, M. tianschanica,* and *M. varia*; and hexaploids—*M. saxatilis* and *M. cancellata.*

The most comprehensive systems of classification of alfalfa have been suggested by the Soviet botanists A.A. Grossgeim, I.T. Vasil'chenko, E.N. Sinskaya, M.V. Kultiasov, and O.Kh. Khasanov. Most of the systems proposed to date do not adequately consider the criteria of variability of characters. Hence infraspecific taxa, or simply interspecific hybrids, have often been treated as independent species.

The global gene pool of alfalfa with respect to self-fertility, nectar productivity, longevity, presence of male sterile forms, and high crossability is concentrated in the Eurasian center of origin.

Within the Central Asian gene center are concentrated species with germ plasm for such characters and properties as multiple-cutting habit, heat (temperature) resistance, early maturity, responsiveness to irrigation, high seed productivity, tolerance for salinity, and tall stems. The wild material of this gene center is the world's forte for drought resistance.

In the Euro-Siberian gene center are concentrated gene variations of such important characters and properties as winter hardiness, cold resistance, resistance to flooding, long sprouting period, survival in pastures, rhizomatous root habit, profuse foliage, softness of stems, ecological variability, resistance to root rots, self-incompatibility, sources of CMS, and crossability.

The Kazakh field-study group of VIR has completed the first stage of work on mobilization of plant resources within the republic, including cultivated and wild populations of alfalfa. Genetic resources of the VIR have been enriched by 3,500 specimens. For the first time in the history of the Institute, a collection of arid fodder plants has been established. This unique gene reserve is actively used in breeding work today.

It was established by the Kazakh expedition that areas of diploid alfalfa species, so important from the viewpoint of fodder, are concentrated in the republic: *M. coerulea*—in the Caspian lowland, *M. trautvetteri*—on the Ustyurt plateau and the Ural-Embensk sands, and *M. difalcata*—in the central Kazakhstan hillocks. Among the tetraploid species *M. sativa* and *M. tianschanica* grow in the hilly belt of western Tien Shan, *M. falcata* is found everywhere but concentrated in the hills of eastern Tien Shan, Dzhungarian-Alatau, Saur-Tarbagatau, and Rudnoi Altai, and *M. varia* is widely distributed in the hillock and foothill zone of the northern Turan plain transitional floristic province.

During field investigations large loci of introgressive hybridization of wild alfalfa species have been identified, which are confined to the hilly regions: Mugodzharo-Ustyurt, Tien Shan, central Kazakhstan, Dzhungar, and eastern Kazakhstan.

The strongest center is situated in the hills of Mugodzhar, where the areas of *M. coerulea*, *M. sativa*, *M. falcata*, and *M. difalcata* intersect. *M. trautvetteri* and *M. varia* are the products of hybridization of these species.

In the Soviet Union 80 varieties of alfalfa have been released for cultivation, including 15 local and 65 improved varieties, comprising five species: *M. sativa*—21 varieties, *M. varia*—53, *M. falcata*—3, *M. quasifalcata*—1, and *M. borealis*—2.

On the basis of many years of study of the world collection of alfalfa, promising initial material has been identified for different directions of breeding work.

1. The most early-maturing (vegetative period up to 100 days) are specimens of common alfalfa and variable alfalfa from China, India, Iran, Egypt, Sudan, Peru, Chile, Argentina, Brazil, Ecuador, France (Gamma, Du Puits, Omega, Flamande, Provence, Warote, Etoile du Nord, Luciole),

Italy (Gigante Cremoneze), Sweden (Alfa, Tuna, Sverre), and local varieties of Bolivia, Uruguay, Panama, Mexico, Morocco, Syria, and Pakistan.

In summer crops, compared with spring crops, the vegetative period of specimens is reduced, on the average, by 25 to 35 days, while the phase of seed germination is reduced by half.

2. Improved and local varieties of the Central Asian gene center as well as specimens from Eurasia, Peru, and Chile are characterized by quick sprouting and tall plants (100 cm and above).

3. High foliage (48 to 52%) in northern Kazakhstan is characteristic of specimens of North Kazakhstan, Khiva, Plain Turkestan, and Trans-Caucasian varietal types; among foreign varieties the following are distinguished in this respect: improved varieties of Canada, the USA, and varieties of Peru (K-5141, K-21284).

On irrigated lands maximum foliage is characteristic for varietal specimens of the Anatolian group of varietal types, and the least foliage of the Central Asian group. In the arid zone the maximum foliage is observed without irrigation in specimens of Tien Shan, and the lowest in South Kazakhstan alfalfa.

4. In terms of crude protein content (20% and above), the best in the collection are varieties developed in our country: Kazan-64/95, Zabai-kalka, Valuyskaya local, Aparan local, Poltava-256, Sretenskaya-77, Karabalykskaya-18, Omsk-2251, Dnepropetrovsk local, Vakhshskaya-233; wild populations of crescentoid alfalfa (K-28900), glutinous, varicolored (K-16714), and semitwisted (K-16691). Among the foreign varieties the highest percentage of crude protein is found in Ainsford (England), Cay-uga (USA), Kleszczewska (Poland), Baska Zms-1 (Yugoslavia), local populations from Turkey (K-3368), the Federal Republic of Germany (K-36903), and Algeria (K-36911).

5. High resistance to root rots is exhibited by the improved varieties of variable alfalfa developed under severe soil-climatic conditions of Siberia, Kazakhstan, and the southeast European part of the USSR. Foreign varieties are not resistant to diseases and pests in Kazakh SSR.

6. Maximum resistance to low temperatures is characteristic of varieties and specimens of common and variable alfalfas of Kazakh SSR, Middle and Low Povolzh'e, western Siberia, and eastern Siberia, as well as yellow, blue, varicolored, Trautvetter's, glandular, semitwisted alfalfas and natural hybrids of wild species. A high correlation was established between field and laboratory methods of evaluation of species and varieties of alfalfa for resistance to low temperatures.

7. The most drought-resistant were wild specimens of yellow, blue, Trautvetter's, and South Kazakhstan alfalfas collected by expeditions from the VIR in the steppe and desert regions of Kazakh SSR; improved and

local varieties from Kara-Kalpak ASSR, western and central Kazakhstan, Lower Povolzh'e, and Kalmytsk ASSR; and varieties of the Krasnokutskaya Breeding Station, steppe regions of Ukrainian SSR, and Khakass autonomous province. Among the foreign specimens varieties from Canada and the USA, and local varieties from central and western China are characterized by drought and heat (temperature) resistance.

8. The following varieties and specimens surpassed the control in yield of green mass and hay in a multiyear evaluation of the alfalfa collection:

a) Steppe zone of northern Kazakhstan—Karabalykskaya-18, Kuzbasskaya, Flora, Nerchinskaya-46, Blue hybrid, and Chernigovskaya;

b) Irrigated lands of the desert zone of western Kazakhstan—Fergana-700, Semirechensk local, Tashkent-3192, Vakhshskaya-233, Iolotanskaya, Azerbaydzhan-265, Mesopotamian and Liguen (Chile), Boreal, Luciole, Prima, Etoile du Nord (France), Baska Zms-1 (Yugoslavia), Acsai (Hungary), Progress, Saranac, Cayuga (USA), Alfa and Tuna (Sweden), and specimens from Peru, Ecuador, Sudan, Kenya, South African Republic (P-58/327), India, Egypt, Algeria, and Pakistan;

c) Under rainfed conditions in the desert zone—Karabalykskaya-18, Karaganda-1, Kuzbasskaya, Barnaulskaya-17, Flora, Brodskaya local, Kazan-64/95, Valuyskaya local, and specimens from Kirgiz SSR (K-8940, 8941), Ladak from Tibet (K-19883 and 23217), wild populations of common alfalfa (K-060239, K-060249), variable alfalfa (K-063125), blue alfalfa (K-15198, K-35009, K-36051), Tian Shan alfalfa (K-34628), and Trautvetter's alfalfa (K-34631).

The following varieties are well known for seed yield: in the steppe zone—Marusinskaya-81, Kemlyanskaya-1, Saranskaya local, Kazan-64/95, Poltava-256, local from China (K-32863), Narragansett (USA), Mesopotamian (K-7221, Iraq); under irrigation in western Kazakhstan—Semirechensk local, Krasnokutsk-3125, Karabalykskaya-18, Blue hybrid-1316, Kainskaya-4146, Amur-33, Ferax (Canada), blue alfalfa (K-36053 and K-36118); under rainfed conditions in the desert zone—Semirechensk local, Uzgen local, Samarkand local, Slavyanskaya local, Manichskaya local, and Azerbaydzhan-2/30, Krasnokutsk-3125, East Kazakhstan-5057, Lyulinetskaya, Kamalinskaya-530, local from Kirgiz SSR (K-6348), local from Kara-Kalpak ASSR (K-8932), local from Chuvash ASSR (K-32792), local from Kirov province (K-32096 and 32097), early-maturing populations from Italy (K-5677), Turkey (K-6001), India (K-23209), Grimm (USA), and Brnenskaya (Czechoslovakia).

The least variable characters (V = 4 to 20%) in alfalfa are: duration of development of first and subsequent cuttings, length and width of pods, germination period, number of internodes on main stem, weight of 1,000 seeds, length of leaflet, foliage percentage, diameter of stem, plant height, number of shoots in bush, content of protein, cellulose, ash, NES, phosphorus, potash, and calcium. High variability ($V = 20$ to 89%) is characteristic of the following characters: number of racemes, pods, and seeds in one plant or an area of $1.0 \, m^2$, weight of seeds from one plant, fresh weight of one plant (in grams), sprouting vigor, plant height on 20th day after cutting, width of leaflet, and content of fat and sodium.

Some distinct correlations were revealed between morphobiological types of plants in the composition of variety Tibet. In the erect, early-maturing biotypes plant height correlates positively with yield of green mass ($r = 0.61$ to 0.77) and inversely with foliage percentage of plants ($r = -0.57$ to 0.65); in biotypes with a spreading form of bush positive correlations occur between fresh weight of plants and tillering ($r = 0.51$ to 0.82), degree of plant disease and tillering ($r = 0.55$ to 0.75), yield of green mass and diameter of stem ($r = 0.68$ to 0.89), and length of leaflet and foliage percentage ($r = 0.40$ to 0.85); in biotypes with a prostrate form of bush correlations are likewise evident between degree of plant disease and diameter of stem ($r = 0.31$ to 0.69).

In wild species of alfalfa positive correlations have been established between duration of development of cuttings and cuttingwise plant height, and between plant height and yield of green mass. Under conditions of regular irrigation positive correlation was observed between total productivity of plants and these indexes: time of formation of cuttings, cuttingwise plant height, foliage percentage, cuttingwise yield of green mass, and cuttingwise mass of hay. Coefficients of correlation between duration of development of cuttings and productivity were weak ($r = 0.15$ to 0.25), between plant height and productivity, medium ($r = 0.40$ to 0.60), and between foliage percentage, yield of green mass, mass of hay, and total productivity of plants, high ($r = 0.80$ to 0.90). The synergistic effect of characters underscores the degree of effective selection and judiciously used can actively influence the breeding process.

Comprehensive botanical, geographic, and genetic-breeding studies of alfalfa provide a deeper understanding of the most important fodder crop in the world, which results in better exploitation of biological properties for developing high-yielding varieties for different economic purposes.

Bibliography*

Ahlgren, G.H. 1949. *Forage Crops*. McGraw-Hill, New York, 418 pp.

Alekseev, A.M. 1948. Vodnyi rezhim rastenii i vliyanie na nego zasukhi (Water Regime of Plants and Effect of Drought). Kazan, pp. 131–139.

Alekseev, A.M. 1953. K voprosu o vliyanii vodnogo rezhima list'ev na protsess fotosinteza (Effect of water regime of leaves on the process of photosynthesis). *Botanicheskii Zhurnal SSSR*, 20, 3, 227–241.

Alekseev, A.M. 1968. Znachenie struktury tsitoplasmy dlya vodnogo rezhima rastetel'nykh kletok (Importance of structure of cytoplasm for water regime of plant cells). In: *Vodnyi Rezhim Rastenii i Ikh Produktivnost'*. Moscow, pp. 5–12.

Alekseev, A.M. 1968. O vodoobmene rastenii (Water exchange in plants). In: *Vodnyi Rezhim Rastenii i Ikh Produktivnost'*. Moscow, pp. 13–21.

Angelov, Z.G. 1976. Gibridizatsiya *M. sativa* s drugimi vidami s tsel'yu polucheniya immunykh form (Hybridization of *M. sativa* with other species to obtain immune forms). Avtoref. Dis. na Soisk. Uchenoi Stepeni Kandidata S.-Kh. Nauk. Sofiya, 40 pp.

Archer, S.G. and C.E. Bunch. 1953. *The American Grass Book*. University of Oklahoma Press, pp. 187–190.

Armstrong, J.M. 1954. Cytological studies in alfalfa polyploids, *Can. J. Botany*, vol. 32, pp. 531–542.

Baitulin, I. and S. Kultaev. 1963. Osobennosti razvitiya kornevykh sistem donnika i lyutserny sinei na solontsovykh pochvakh v svyzi s raznoi obrabotkoi (Peculiarities of development of root systems of sweet clover and blue alfalfa in alkaline soils in the context of various treatments). *Vestnik S.-Kh. Nauki*, no. 2, pp. 13–23.

Balázs, F. 1960. A gyepek botanikai és gazdasági értekelese. Mezogazdasagi, Kiado, Budapest, pp. 107–134.

Balázs, F. 1961. Fenérjetartalom változasok a lucernában, *Magyar Tud Akad. Agrartud. Oszt. Kozl.*, nos. 1–3, pp. 99–112.

Belov, A.I. 1931. Lyutserva Srednei Azii (Alfalfa of Central Asia). *Trudy po Prikl. Bot., Gen. i Sel., Prilozhenie*, no. 48, pp. 3–125.

*Some references are incomplete in the Russian original—General Editor.

Belov, A.I. 1931a. Kul'tura lyutserny v Srednei Azii (Alfalfa Cultivation in Central Asia). Tashkent, pp. 91–109.

Belov, A.I. 1965. Proiskhozhdenie i evolyutsiya kul'turnykh lyutsern Srednei Azii (Origin and evolution of cultivated alfalfas of Central Asia). In: *Problemy Sovremennoi Botaniki.* Moscow-Leningrad, vol. 2, pp. 293–298.

Bingham, E.T. 1968. Aneuploids in seedling populations of tetraploid alfalfa, *Medicago sativa* L., *Crop Sci.*, 8, 5, 571–574.

Bingham, E.T. 1968a. Transfer of diploid *Medicago* subsp. germ plasm to tetraploid *M. sativa* L. in 4X–2X crosses, *Crop Sci.*, 8, 6, 760–762.

Bingham, E.T. 1969. Haploids from cultivated alfalfa, *Medicago sativa* L., *Nature*, 221, 5183, 4–8.

Bingham, E.T. 1971. Isolation of haploids of tetraploid alfalfa, *Crop Sci.*, 11, 3, 433–435.

Bingham, E.T. and A. Binek. 1969. Comparative morphology of haploids from cultivated alfalfa, *Medicago sativa* L., *Crop Sci.*, 9, 6, 433–435.

Bingham, E.T. and C.B. Gillies. 1971. Chromosome pairing, fertility, and crossing behavior of haploids of tetraploid alfalfa, *Medicago sativa* L., *Canad. J. Genet. Cytol.*, 13, 2, 195–202.

Bobrov, E.G. 1972. Istoriya i sistematika listvennits (History and Systematics of Larches). Leningrad, 96 pp.

Bócsa, I. and J.A. Buglos. 1974. A lucerne nyersfehérjere való nemesitésének néhány mintázástechnikai kérdése, *Növénytermeles*, 23, 1, 1–5.

Bohart, G.E. 1963. How to manage the alfalfa leaf-cutting bee (*Megachile rotundata* Fabr.) for alfalfa pollination, *Agr. Exp. Sta., Utah State Univ.*, Circ. 144, pp. 240–246.

Bohart, G.E. 1972. Management of wild bees for the pollination of crops, *Ann. Rev. Entomol.*, vol. 17, pp. 384–389.

Bolton, J.L. 1962. *Alfalfa.* Interscience Publishers, New York, 474 pp.

Bolton, J.L., B.P. Goplen and H. Baenziger. 1972. World distribution and historical developments. In: *Alfalfa Science and Technology.* American Society of Agronomy, Madison, Wisconsin, pp. 1–34.

Bordakov, L.P. 1929. Geografiya, morfologiya, sistematika i biologiya lyutserny (Geography, morphology, taxonomy, and biology of alfalfa). In: *Trudy Vses. S"ezda po Genetike, Selektsii, Semenovodstva i Plemennomu Zhivotnovodstvu.* Leningrad, vol. 3, pp. 113–116.

Bordakov, L.P. 1934. Opyt sistematicheskogo izucheniya vida *Medicago sativa* L. (Experimental taxonomic study of the species *Medicago sativa* L.). *Trudy po Prikl. Botan., Gen. i Sel.*, 7, 1, 3–48.

Bordakov, L.P. 1936. Sinyaya posevnaya lyutserna (Cultivated Blue Alfalfa). Moscow, pp. 3–51.

Bradner, N.R. and W.R. Childers. 1968. Cytoplasmic male sterility in alfalfa, *Canad. J. Plant Sci.*, 48, 1, 111–112.

Brezhnev, D.D. 1967. Ispol'zovanie mirovykh rastitel'nykh resursov v selektsii sel'skokhozyaistvennykh kul'tur (Use of world plant resources in breeding agricultural crops). In: *Dostizheniya Otechestvennoi Selektsii.* Moscow, pp. 21–37.

Brezhnev, D.D. 1974. Rastitel'nye resursy na sluzhbu Nechernozemnoi zony (Plant resources for the Nechernozem zone). *Byull. VIR,* nos. 44–45, pp. 9-13.

Brezhnev, D.D. 1975. Shirokaya programma issledovanii (Extensive program of research). *Trudy po Prikl. Bot., Gen. i Sel.,* 54, 1, 7–26.

Brezhnev, D.D. and G.E. Shmaraev. 1975. Sovremennaya sel'khozyaist-vennaya nauka v Velikobritanii (Present-day agricultural science in Great Britain). *Vestnik S.-Kh. Nauki.* Moscow, no. 4, pp. 117–124.

Busbice, T.H. and C.P. Wilsie. 1966. Genetics of *Medicago sativa* L. II. Inheritance of dwarf character Dw_2, *Crop Sci.*, 6, 5, 231–234.

Busbice, T.H. and C.P. Wilsie. 1966a. Inbreeding depression and hete-rosis in autotetraploids with application to *Medicago sativa* L., *Euphytica,* vol. 15, pp. 327–330.

Busbice, T.H., R.R. Hill, Jr. and H.L. Carnahan. 1972. Genetics and breeding procedures. *Alfalfa Science and Technology.* Madison, Wisconsin, pp. 283-319.

Buss, G.R. and R.W. Cleveland. 1968. Karyotype of a diploid *Medicago sativa* L. analyzed from sporophytic and gametophytic mitosis, *Crop Sci.,* 8, 6, 231–248.

Carnahan, H.L., J.W. Miller and M.H. Yama. 1969. Registration of 520 alfalfa (Reg. No. 44), *Crop Sci.,* vol. 9, pp. 847–848.

Clement, W.M., Jr. 1963. Chromosome relationships in diploid hybrid between *Medicago sativa* L. and *M. dzhawakhetica* Bortz., *Canad. J. Genet. Cytol.,* 5, 4, 147–150.

Clement, W.M., Jr. 1968. The effect of the basic color factor on xantho-phyll pigmentation in diploid alfalfa, *Canad. J. Genet. Cytol.,* 10, 3, 147–150.

Clement, W.M., Jr. and E.H. Stanford. 1966. Red root in alfalfa. Inheri-tance and relationship with flower color, *Crop Sci.,* pp. 451–453.

Cleveland, R.W. and E.H. Stanford. 1959. Chromosome pairing in hybrids between tetraploid *Medicago sativa* L. and diploid *M. falcata* L., *Agr. J.,* 51, 8, 488–492.

Cooper, D.S. 1935. Chromosome numbers in the Leguminosae, *Amer. J. Bot.,* 23, 3, 471–477.

Cooper, D.S. 1939. Artificial induction of polyploidy in alfalfa, *Amer. J. Bot.,* vol. 26, pp. 65–67.

Daday, H. 1962. Breeding for creeping root in lucerne (*Medicago sativa* L.), *Austral. J. Agr. Res.*, 13, 5, 813–820.

Daday, H. 1963. African lucerne, *Field Station Record*, 2, 1, 1–16.

Daday, H. 1963a. They've bred lucerne you can graze, *Austral. Country Mag.*, Nov., pp. 39–40.

Daday, H. 1965. General and specific combining ability for forage yield in lucerne (*Medicago sativa* L.), *Australian J. Agr. Res.*, 16, 3, 293–299.

Daday, H. 1965a. Performance of lucerne varieties on the south coast of New South Wales, *Austral. J. Exper. Agr. Animal Husbandry*, 5, 16, 44–45.

Daday, H. 1966. De Puits lucerne, *Field Station Record*, 5, 2, 78–79.

Daday, H. 1968. Heritability and genotypic and environmental correlations of creeping roots and persistency in *Medicago sativa* L., *Austral. J. Agr. Res.*, 19, 1, 27–34.

Daday, H. 1968a. New grazing lucerne here... and the name is... "Cancreep", *Austral. Country Mag.*, 24, 4, 198–201.

Daday, H. and G.G. Greenham. 1960. Genetic studies on cold hardiness in *Medicago sativa* L., *Heredity*, 51, 6, 249–255.

Daday, H., B.E. Mottersbead and V.E. Rogers. 1961. Performance and interactions in varieties of lucerne (*Medicago sativa* L.), *Austral. J. Exper. Agr. Animal Husbandry*, 1, 2, 67–72.

De Candolle, A.P. 1825. *Prodomus Systematis*. Paris, vol. 2, 606 pp.

De Candolle, A.P. 1919. *Origin of Cultivated Plants*. D. Appleton, New York-London, pp. 102–104.

Demarly, G. 1968. Le selection des varietes synthetiques. *Proceedings 5th Eucarpia Congr.*, Milan, 520 pp.

Dessureaux, E. 1968. Effect of selection for alfalfa seed-setting in an inbreeding system, *Forage Notes*, 14, 2, 19–20.

Dessureaux, L. 1968a. Seed setting of alfalfa as affected by various methods of Pollination, *Forage Notes*, 14, 2, 8–10.

Dessureaux, L. 1969. Inbreeding and heterosis in autotetraploid alfalfa. I. Fertility, *Canad. J. Genet. Cytol.*, 11, 12, 15–16.

Dmitrieva, L.V. 1958. Izmenenie vodouderzhivayushchei sposobnosti lyutserny tyan'shanskoi v usloviyakh kul'tury (Change in water-retention capacity of Tian Shan alfalfa under cultivation). *Byull. Glavnogo Botanicheskogo Sada AN SSSR*, no. 31, pp. 39–44.

Dmitrieva, L.V. 1959. Izmenenie anatomicheskoi struktury lista lyutserny tyan'shanskoi v usliviyakh kul'tury (Change in anatomical structure of leaves of Tian Shan alfalfa under cultivation). *Byull. Glavnogo Botanicheskogo Sada An SSSR*, no. 33, pp. 66–73.

Dmitrieva, L.V. 1960. K sravnitel'nomu izucheniyu intensivnosti transpiratsii lyutserny tyan'shanskoi pri ee akklimatizatsii (Comparative study of transpiration rate of Tian Shan alfalfa during acclimatization). *Byull. Glavnogo Botanicheskogo Sada AN SSSR*, no. 31, pp. 63–68.

Dmitrieva, L.V. 1961. Izmenenie produktivnosti lyutserny tyan'shanskoi v mezofil'nykh usloviyakh kul'tury (Change of productivity of Tian Shan alfalfa under mesophytic conditions of cultivation). *Byull. Glavnogo Botanicheskogo Sada AN SSSR*, no. 42, pp. 76–78.

Dmitrieva, L.V. 1962. Osobennosti vodnogo defitsita list'ev lyutserny tyanshanskoi v usloviyakh kul'tury (Peculiarities of water deficit of leaves of Tian Shan alfalfa under cultivation). *Trudy. Glavnogo Botanicheskogo Sada AN SSSR*, vol. 8, pp. 59–64.

Dmitrieva, L.V. 1967. Izmenenie prisposobitel'nykh osobennostei lyutserny tyan'shanskoi v opyte vvedeniya ee v kul'turu (Change of adaptative peculiarities of Tian Shan alfalfa in cultivation experiments). In: *Lyutserna Tyan'shanskaya i Opyt Ee Introduktsii*. Moscow, pp. 183–220.

Dmitrochenko, A.P. 1954. Kormlenie molochnykh korov (Feeding of Milch Cows). Moscow-Leningrad, 305 pp.

Dubinin, N.P. 1961. Problemy radiatsionnoi genetiki (Problems of Radiation Genetics). Moscow, 468 pp.

Dubinin, N.P. 1971. Geneticheskie printsipy selektsii rastenii (Genetic principles of plant breeding). In: *Geneticheskie Osnovy Selektsii Rastenii*. Moscow, pp. 7–32.

Dubinin, N.P. and V.K. Shcherbakov. 1965. Teoreticheskie voprosy i dostizheniya pri ispol'zovanii poliploidii v selektsii rastenii (Theoretical problems and achievements in the use of polyploidy in plant breeding). In: *Poliploidiya i Selektsiya*. Moscow-Leningrad, pp. 65–79.

Ermakov, A.I., V.V. Arasimovich, M.I. Smirnova-Ikonnikova and I.K. Murri. 1972. Metody biokhimicheskogo issledovaniya rastenii (Methods of Biochemical Research in Plants). Moscow, 456 pp.

Evans, K.H., R.L. Davis and W.E. Nyguist. 1966. Interaction of plant spacing and combining ability in a light-clone diallele of *Medicago sativa* L., *Crop Sci.*, 6, 5, 451–454.

Fedorov, A.K. 1968. Biologiya mnogoletnikh trav (Biology of Perennial Grasses). Moscow, 176 pp.

Filatov, F.I. 1951. Agrobiologicheskie osnovy vozdelyvaniya mnogoletnikh trav na yugo-vostoke SSSR (Agrobiological Basis in the Cultivation of Perennial Grasses in Southeastern USSR). Saratov, 279 pp.

Gartner, A. and R.L. Davis. 1966. Effects of self-compatibility on chance crossing of *Medicago sativa* L., *Crop. Sci.*, 6, 1, 210–211.

Genkel', P.A. 1946. Ustoichivost' rastenii k zasukhe i puti ee povysheniya (Drought resistance of plants and ways to increase it). *Trudy In-ta Fiziologii Rastenii im. K.A. Timiryazeva*. Moscow, 5, 1, 152–156.

Genkel', P.A. 1960. Fiziologiya zakalivaniya rastenii k zasukhe v svyazi s problemoi povysheniya produktivnosti kul'turnykh rastenii (Physiology of hardening of plants against drought in the context of increasing productivity of cultivated plants). In: *Tezisy Dokladov Kazanskogo Un-ta Kazan'*, pp. 15–18.

Genkel', P.A. 1965. Fiziologiya rastenii s osnovami mikrobiologii (Plant Physiology with Fundamentals of Microbiology). Moscow, 536 pp.

Gillies, C.B. 1968. The pachytene chromosomes of a diploid *Medicago sativa*, *Canad. J. Genet. Cytol.*, 10, 4, 788–793.

Gillies, C.B. 1970. Alfalfa chromosomes. 1. Pachytene karyotype of a diploid *Medicago falcata* L. and its relationship to *M. sativa* L., *Crop Sci.*, 10, 3, 172–175.

Gillies, C.B. 1970a. Alfalfa chromosomes. 2. Pachytene karyotype of a tetraploid *Medicago sativa* L., *Crop Sci.*, 10, 2, 169–191.

Gillies, C.B. 1971. Alfalfa chromosomes. 3. *Medicago glomerata* Balb. pachytene karyotype, *Crop Sci.*, 11, 3, 357–403.

Golodkovskii, L.I. and V.L. Golodkovskii. 1937. Kornevaya sistema lyutserny i plodorodie (Root System of Alfalfa and Fertility). Tashkent, pp. 76–80.

Golodkovskii, V.L. and A.D. Pyataeva. 1936. Estestvennye gibridy lyutserny v gorakh Karatau (Natural hybrids of alfalfa in the Karatau mountains). *Sotsialisticheskaya Nauka i Tekhnika*. Tashkent, no. 11, pp. 96–101.

Golodkovskii, V.L., Kh.I. Ibragimova and Kh.U. Uzimov. 1971. Biologiya semennoi lyutserny (sistematika, fotoperiodizm, vliyanie fosfornykh udobrenii, polivnoi rezhim) (Biology of seed Alfalfa: Taxonomy, Photoperiodism, Effect of Phosphate Fertilizers, and Irrigation Regime). Tashkent, 183 pp.

Goloskokov, V.P. 1960. Lyutserna i klevera Kazakhstana—lushchie kormovye rasteniya (Alfalfa and clover of Kazakhstan—the best fodder plants). *Izv. AN Kazakhskoi SSR (Ser. Biologiya i Pochvovedeniya)*, 1, 7, 15–21.

Golush, B.M. and N.A. Sharina. 1940. Fiziko-khimicheskie izmeneniya plazmy pri zamorazhivanii (Physicochemical changes in plasm during freezing). *Izv. AN SSSR*, no. 4, pp. 356–359.

Goncharov, P.L 1965. Lyutserna v Irkutskoi oblasti (Alfalfa in Irkutsk Province). Irkutsk, 106 pp.

Goncharov, P.L. 1970. Raschlenenie populyatsii, otbor na kachestvo i ispol'zovanie geterozisa v selektsii lyutserny (Segregation of population, selection for quality, and use of heterosis in alfalfa breeding). *Trudy Krasnoyarskogo NIISKh*, vol. 6, pp. 15–28.

Goncharov, P.L. 1970. Ispol'zovanie geterozisa dlya povysheniya produktivnosti lyutserny (Use of heterosis for increasing productivity of alfalfa). *Selektsiya i Semenovodstvo*, no. 6, pp. 23–25.

Goncharov, P.L. 1971. Selektsiya lyutserny v Vostochnoi Sibiri i perspektivy sozdaniya geterozisnykh gibridov (Alfalfa breeding in eastern Siberia and prospects of developing heterotic hybrids). *Dokl. VASKhNIL*, no. 6, pp. 8–9.

Goncharov, P.L. 1972. Metody selektsionno-semenovodcheskoi raboty s mnogoletnimi i odnoletnimi travami na Tulunskoi selektsionnoi stantsii (Methods of breeding and seed production of perennial and annual grasses in Tulunsk Plant-Breeding Station). In: *Dokl. i Soobshch. po Kormoproizvodstvu (VIK)*. Moscow, no. 4, pp. 48–53.

Goncharov, P.L. 1974. Lyutserna v Pribaikal'e (Alfalfa in Baikal). *Sibirskii Vestnik. S.-Kh. Nauki*, no. 3, pp. 52–58.

Greenham, C.G. and H. Daday. 1957. Electrical determination of cold hardiness in *Trifolium repens* L. and *Medicago sativa* L., *Nature*, 180, 14, 1–7.

Greenham, C.G. and H. Daday. 1960. Further studies on the determination of cold hardiness in *Trifolium repens* L. and *Medicago sativa* L., *Austral. J. Agric. Res.*, 11, 1, 1–15.

Grigor'ev, Yu.S. 1955. Sravnitel'no-ekologicheskoe issledovanie kserofitizatsii vysshikh rastenii (Comparative Ecological Studies on Xerophily of Higher Plants). AN SSSR, Moscow-Leningrad, 157 pp.

Grigoryan, B.E. 1973. Kombinirovannoe deistvie fizicheskikh i khimicheskikh faktorov na mutatsionnyi protsess u lyutserny (Combined effect of physical and chemical factors on mutation in alfalfa). Avtoref. Dis. na Soisk. Uchenoi Stepeni Doktora S.-Kh. Nauk, Baku, 24 pp.

Gritsenko, T.G. 1950. Svobodnaya mezhsortovaya gibridizatsiya lyutserny (Free intervarietal hybridization of alfalfa). *Agrobiologiya*, no. 3, pp. 138–142.

Gritsenko, T.G. 1956. Osnovnye itogi nauchno-issledovatel'skoi raboty po selektsii i semenovodstvu lyutserny sinei no opytnykh stantsiyakh Soyuz NIKhI za 1948–1954 gg. (Major results of research work on breeding and seed production of blue alfalfa in experimental stations in Soyuz NIKhI from 1948 to 1954). *Itogi Rabot Soyuz NIKhI za 1954*, no. 2, pp. 85–102.

Grossgeim, A.A. 1919. Obzor Krymsko-Kavkazskikh predstavi-telei roda *Medicago* L. (Review of Crimean-Caucasian representatives of the genus *Medicago* L.). *Zap. Nauch.-Prikl. Otd. Tiflisskogo Botan. Sada*, no. 1, pp. 78–121.

Grossgeim, A.A. 1945. Lyutserna—*Medicago* L. (Alfalfa—*Medicago* L.). In: *Flora SSSR*. AN SSSR, Moscow-Leningrad, vol. 11, pp. 129–176.

Grubov, V.I. 1953. Konspekt flory Mongol'skoi Narodnoi Respubliki (Résumé of flora of the Mongolian People's Republic). In: *Trudy Mongol'skoi Komissii.* Moscow, no. 67, 308 pp.

Grun, P. 1951. Variations in the meiosis of alfalfa, *Amer. J. Bot.*, vol. 38, pp. 475–488.

Gunn, C.R., W.H. Skrdla, and H.C. Spencer. 1968. Classification of *Medicago sativa* L. using legume characters and flower colors, *Technical Bull., Washington,* no. 1574, 85 pp.

Gusev, N.A. 1960. Nekotorye metody issledovaniya vodnogo rezhima rastenii (Some Methods for Studying the Water Regime of Plants). Leningrad, 60 pp.

Gusev, N.A. 1966. K voprosu o sostoyanii vody v rasteniyakh (Problem of water status quo in plants). *Fiziologiya Rastenii,* 13, 4, 122–158.

Gusev, N.A. 1968. O nekotorykh parametrakh i metodakh issledovaniya vodnogo rezhima rastenii (Some parameters and methods for studying the water regime of plants). In: *Vodnyi Rezhim Rastenii i Ikh Produktivnost'.* Moscow, pp. 22–37.

Guy, P. 1972. Structure genotypique d'un hybride autotétraploid multiplié en panmixie. 2. Eléments de généralisation, *Ann. Amelior. Plantes,* 22, 3, 239–261.

Guy, P. 1975. L'amélioration de la luzerne pour la résistance a ses ennemis végétaux et animaux, *Fourrages,* no. 64.

Guy, P. 1976. INRA, Station d'Amelioration Plantes Fourrageres Lusignan, 48 pp.

Guy, P. et al. 1975. Les principales espéces de légumineuses et graminées fourragéres et les variéties inscrites au catalogue français, *Fourrages,* no. 64, pp. 21–23.

Hansen, N.E. 1909. The wild alfalfa and clovers of Siberia with a perspective view of the alfalfas of the world. *Bureau of the Plant Industry, Washington, Bull.* no. 150, 96 pp.

Hanson, C.H. 1969. Registration of alfalfa germ plasm, *Crop Sci.,* 9, 4, 526–527.

Hanson, C.H. and T.A. Campbell. 1972. Vacuum-dried pollen of alfalfa (*Medicago sativa* L.) viable after eleven years, *Crop Sci.,* 12, 6, 874.

Hanson, C.H. and R.L. Davis. 1972. Highlights in the United States alfalfa science and technology, *J. Amer. Soc. Agric.,* pp. 35–51.

Hawn, E.J. and M.K. Hanna. 1967. Influence of stem nematode infestation on bacterial wilt reaction and forage yield of alfalfa varieties, *Can. J. Plant Sci.,* 47, 2, 203–208.

Hayward, H.E. 1938. *The Structure of Economic Plants.* New York, 674 pp.

Heinrichs, D.H. 1967. Alfalfa varieties—height of cutting studies, *Forage Notes,* 13, 2, 301–304.

Heinrichs, D.H. 1973. Breeding and management for nutrient yield and quality in legumes, agronomic and biological practicability, *Forage Notes*, 18, 2, 511–514.

Heinrichs, D.H. 1973a. Influence of light source on the growth of alfalfa cultivars, *Canad. J. Plant Sci.*, 53, 2, 291–294.

Heinrichs, D.H. and F.H.W. Morley. 1960. Inheritance of resistance to winter injury and its correlation with creeping rootedness in alfalfa, *Canad. J. Plant Sci.*, 40, 3, 591–594.

Heinrichs, D.H., J.E. Troelsen and K.W. Clark. 1960. Winter hardiness evaluation in alfalfa, *Canad. J. Plant Sci.*, 40, 4, 278–281.

Hendry, G.W. 1923. Alfalfa in history, *J. Amer. Soc. Agr.*, vol. 15, pp. 171–176.

Heyn, C.C. 1956. Index of some chromosome counts in the genus *Medicago*, *Caryologia*, 9, 1, 175–183.

Heyn, C.C. 1963. The annual species of *Medicago*. Scripta Hierosolymitana publications of the Hebrew Univ., Jerusalem, vol. 12, pp. 317–321.

Hill, R.R. 1966. Designs to estimate effects of clone substitution in alfalfa synthesis, *Crop Sci.*, 6, 5, 72–74.

Il'ina, E.Ya. 1964. Morfologicheskaya priroda i vozrastya izmeneniya zony kushcheniya lyutserny sinegibridnoi (Morphological nature and age-dependent changes in the tillering zone of blue hybrid alfalfa). *Botanicheskii Zhurnal SSSR*, 49, 5, 685–689.

Il'ina, E.Ya. 1966. Yarusnoe izmenenie morfologo-anatomicheskoi struktury list'ev lyutserny sinegibridnoi (Changes in morphological and anatomical structure of leaves of blue hybrid alfalfa in different tiers). *Zap. Sverdlovskaya Otd-Niya Vsesoyuz. Botan. O-va*, no. 4, pp. 137–143.

Ivanov, A.F. and G.A. Medvedev. 1977. Vozdelyvanie lyutserny v usloviyakh orosheniya (Cultivation of Alfalfa under Conditions of Irrigation). Moscow, 112 pp.

Ivanov, A.I. 1962. Opylenie lyutserny v Tselinnom krae (Pollination of alfalfa in the Tselinnyi territory). *Vestnik S.-Kh. Nauki.* Alma-Ata, no. 11, pp. 36–43.

Ivanov, A.I. 1966. Nakoplenie kornevoi massy razlichnymi vidami i sortami lyutserny v Tselinogradskoi oblasti (Accumulation of root mass by different species and varieties of alfalfa in Tselinograd province). *Vestnik S.-Kh. Nauki.* Alma-Ata, no. 6, pp. 25–30.

Ivanov, A.I. 1968. Iskhodnyi material dlya selektsii lyutserny (Initial material for alfalfa breeding). *Selektsiya i Semenovodstvo*, no. 4, pp. 44–46.

Ivanov, A.I. 1968a. Selektsionnaya tsennost' lyutserny razlichnogo geograficheskogo proiskhozhdeniya v usloviyakh stepi Severnogo Kazakhstana (Breeding value of alfalfa of different geographic origin under steppe conditions in northern Kazakhstan). *Trudy po Prikl. Bot., Gen. i Sel.*, 38, 3, 124–167.

Ivanov, A.I. 1969. Ochagi zemledeliya Mongolii (Farming centers in Mongolia). *Trudy po Prikl. Bot., Gen. i Sel.*, 40, 2, 164–183.

Ivanov, A.I. 1970. Vliyanie regulyatorov rosta na lyutserny v usloviyakh zhestkoi bogary i poliva Severnogo Priaral'ya (Effect of growth regulators on alfalfa under rainfed and irrigated conditions in northern Aral). *Doklady VASKhNIL*, no. 7, pp. 13–16.

Ivanov, A.I. 1970. Tsennye obraztsy kollektsii lyutserny dlya selektsii v Severnom Kazakhstane (Valuable specimens of alfalfa collected for breeding in northern Kazakhstan). *Vestnik S.-Kh. Nauki*, no. 3, pp. 32–34.

Ivanov, A.I. 1970a. Deistvie rostovykh veshchastv na vodnyi rezhim, biokhimicheskii sostav i produktivnost' lyutserny v usloviyakh Priaral'-skoi pustyni (Effect of growth regulators on the water regime, biochemical composition, and productivity of alfalfa in the Aral desert). *Trudy po Prikl. Bot., Gen. i Sel.*, 43, 1, 275–290.

Ivanov, A.I. 1971. Osvoenie pustynnykh zemel' Severnogo Priaral'ya (Reclamation of desert lands of northern Aral). *Trudy po Prikl. Bot., Gen. i Sel.*, 44, 2, 7–34.

Ivanov, A.I. 1972. Iskhodnyi material dlya selektsii lyutserny na morozostoikost' (Initial material for breeding alfalfa for frost resistance). In: *Dokl. i Soobshch. po Kormoproizvodstvu*. Moscow, no. 4, pp. 32–38.

Ivanov, A.I. 1972. Osobennosti vodnogo rezhima lyutserny na oroshaemykh i bogarnykh zemlyakh Kazakhstana (Peculiarities of the water regime of alfalfa in irrigated and rainfed lands of Kazakhstan). In: *Dokl. i Soobshch. po Kormoproizvodstvu*. Moscow, 47, 3, 98–138.

Ivanov, A.I. 1973. Tsentry formoobrazovaniya mnogoletnikh vidov lyutserny na territorii Kazakhskoi SSR i ikh rol' v evolyutsii i selektsii (Centers of development of perennial species of alfalfa in Kazakh SSR and their role in evolution and breeding). In: *Tezisy Dokl. VI Simpoziuma po Novym Kormovym Silosnym Rasteniyam*. Saransk, pp. 99–100.

Ivanov, A.I. 1973a. Introgressivnaya gibridizatsiya v roda *Medicago* L. na territorii Kazakhskoi SSR i ee rol' v evolyutsii i selektsii (Introgressive hybridization in the genus *Medicago* L. in Kazakh SSR and its role in evolution and breeding). *Byull. VIR*, no. 30, pp. 60–62.

Ivanov, A.I. 1973b. Diagnostika sortov lyutserny na morozostoikost' po fiziologicheskim pokazatelyam (Rating of alfalfa varieties for frost resistance based on physiological indexes). In: *Tezisy Dokl. Seminara po Zimostoikosti Ozimykh Kul'tur i Mnogoletnikh Trav*, Kiev, pp. 68–70.

Ivanov, A.I. 1974. Genofond *Medicago* L. v tsentrakh proiskhozhdeniya kul'turnykh rastenii i perspektivy ego ispol'zovaniya v selektsii (Gene pool of *Medicago* L. in centers of origin of cultivated plants and prospects of its utilization in breeding). *Trudy po Prikl. Bot., Gen. i Sel.*, 52, 2, 53–76.

Ivanov, A.I. 1975. Metodicheskie ukazeniya po izucheniyu mirovoi killetskii mnogoletnikh trav (Methodological Notes for Studying the World Collection of Perennial Grasses). Leningrad, 21 pp.

Ivanov, A.I. 1975a. Skhema filogenii podroda *Falcago* roda *Medicago* L. Phylogenetic scheme of the subgenus *Falcago* of the genus *Medicago* L.). In: *Metodicheskie Ukazaniya po Izucheniyu Mirovoi Kollektsii Mnogoletnikh Trav*, no. 48, pp. 78–79.

Ivanov, A.I. 1975b. Filogenez *Medicago* L. podroda *Falcago* (Reichb.) Grossh. [Phylogeny of *Medicago* L., subgenus *Falcago* (Reichb.) Grossh.]. In: *Tezisy Dokl. XII Botan. Kongressa AN SSSR*. Leningrad, vol. 2, p. 520.

Ivanov, A.I. 1976. Rasprostranenie lyutserny po stranam i kontinentam (Distribution of alfalfa in different countries and continents). *Trudy po Prikl. Bot., Gen. i Sel.*, 56, 2, 151–152.

Ivanov, A.I. and I.S. Borodkin. 1970. Rezul'taty ispytaniya sortov mirovoi kollektsii lyutserny v sukhostepnoi zone severnogo Kazakhstana (Results of trials of varieties of the world collection of alfalfa in the dry steppe zone of northern Kazakhstan). *Trudy VNIIZKh.* Alma-Ata, vol. 3, pp. 11–2119 [*sic*].

Ivanov, A.I. and I.E. Kozulya. 1971. Oroshenie sel'skokhozyaistvennykh kul'tur mineralizovannymi vodami v peschanykh pustynyakh Zapadnogo Kazakhstana (Irrigation of agricultural crops with mineralized waters in the sandy deserts of western Kazakhstan). *Trudy po Prikl. Bot., Gen. i Sel.*, 44, 2, 257–268.

Ivanov, A.I. and A.G. Lapin. 1971. Vodnyi rezhim i zimostoikost' sortov lyutserny (Water regime and winter hardiness of alfalfa varieties). *Trudy po Prikl. Bot., Gen. i Sel.*, 44, 2, 157–163.

Ivanov, A.I. and A.V. Bukhteeva. 1972. Tsennye mnogoletnye travy Severoturanskoi provintsii i vysokogornykh raionov Vostochnogo Tyan'-Shanya i Dzhungarskogo Alatau (Valuable perennial grasses of northern Turan province and high-altitude hilly regions of eastern Tien Shan and Dzhungarian-Alatau). *Trudy po Prikl. Bot., Gen. i Sel.*, 49, 1, 15–32.

Ivanov, A.I. and A.V. Bukhteeva. 1973. Resursy mnogoletnikh kormovykh rastenii Vostochnogo Kazakhstana (Perennial fodder plant resources of eastern Kazakhstan). *Trudy po Prikl. Bot., Gen. i Sel.*, 50, 3, 3–38.

Ivanov, A.I. and O.A. Ivanova. 1974. Reaktsiya vidov kostra na dlinu dnya (Response of brome grass species to daylength). *Trudy po Prikl. Bot., Gen. i Sel.*, 52, 2, 176–186.

Ivanov, A.I. and O.A. Ivanova. 1974a. Reaktsiya sortov lyutserny na dlinu dnya (Response of alfalfa varieties to daylength). *Byull. VIR*, no. 38, pp. 67–71.

Ivanov, A.I. and A.V. Bukhteeva. 1975. Tsenoarealy vazhneishikh kormovykh rastenii Kazakhstana (Cenocenters of important fodder Plants of Kazakhstan). *Trudy po Prikl. Bot., Gen. i Sel.*, 54, 3, 3–17.

Ivanov, A.I. and O.A. Ivanova. 1975. Osobennosti razvitiya sortov lyutserny v usloviyakh raznogo fotoperioda (Peculiarites of development of alfalfa varieties under different photoperiods). *Byull. VIR*, no. 55, pp. 26–30.

Ivanov, A.I., I.E. Kozulya and V.N. Shvitkin. 1970. Sorta lyutserny Severnogo i Zapadnogo Kazakhstana kak iskhodnyi material dlya selektsii (Alfalfa varieties of northern and western Kazakhstan as initial material for breeding). *Trudy po Prikl. Bot., Gen. i Sel.*, 43, 2, 250–259.

Ivanov, L.A. 1918. Transpiratsiya drevesnykh porod v polivnykh usloviyakh Turkmenskoi SSR (Transpiration of woody stocks under irrigated conditions of Turkmenian SSR). *Lesnoi Khozyaistvo*, no. 5, pp. 27–29.

Ivanov, L.A., A.A. Silina and Yu.O. Tsel'niker. 1950. O metode bystrogo v zveshivaniya dlya opredeleniya transpiratsii v estestvennykh usloviyakh (Quick weighing method for determination of transpiration under natural conditions). *Botanicheskii Zhurnal SSSR*, 35, 2, 167–184.

Ivanov, N.N. 1947. Problema belka v rastenievodstve (Problem of Protein in Crop Husbandry). 110 pp.

Janossy, A. and I. Sulyok. 1967. Investigation on plant collection of lucerne, *Acta Agr. Acad. Scient. Hung.*, vol. 16, pp. 397–406.

Johansen, B.R. 1968. Isolation distance in lucerne. *Yearb. R. Vet. Agr. College, Copenhagen*, pp. 7–9.

Johansen, B.R. 1968a. Storage of lucerne pollen on filter paper. *Yearb. R. Vet. Agr. College, Copenhagen*, p. 6.

Julen, J. 1944. Investigations on diploid, triploid and tetraploid lucerne, *Hereditas*, vol. 30, pp. 567–582.

Julen, J. 1974. Sverge och Netun-tva nya lusernsorter, *Aktuellt Svalof*, no. 1, pp. 143–154.

Jung, G.A. 1962. Effect of uracil, thiouracil and quanine on cold resistance and nitrogen metabolism of alfalfa, *Plant Physiol.*, 37, 6, 359–364.

Jung, G.A. and D. Smith. 1960. Influence of extended storage at constant low temperature on cold resistance and carbohydrate reserves of alfalfa and medium red clover, *Plant Physiol.*, 35, 1, 364–366.

Kauffeld, N.M., E.L. Sorensen and R.H. Painter. 1969. Stability of attractiveness of alfalfa clones to honeybees under varying locations, seasons, and years, *Crop Sci.*, 9, 2, 225–228.

Kazaryan, E.S. 1967. Mikroelementnyi sostav dikorastushchikh kormovykh rastenii (Micro-element composition of wild fodder plants). *Luga i Pastbishcha*, no. 1, pp. 31–43.

Kedrov-Zikhman, O.O. 1974. Polikross-test v selektsii rastenii (Polycross Test in Plant Breeding). Minsk, 127 pp.

Keller, B.A. 1933. Ocherki po biologi rastenii (Notes on the biology of plants). *Sovetskaya Botanika,* no. 2, pp. 5–38.

Keller, B.A. 1933a. Botanika s osnovami fiziologii (Botany with Fundamentals of Physiology). Moscow-Leningrad, pts. 3 and 4, 270 pp.

Keller, B.A. 1948. Osnovy evolyutsii rastenii (Fundamentals of Evolution of Plants). Moscow, 207 pp.

Khalin, G.A. 1970. Sravnitel'naya morozoustoichivost' mnogoletnikh kormovykh trav v zavisimosti ot uslovii vyrashchivaniya (Comparative frost resistance of perennial fodder grasses depending on conditions of cultivation). *Trudy po Prikl. Bot., Gen. i Sel.,* 43, 2, 64–92.

Khananyan, S.Kh. 1936. Kul'tura lyustserny v usloviyakh orosheniya (Alfalfa Crop under Conditions of Irrigation). Moscow-Leningrad, 104 pp.

Khasanov, O.Kh. 1958. K voprosu proiskhozhdeniya dikorastushchikh lyutsern (*Medicago* L.) Zapadnogo Tyan'-Shanya [Origin of wild alfalfas (*Medicago* L.) of western Tien Shan]. *Sb. Rabot AN Uzbekskoi SSR,* no. 1, pp. 78–81.

Khasanov, O.Kh. 1962. Dikorastushchie lyutserny Chirchik-Angrenskogo Basseina (Wild Alfalfas of the Chirchik-Angrenskii Basin). Tashkent, 156 pp.

Khasanov, O.Kh. 1971. O genezise i formirovanii dikorastushchikh lyutsern Srednei Azii (Genesis and formation of wild alfalfas of Central Asia). *Dokl. AN Uzbekskoi SSR,* no. 7, pp. 154–156.

Khasanov, O.Kh. 1972. Dikorastushchie lyutserny Srednei Azii (Wild Alfalfas of Central Asia). Tashkent, 172 pp.

Kirkbride, D. 1962. The pre-pottery farmers, *Discovery,* July.

Klinkowski, M. 1931. Ein Beitrag zur Geographie der Luzerne, *Repert. Spec. Nov. Veget., Beih,* vol. 62, pp. 35–39.

Klinkowski, M. 1933. Lucerne, its ecological position and distribution in the world. *Great Britain, Wales, Imperial Bureau of Plant Genetics, Herbage Plants. Bull.* no. 12, pp. 1–61.

Kolikov, M.S. 1939. Estestvennye kormovye ugod'ya Severnogo Priaral'ya

(Natural fodder lands of northern Aral). In: *Osvoenie Pustyn', Polu-pustyn' i Vysokogorii*. Moscow, pp. 117–140.

Kolosov, I.I. 1962. Poglotitel'naya deyatel'nost' kornevykh sistem rastenii (Absorption Activity of Plant Roots). Moscow, 387 pp.

Konstantinov, P.N. 1932. Lyutserna i ee kul'tura na Yugovostoka Evropeiskoi chasti SSR (Alfalfa and Its Cultivation in the Southeast European Part of the USSR). Samara, 61 pp.

Konstantinov, P.N. 1936. Lyutserna (Alfalfa). Moscow, 26 pp.

Konstantinova, A.M. 1948. Puti ispol'zovaniya dikikh lyutsern pri soz-danii sortov v novykh raionakh lyutsernoseyaniya (Ways of using wild alfalfas in the development of varieties in new regions of alfalfa cultivation). *Selektsiya i Semenovodstvo*, no. 8, pp. 35–42.

Konstantinova, A.M. 1960. Selektsiya i semenovodstvo mnogoletnikh trav (Breeding and Seed Production of Perennial Grasses). 387 pp.

Konstantinova, A.M. 1970a. Zadachi issledovanii po ispol'zovaniyu geterozisa pervogo pokoleniya v selektsii lyutserny (Tasks before researchers in utilization of heterosis of the first generation in alfalfa breeding). *Selektsiya i Semenovodstvo*, no. 3, pp. 28–32.

Konstantinova, A.M. 1972. Ispol'zovanie geterozisa gibridov F_1 v selektsii lyutserny (Utilization of heterosis of F_1 hybrids in alfalfa breeding). In: *Dokl. i Soobshch. po Kormoproizvodstvu*. Moscow, pp. 98–102.

Konstantinova, A.M. 1972a. Selektsiya lyutserny dlya severnykh raionov lyutsernoseyaniya (Alfalfa breeding in the northern regions of alfalfa cultivation). In: *Selektsiya i Semenovodstvo Zernovykh i Kormovykh Kul'tur*. Moscow, pp. 305–310.

Konstantinova, A.M. 1974. Selektsiya lyutserny na mnogoukosnost' (Al-falfa breeding for multiple cuttings). In: *Kormoproizvodstvo*. Moscow, no. 7, pp. 121–132.

Konstantinova, A.M. 1974a. Ispol'zovanie gibridizatsii v selektsii mno-goletnikh trav (Use of hybridization in breeding perennial grasses). In: *Kormoproizvodstvo*. Moscow, pp. 275–282.

Konstantinova, A.M. and G.F. Kuleshov. 1974. Selektsiya i semeno-vodstvo mnogoletnikh kormovykh trav (Breeding and seed production of perennial fodder grasses). In: *Pastbishcha i Senkosy SSSR*. Moscow, pp. 140–151.

Konstantinova, A.M. et al. 1970. Ispol'zovanie geterozisa gibridov lyut-serny pervogo pokoleniya (Utilization of Heterosis of First-Generation Hybrids of Alfalfa). Moscow, 24 pp.

Koperzhinskii, V.V. 1950. Otnoshenie lyutserny k klimatu i pochve (Soil and climatic requirements of alfalfa). In: *Lyutserna*. Moscow, pp. 30–37.

Koperzhinskii, V.V. 1950. Uoobrenie lyutserny i ee travosmesei (Application of fertilizers to alfalfa and its grass mixtures). In: *Lyutserna.* Moscow, pp. 118–138.

Koperzhinskii, V.V. 1950. Oplodotvorenie tsvetkov i obrazovanie semyan (Pollination of flowers and seed-setting). In: *Lyutserna.* Moscow, pp. 194–210.

Koperzhinskii, V.V. and A.A. Shchibrya. 1950. Biologiya tsveteniya i obrazovanie semyan lyutserny (Biology of flowering and seed-setting of alfalfa). In: *Lyutserna.* Moscow. p. 391.

Korneev, N.A. 1955. Mnogoletnie travy dlya sevooborotov Zapadnogo Kazakhstana (Perennial grasses for crop rotation in western Kazakhstan). *Trudy In-ta Zemledeliya im. V.R. Vil'yamsa,* vol. 4, pp. 120–138.

Koryakina, V.F. and A.I. Smetannikova. 1970. Fiziologiya klevera i lyutserny (Physiology of clover and alfalfa). In: *Fiziologiya Sel'skokhozyaistvennykh Rastenii.* Moscow, vol. 6, pp. 256–384.

Kossovich, P.S. 1903. Razvitie kornei v zavisimosti ot temperatury pochvy v period rosta rastenii (Root development depending on soil temperature during the period of plant growth). *Zhurnal Opytnoi Agronomii,* vol. 4, pp. 17–23.

Kossovich, P.S. 1904. Kolichestvennoe opredelenie uglekisloty, vydelyaemoi kornyami vo vremya ikh razvitiya (Quantitative determination of carbonic acid released by roots during their development). *Zhurnal Opytnoi Agronomii,* vol. 5, pp. 21–26.

Kristkalne, S.Kh. 1960. Intensivnost' transpiratsii v list'yakh lyutserny tyan'shanskoi v usloviyakh Latviiskoi SSR (Intensity of respiration in leaves of Tian Shan alfalfa under conditions of Latvian SSR). In: *Rastitel'nost' Latviiskoi SSR.* Riga, vol. 3, pp. 205–212.

Kristkalne, S.Kh. 1963. Vodouderzhivayushchaya sposobnost' lyutserny tyan'shanskoi v usloviyakh Latviiskoi SSR (Water-retention capacity of Tian Shan alfalfa under conditions of Latvian SSR). In: *Rastitel'nost' i Ee Ispol'zovanie v Narodnom Khozyaistve.* Riga, pp. 83–89.

Kristkalne, S.Kh. 1964. Ekologo-fiziologicheskie osobennosti lyutserny tyan'shanskoi v usloviyakh Latviiskoi SSR (Ecological and Physiological peculiarities of Tian Shan alfalfa under conditions of Latvian SSR). Avtoref. Dis. na Soisk. Uchen. Step. Kand. Nauk, Riga, 24 pp.

Kuleshov, G.F. 1974. Rol' instituta v razvitii otechestvennoi selektsii i perspektivy sozdaniya intensivnykh sortov kormovykh kul'tur (Role of the Institute in the development of Soviet Plant breeding and prospects for developing intensive varieties of fodder crops). In: *Kormoproizvodstvo.* Moscow, pp. 260–275.

Kuleshov, G.F. and N.S. Bekhtin. 1975. Sozdanie sortov trav intensivnogo tipa i ikh ispol'zovanie (Development of varieties of the intensive type and their use). Korma, no. 5, pp. 26–27.

Kuleshov, G.F., N.S. Bekhtin and Yu.M. Piskovatskii. 1974. Rezul'taty otsenki slozhnogibridnykh senokosnykh i pastbishchnykh populyatsii mnogoletnikh zlakovykh trav (Results of evaluation of complex hybrid hay and pasture populations of perennial cereal grasses). In: *Kormoproizvodstvo*. Moscow, no. 7, pp. 124–127.

Kul'tiasov, M.V. 1946. Novyi vid zheltotsvetkovoi lyutserny iz Zapadnogo Tyan'-Shanya (A new species of yellow-flowered alfalfa from western Tien Shan). *Spisok Semyan*, no. 1. *Byul. Glavn. Botan. Sada AN SSSR*. Moscow, pp. 17–18.

Kul'tiasov, M.V. 1947. Prirodnye formy sinetsvetkovoi lyutserny iz Zapadnogo Tyan'-Shanya (Natural forms of blue-flowered alfalfa from western Tien Shan). *Uchen. Zap. Mosk. Obl. Ped. In-ta*, 10, 3, 125–132.

Kul'tiasov, M.V. 1953. Ekologo-istoricheskii metod v introduktsii rastenii (Ecological and historical method of plant introduction). *Byul. Gl. Botan. Sada AN SSSR*. Moscow, no. 15, pp. 257–270.

Kul'tiasov, M.V. 1967. Ekogeneticheskii analiz mnogoletnikh lyutsern (Ecological and genetic analysis of perennial alfalfas). In: *Lyutserna Tyan'shanskaya i Opyt Ee Introduktsii*. Moscow, 288 pp.

Kursanov, A.L. 1957. Kornevaya sistema rastenii kak organ obmena veshchestv (Root system of plants as an organ of metabolism). *Izvestiya AN SSSR (Ser. Biol. Nauk)*, no. 6, pp. 689–705.

Kuz'min, V.P. 1961. Rezul'taty selektsii polevykh kul'tur v stepnoi zone Kazakhstana (Results of breeding field crops in the steppe zone of Kazakhstan). *Trudy VNIIZKh*, vol. 1, pp. 102–111.

Kuz'min, V.P. 1962. Selektsiya polevykh kul'tur v Tselinnom krae (Breeding of field crops in the Tselinnyi territory). *Kolkhoznoe Proizvodstvo*, no. 1, pp. 26–29.

Kuz'min, V.P. 1962a. O zernobobovykh kul'turakh v Tselinnom krae (Leguminous crops in the Tselinnyi territory). *Vestnik S.-Kh. Nauki*. Alma-Ata, no. 8, pp. 26–31.

Kuz'min, V.P. 1962b. Rezervy povysheniya urozhainosti zernovykh kul'tur v Tselinnom krae putem selektsii (Possibility of increasing yield potential of cereal crops in the Tselinnyi territory through plant breeding). *Vestnik AN Kazakhskoi SSR*, no. 7, pp. 18–23.

Kuz'min, V.P. 1965. Selektsiya i semenovodstvo zernovykh kul'tur v Tselinnom krae Kazakhstana (Breeding and Seed Production of Cereal Crops in the Tselinnyi territory of Kazakhstan). Moscow-Tselinograd, 199 pp.

Kuz'min, V.P. and A.I. Ivanov. 1964. Porazhaemost' lyutserny kornevymi gnilyami i selektsiya na ustoichivost' k nim (Susceptibility of alfalfa to root rots and breeding for resistance to them). *Vestnik S.-Kh. Nauki*. Alma-Ata, no. 3, pp. 11–17.

Kuznetsov, V.M. 1967. Rezul'taty opytov zonal'noi seti botanicheskikh sadov SSSR po introduktsii lyutserny tyan'shanskoi (Results of experiments with zonal network in botanical gardens of the Soviet Union on the introduction of Tian Shan alfalfa). In: *Lyutserna Tyan'shanskaya i Opyt Ee Introduktsii*. Moscow, pp. 259–287.

Larin, I.V. 1937. Kormovye rasteniya estestvennykh senokosov i pastbishch SSSR (Fodder plants of natural haylands and pastures of the Soviet Union). *Trudy VASKhNIL*. Moscow-Leningrad, vol. 1, 944 pp.

Larin, I.V. 1939. K voprosu ob organizatsii nauchno-issledovatel'skoi raboty po ukrepleniyu kormovoi bazy v pustynyakh SSSR (Organization of research work for strengthening the fodder base in the deserts of the Soviet Union). *Sovetskaya Botanika*. Moscow-Leningrad, no. 5, pp. 15–19.

Larin, I.V. 1950. Kormovye rasteniya estestvennykh senokosov i pastbishch SSSR (Fodder plants of natural haylands and pastures of the Soviet Union). *Trudy VASKhNIL*. Moscow-Leningrad, vol. 2, 948 pp.

Larin, I.V. 1969. Sovremennoe sostoyanie i perspektivy ispol'zovaniya i uluchsheniya pustynnykh pastbishch (Present status and prospects of utilization and improvement of desert pastures). *Problemy Osvoeniya Pustyn'*, no. 3, pp. 8–10.

Ledingham, G.F. 1940. Cytological and developmental studies of *Medicago sativa* and a diploid form of *M. falcata, Genetics*, vol. 25, pp. 1–15.

Lesins, K. 1952. Some data on the cytogenetics of alfalfa, *Heredity*, vol. 43, pp. 181–184.

Lesins, K. 1957. Cytogenetic study on a tetraploid plant at the diploid chromosome level, *Canad. J. Bot.*, 35, 2, 181–196.

Lesins, K. 1959. Note on a hexaploid *Medicago*: *M. cancellata* M.B., *Canad. J. Genet. Cytol.*, 1, 2, 133–134.

Lesins, K. 1961. Interspecific crosses involving alfalfa. 2. *Medicago cancellata* M.B. × *M. sativa* L., *Canad. J. Genet. Cytol.*, vol. 3, pp. 316–324.

Lesins, K. 1961a. Mode of fertilization in relation to breeding methods in alfalfa, *Z. Pflanzenzucht.*, no. 1, pp. 31–54.

Lesins, K. 1962. Interspecific crosses involving alfalfa. 3. *Medicago sativa* L. × *M. prostrata* Jacq., *Canad. J. Genet. Cytol.*, 4, 1, 14–23.

Lesins, K. 1968. Interspecific crosses involving alfalfa. 4. *M. dicago glomerata* × *M. sativa* with reference to *M. prostrata, Canad. J. Genet. Cytol.*, 10, 3, 536–544.

Lesins, K. 1969. Relationship of taxa in genus *Medicago* as revealed by hybridization. 4. *M. hybrida* × *M. sulfuricosa, Canad. J. Genet. Cytol.*, 11, 2, 340–345.

Lesins, K. 1971. Interspecific crosses involving alfalfa. 5. *Medicago saxatilis*

× *M. sativa* with reference to *M. cancellata* and *M. rhodopaes, Canad. J. Genet. Cytol.*, 12, 1, 437–442.

Lesins, K. 1972. Interspecific crosses involving alfalfa. 7. *Medicago sativa* × *M. rhodopaes, Canad. J. Genet. Cytol.*, 14, 2, 221–226.

Lesins, K. and I. Lesins. 1960. Sibling species in *Medicago prostrata* Jacq., *Canad. J. Genet. Cytol.*, 2, 4, 416–417.

Lesins, K. and I. Lesins. 1961. Some little-known *Medicago* species and their chromosome complements, *Canad. J. Genet. Cytol.*, 3, 1, 7–9.

Lesins, K. and I. Lesins. 1962. Trueness-to-species in seed samples of *Medicago* with a note on 2n = 14 species, *Canad. J. Genet. Cytol.*, 4, 3, 337–339.

Lesins, K. and I. Lesins. 1963. Pollen morphology and species relationship in *Medicago* L., *Canad. J. Genet. Cytol.*, 5, 3, 348–350.

Lesins, K. and I. Lesins. 1963a. Some little-known *Medicago* species and their chromosome complements. 2. Species from Turkey, *Canad. J. Genet. Cytol.*, 5, 2, 270–280.

Lesins, K. and I. Lesins. 1964. Diploid *Medicago falcata* L., *Canad. J. Genet. Cytol.*, 6, 2, 152–163.

Lesins, K. and I. Lesins. 1965. Little-known *Medicago* species and their chromosome complements. 3. Some Mediterranean species, *Canad. J. Genet. Cytol.*, vol. 7, pp. 18–22.

Lesins, K. and I. Lesins. 1966. Little-known Medicagoes and their chromosome complements. 4. Some mountain species, *Canad. J. Genet. Cytol.*, 8, 1, 8–13.

Lesins, K. and C.B. Gillies. 1972. Taxonomy and cytogenetics of *Medicago* L. *Alfalfa Science and Technology*. Amer. Soc. Agr., Madison, Wisconsin, pp. 53–86.

Litvinov, L.S. 1933. Metody otsenki zasukhoustoichivosti (Methods of evaluation of drought resistance). *Semenovodstvo*, no. 6, pp. 16–20.

Lubenets, P.A. 1936. Lyutserna kak iskhodnyi material dlya selektsii (v usloviyakh Azovo-Chernomorskogo kraya) (Alfalfa as Initial Material for Breeding under Conditions of the Azov-Chernomorsk Territory). Leningrad, 82 pp.

Lubenets, P.A. 1953. Vidovoi sostav i selektsionnaya otsenka kul'turnykh i dikorastushchikh lyutsern (Specific composition and breeding evaluation of cultivated and wild alfalfas). *Trudy po Prikl. Botan., Gen. i Sel.*, 30, 2, 3–135.

Lubenets, P.A. 1956. Lyutserna (Alfalfa). Moscow-Leningrad, 240 pp.

Lubenets, P.A. 1961. Kollektsiya lyutserny (Alfalfa collection). *Katalog-Spravochnik*. Leningrad, no. 6, 46 pp.

Lubenets, P.A. 1968. Vysokoproduktivnye geterozisnye gibridy lyutserny (High-yielding heterotic hybrids of alfalfa). *Dokl. VASKhNIL*, no. 9, pp. 11–13.

Lubenets, P.A. 1972. Lyutserna—*Medicago* L. [Kratkii obzor roda i klassifi-katsiya podroda *Falcago* (Reichb.) Grossh.] [Alfalfa—*Medicago* L. Brief review of the genus and classification of the subgenus *Falcago* (Reichb.) Grossh.]. *Trudy po Prikl. Bot., Gen. i Sel.*, 47, 3, 3–68.

Lubenets, P.A. 1972a. Geterozisnye gibridy lyutserny (Heterotic hybrids of alfalfa). *Sel'skokhozyaistvennyi Byul.*, 7, 2, 240–243.

Lubenets, P.A. 1974. Iskhodnyi material dlya sozdaniya vysokouro-zhainykh sortov i geterozisnykh gibridov lyutserny (Initial material for development of high-yielding varieties and heterotic hybrids of alfalfa). *Trudy po prikl. Bot., Gen. i Sel.*, 52, 2, 3–52.

Lubenets, P.A. 1974a. Rezul'taty issledovaniya mirovykh resursov dlya selektsii lyutserny s vysokim soderzhaniem belka (Results of research on world resources for breeding alfalfa with a high protein content). *Byull. VIR*, no. 42, pp. 3–9.

Lubenets, P.A. and A.I. Ivanov. 1969. Dikorastushchie mnogoletnie travy—tsennyi iskhodnyi material dlya selektsii i prakticheskogo ispol'zovaniya (Wild perennial grasses—valuable initial material for breeding and practical use). In: *Vvedenie v Kul'tura Kormovykh Rastenii Dlya Uluchsheniya Polupustynnykh i Pustynnykh Pastbishch. MSKh SSSR, VNIITEIS.* Moscow, pp. 36–45.

Lubenets, P.A. and A.I. Ivanov. 1971. Tsennye dikorastushchie populyat-sii kormovykh kul'tur aridnoi zony Kazakhstana i ikh ispol'zovanie v selektsii (Valuable wild populations of fodder crops of the arid zone of Kazakhstan and their utilization in breeding). *Byull. VIR*, no. 19, pp. 37–42.

Lubenets, P.A. and A.I. Ivanov. 1971a. Issledovaniya po mnogoletnim travam (Studies on perennial grasses). *Trudy po prikl. Bot., Gen. i Sel.*, 44, 2, 35–43.

Lubenets, P.A. and A.I. Ivanov. 1971b. Mobilizatsiya tsennykh v kor-movom otnoshenii dikorastushchikh mnogoletnikh trav Zapadnogo Kazakhstana i voprosy ikh okhrany (Mobilization of wild perennial grasses of western Kazakhstan, valuable from the point of view of fod-der, and problems of their protection). In: *Materialy Soveshch. po Okhrane Ob'ektov Rastitel'nogo Mira Respublik Srednei Azii i Kazakhstana.* FAN, Tashkent, pp. 181–188.

Lubenets, P.A. and A.I. Ivanov. 1971c. Mobilizatsiya, izuchenie i okhrana rastitel'nykh resursov aridnoi zony Kazakhstana (Mobilization, study, and protection of plant resources of the arid zone of Kazakhstan). *Trudy po Prikl. Bot., Gen. i Sel.*, 45, 2, 11–31.

Lubenets, P.A. and A.I. Ivanov. 1973. Iskhodnyi material dlya selektsii mnogoletnikh trav na zimostoikost' (Initial material for breeding peren-nial grasses for winter hardiness). In: *Tezisy Dokl. Vsesoyuz. Soveshch.*

po Zimostroikosti Zernovykh Kul'tur i Mnogoletnikh Trav. Kiev, pp. 62–64.

Lubenets, P.A. and A.V. Yashchenko. 1975. Geterozis u lyutserny (Heterosis in alfalfa). *Byull. VIR*, no. 55, pp. 35–38.

Lubenets, P.A. and A.I. Ivanov. 1976. Morozostoikost' obraztsov mirovoi kollektsii lyutserny (Frost resistance of samples of the world collection of alfalfa). In: *Zimostoikost' Ozimykh Khlebov i Mnogoletnikh Trav*. Kiev, pt. 2, pp. 148–155.

Lubenets, P.A., I.N. Fedorenko and L.I. Bulygina. 1971. Geterozisnye gibridy lyutserny (Heterotic hybrids of alfalfa). *Byull. VIR*, no. 17, pp. 3–8.

Lubenets, P.A., A.I. Ivanov and N.A. Mukhina. 1971. Metodicheskie ukazaniya po izucheniyu mirovoi kollektsii mnogoletnikh kormovykh trav (Methodological Notes for Studying the World Collection of Perennial Fodder Grasses). Leningrad, 19 pp.

Lutkov, A.N. 1966. Poliploidiya v evolyutsii i selektsii rastenii (Polyploidy in the evolution and breeding of plants). In: *Eksperimental'naya Poliploidiya v Selektsii Rastenii*. Novosibirsk, pp. 7–34.

Makarova, G.I. 1965. Mnogoletnie kormovye travy Sibiri (Perennial Fodder Grasses of Siberia). Novosibirsk, 205 pp.

Maksimov, N.A. 1941. Vliyanie zasukhi na fiziologicheskie protsessy v rasteniyakh (Effect of drought on physiological process in plants). In: *Sb. Rabot po Fiziologii Rastenii*. Moscow-Leningrad, pp. 299–309.

Maksimov, N.A. 1952. Izbrannye raboty po zasukhoustoichivosti i zimostoikosti rastenii (Selected Works on Drought Resistance and Winter Hardiness of Plants). Moscow, vol. 1, 575 pp.

Mashtakov, F.M. 1955. Kratkie itogi selektsionnoi raboty s kormovymi travami v Kustanaiskoi oblasti (Summary of results of breeding work with fodder grasses in Kustanaisk province). *Trudy In-ta Zemledeliya im. V.R. Vil'yamsa*. Alma-Ata, vol. 4, pp. 105–119.

Maslinkov, M. et al. 1972. Lyutserna (Alfalfa). Plovdiv, 188 pp.

McLennan, H.A., J.M. Armstrong and K.J. Kasha. 1966. Cytogenetic behavior of alfalfa hybrids from tetraploid by diploid crosses, *Canad. J. Genet. Cytol.*, 8, 3, 544–555.

Meerson, Ya.M. 1939. Kornevaya sistema lyutserny i travosmesei v usloviyakh oroshaemogo zemledeliya (Root system of alfalfa and grass mixtures under conditions of irrigated farming). *Sovetskaya Agronomiya*, no. 7, pp. 35–43.

Megee, C.R. 1935. A search for factors determining winter hardiness in alfalfa, *J. Amer. Soc. Agr.*, 27, 9, 685–698.

Melent'eva, E.V. 1956. Nakoplenie massy kornei u lyutserny i soderzhanie v nikh azota i fosfora (Accumulation of root mass in alfalfa and its nitrogen and phosphorus content). *Izv. AN Uzbekskoi SSR*, no. 11, pp. 17–21.

Metcalfe, C.R. and L. Chalk. 1950. Anatomy of dicotyledons, *Oxford Bull.* no. 3, vol. 1, pp. 427–440.

Mikhailovskaya, I.S. 1972. Vozrastnye anatomo-morfologicheskie izmeneniya podzemnykh organov zheltoi lyutserny (*M. falcata* L.) [Anatomical and morphological changes of underground organ of the yellow alfalfa (*M. falcata* L.) with age]. *Byull. MOIP*, 77, 1, 88–102.

Miller, D.A., J.P. Shrivastva and J.A. Jackobs. 1969. Alfalfa yield components in solid seeding, *Crop Sci.*, 9, 4, 440–443.

Miller, J.W., H.L. Carnahan and M.H. Yama. 1969. Registration of 2 "Atra 55" alfalfa (Reg. No. 45), *Crop Sci.*, vol. 9, pp. 348–451.

Mokeeva, E.A. 1940. Biologo-anatomicheskoe issledovanie lyutserny (*Medicago sativa* L.) [Biological and Anatomical Studies of Alfalfa *Medicago sativa* L.)]. Tashkent, 124 pp.

Mokeeva, E.A. 1957. Lyutserna sinyaya (*M. sativa* L.). Stroenie i razvitie [Blue Alfalfa (*M. sativa* L.). Structure and Development]. Tashkent, 163 pp.

Nakonechnyi, M.F. 1941. Vliyanie shiriny mezhduradii na razvitie kornevoi sistemy lyutserny i vosstanovlenie plodorodiya pochvy (Effect of width of inter-row space on development of alfalfa root system and restoration of soil fertility). *Opytnaya Agronomiya*, no.1, pp. 72–76.

Navalikhina, N.K. 1965. Experimental'noe poluchenie tetraploidov u krasnogo klevera (Experimental development of tetraploid red clover). In: *Poliploidiya i Selektsiya*. Moscow-Leningrad, pp. 285–292.

Nielsen, H.M. and B. Andreasen. 1970. Performance of synthetics and related inbreds, single and double crosses from four clones of lucerne, *Medicago sativa* L. *Yearb. R. Vet. Agr. College*. Copenhagen, pp. 153–169.

Novoselova, A.S. and R.G. Piskovatskaya. 1972. Sinteticheskie populyatsii tetraploidov krasnogo klevera (Synthetic populations of tetraploid red clover). *Korma*, no. 1, pp. 38–40.

Novoselova, A.S. and R.G. Piskovatskaya. 1972a. Metod slozhnogibridnykh populyatsii v selektsii mnogoletnikh trav (Method of complex hybrid populations in breeding perennial grasses). In: *Dokl. i Soobshch. po Kormoproizvodstvu*. VIK, Moscow, no. 4, pp. 87–97.

Novoselova, A.S. and S.N. Cheprasova. 1974. Estestvennye populyatsii i rol' otbora v selektsii klevera krasnogo (Natural populations and role of selection in breeding of red clover). In: *Kormoproizvodstvo*. Moscow, pp. 283–289.

Novoselova, A.S. and R.G. Piskovatskaya. 1975. Ispol'zovanie effekta geterozisa v selektsii tetraploidov klevera krasnogo (Use of heterosis in breeding of tetraploid red clover). *Korma*, no. 4, pp. 45–47.

310

Oakley, R.A. and H.L. Westover. 1921. Utilization of alfalfa/USDA. *Washington Bull*. no. 1229, 98 pp.

Ovchinnikov, B.F. 1937. Osnovnye problemy semenovodstva lyutserny v SSSR (Main problems of seed production of alfalfa in the Soviet Union). In: *Trudy VASKhNIL (Kormovye Kul'tury)*. Moscow, vol. 25, pt. 2, pp. 64–74.

Ovchinnikov, B.F. et al. 1934. Lyutserna (Alfalfa). Moscow, 171 pp.

Palmer, T.P. 1960. Winter growth of lucerne (*Medicago sativa*). 2. Genetic variation in a population of Hunter River lucerne, *N.Z.J. Agr. Res.*, 3, 4, 641–646.

Palmer, T.P. 1967. Lucerne breeding in New Zealand. In: *Lucerne Crop* edited by R.H.M. Langer, A.H. and A.W. Reed. Wellington, pp. 135–148.

Penskoi, I.K. 1940. Dinamika osmoticheskogo davleniya i kolloidov v kletkakh kornei lyutserny v zimne-vesenni period (Dynamics of osmotic pressure and colloids in cells of alfalfa roots in the winter-spring period). In: *Zap. Voronezhskogo SKhI*. Voronezh, 19, 3, 53–55.

Petinov, N.S. 1962. Fiziologiya oroshaemykh sel'skokhozyaistvennykh rastenii (Physiology of irrigated Agricultural Plants). Moscow, 160 pp.

Petinov, N.S. and V.S. Shaidurov. 1963. Opredelenie srokov poliva lyutserny po fiziologicheskim pokazatelyam (Determination of irrigation time of alfalfa based on physiological indexes). *Fiziologiya Rastenii*, 10, 5, 605–607.

Piper, C.V. 1935. *Forage Plants and Their Culture*. McMillan, New York, 671 pp.

Ponomarev, A.N. 1950. Dnevnoi Khod opyleniya lyutserny (Diurnal course of alfalfa pollination). *Dokl. AN SSSR*, 74, 4, 827–830.

Ponomarev, A.N. 1954. Ekologiya tsveteniya i opyleniya zlakov i lyutserny (Ecology of flowering and pollination of cereals and alfalfa). *Botan. Zhurnal SSSR*, 39, 6, 706–720.

Popov, V.M. 1950. Znachenie lyutserny i ee travosmesei i istoriya kul'tury (Importance of alfalfa and its grass mixtures and history of the crop). In: *Lyutserna*. Moscow, 391 pp.

Poznokhirin, F.L. 1961. Kul'tura lyutserny v stepi (Alfalfa Cultivation in the Steppes). Ukrainskaya Akademiya Sel'skokhozyaistvennykh Nauk, Kiev, 244 pp.

Prirodnoe raionirovanie Severnogo Kazakhstana (Natural Division of Northern Kazakhstan). 1960. Moscow, 468 pp.

Protsenko, D.F. 1952. Fiziologicheskaya kharakteristika morozoustoichivosti razlichnykh sortov lyutserny (Physiological characteristics of frost resistance in different varieties of alfalfa). In: *Nauchn. Zap. Kievskogo Un-ta*, 11, 1, 102–109.

Rabinovich, V.M. 1939. Agrotekhnika i zimostoikost' lyutserny (Agronomic practices and winter hardiness of alfalfa). In: *Kormovye Travy*. Moscow, pp. 114–130.

Rabinovich, V.M. 1967. Selektsiya lyutserny v lesostepi Ukrainy (Alfalfa breeding in the Ukrainian forest-steppe). In: *Dostizheniya Otechestvennoi Selektsii*. Moscow, pp. 318–324.

Rapoport, I.A. 1966. Osobennosti i mekhanizm deistviya supermutagenov (Peculiarities and mechanism of action of supermutagens). In: *Supermutageny*. Moscow, pp. 9–22.

Razumov, V.I. 1961. Sreda i razvitie rastenii (Environment and Development of Plants). Moscow-Leningrad, 367 pp.

Rogers, V.E. 1967. Adaptability of lucerne to soil and climate. In: *Lucerne Crop* edited by R.H.M. Langer, A.H. and A.W. Reed. Wellington, pp. 179–182.

Rotili, P. 1974. The importance of the "genotype" association effects in the evaluation of the combining ability in lucerne. *Medicago sativa* Group Meeting. *Slupia Wielka (Polonia)*, Sept., 1974, pp. 36–39.

Rotili, P. and L. Zannone. 1971. The effect of selfing in the S_1—S_2—S_3— S_4 generations of *Medicago sativa*. *Proceedings of the 6th Congr. of Eucarpia, Cambridge*, pp. 48–54.

Rotili, P. and L. Zannone. 1971a. The use of competition in the breeding of lucerne. Eucarpia *Medicago sativa* group. Report of meeting held in Lodi, Milano, vol. 3, pp. 115–118.

Rotili, P. and L. Zannone. 1973. General and specific combining ability in lucerne at different levels of inbreeding and performance of second-generation synthetics measured in competitive conditions. 1st experiment. *Colt. Foraggere, Lodi*, pp. 8–14.

Rubtsov, N.I. et al. 1972. Opredelitel' vysshikh rastenii Kryma (Key to Higher Plants of Crimea). Leningrad, 550 pp.

Sabinin, D.A. 1955. Fiziologicheskie osnovy pitaniya rastenii (Physiological Basis of Plant Nutrition). Moscow, 512 pp.

Sapozhnikov, D.I. 1959. Dolichestvennoe opredelenie khlorofillov A i B pri pomoshchi bumazhnoi khromatografii (Quantitative estimation of chlorophylls *a* and *b* using paper chromatography). *Fiziologiya Rastenii*, 6, 3, 376–379.

Savel'ev, N.M. 1960. Biologicheskie osnovy vozdelyvaniya semennoi lyutserny v zapadnoi Sibiri (Biological Basis for Cultivation of Seed Alfalfa in Western Siberia). Moscow, 351 pp.

Savinkin, A.P. 1964. K voprosu izucheniya vodnogo balansa bogarnykh posevov pshenitsy i lyutserny v usloviyakh glinistoi pustyni Dzhezkazgana (Problem of water balance of rainfed crops of wheat and alfalfa under conditions of the argillaceous desert of Dzhezkazgan). *Trudy*

In-ta Bot. AN Kazakhskoi SSR, vol. 20, pp. 199–218.

Selyaninov, G.T. 1966. Agroklimaticheskaya karta mira (Agroclimatic Map of the World). 11 pp.

Shain, S.S. 1948. Iz istori otechestvennogo travoseyaniya (From the history of grass cultivation in our country). *Sovetskaya Agronomiya*, no. 1, pp. 90–96.

Shain, S.S. 1964. Biologicheskie osobennosti lyutserny (Biological peculiarities of alfalfa). In: *Lyutserna*. Moscow, pp. 25–36.

Shcherbina, D.E. and P.P. Perchik. 1973. Znachenie poliploidii v evolyutsii lyutserny ot dikikh k kul'turnoi formam (Importance of polyploidy in the evolution of alfalfa from wild to cultivated forms). *Tsitologiya i Genetika*, 7, 3, 238–243.

Shchibrya, A.A. 1947. Rol' medonosnykh pchel i dikikh nasekomykh v opylenii lyutserny (Role of honeybees and wild insects in the pollination of alfalfa). *Selektsiya i Semenovodstvo*, no. 8, pp. 58–66.

Shchibrya, A.A. 1950. Botanicheskoe opisanie i klassifikatsiya lyutserny (Botanical description and classification of alfalfa). In: *Lyutserna*. Moscow, pp. 15–20.

Shebalina, M.A. and M.S. Kolikov. 1955. Mnogoletnie kormovye travy (Perennial Fodder Grasses). Leningrad, 232 pp.

Shkatova, L.F. 1966. Vodnyi rezhim rastenii lyutserny pri vegetativnom sposobe ee razmnozheniya (Water regime of alfalfa plants during vegetative multiplication). In: *Estestvennogeograficheskie Nauki*. Voronezhskii Ped. In-t, pp. 94–101.

Shumnyi, V.K. 1973. Issledovanie deistviya genov v svyazı s problemoi geterozisa u rastenii (Studies on the Effect of Genes in the Context of Heterosis in Plants). Novosibirsk, 24 pp.

Shumnyi, V.K. and E.V. Kvasova. 1971. Izmenenie samofertil'nosti klonov lyutserny v raznykh usloviyakh vyrashchivaniya (Change in the self-fertility of alfalfa clones under different conditions of cultivation). *Izv. Sib. Otdeleniya AN SSSR (Ser. Biol. Nauk)*, 2, 10, 60–64.

Simon, J.P. 1967. Relationship in annual species of *Medicago*. 4. Interspecific graft affinities between selected species, *Austral. J. Bot.*, 15, 1, 75–82.

Simon, J.P. 1967a. Relationship in annual species of *Medicago*. 5. Analysis of phenolics by means of one-dimensional chromatographic techniques, *Austral. J. Bot.*, 15, 1, 35–73.

Simon, J.P. and A. Simon. 1965. Relationship in annual species of *Medicago, Austral. J. Agr. Res.*, 16, 1, 37–60.

Simon, J.P. and A.J. Millington. 1967. The inheritance of marker genes in *Medicago truncatula* Gaerth. 2. Their suitability for use in a plant-breeding programme, *Austral. J. Agr. Res.*, 18, 6, 887–890.

Simon, J.P. and A.J. Millington. 1967a. Relationship in annual species of

Medicago. 4. The complex *M. littoralis* Rhode—*M. truncatula* Gaerth., *Austral. J. Bot.*, 15, 1, 83–93.

Sinskaya, E.N. 1935. Selektsiya kormovykh trav (Breeding of fodder grasses). In: *Teoreticheskie Osnovy Selektsii*. Moscow-Leningrad, vol. 2, pp. 587–658.

Sinskaya, E.N. 1938. Vidoobrazovanie lyutserny v oblasti Glavnogo Kavkazskogo khrebta i Dagestana (Speciation of alfalfa in the Greater Caucasian montane region and in Dagestan). *Botan. Zhurnal SSSR*, no. 4, pp. 321–335.

Sinskaya, E.N. 1948. Dinamika Vida (Dynamics of Species). Moscow-Leningrad, 526 pp.

Sinskaya, E.N. 1950. Kul'turnaya flora SSSR (Cultivated Flora of the Soviet Union). Moscow-Leningrad, vol. 13, pp. 3–344.

Sinskaya, E.N. 1960. Vazhneishie dikorastushchie kormovye rasteniya Severnogo Kavkaza (Important wild fodder plants of northern Caucasus). *Trudy po Prikl. Bot., Gen. i Sel.*, 33, 3, 149–204.

Sinskaya, E.N. 1969. Istoricheskaya geografiya kul'turnoi flory (na zare zemedeliya) [Historical Geography of Cultivated Flora (at the Dawn of Agriculture)]. Leningrad.

Sinskaya, E.N. and Z.P. Maleeva. 1959. Ploidnost' u mnogoletnikh vidov lyutserny (Ploidy level in perennial species of alfalfa). *Botan. Zhurnal SSSR*, 44, 8, 1103–1113.

Smetannikova, A.I. 1950. Anatomicheskie dannye po lyutserne (Anatomical data on alfalfa). In: *Kul'turnaya Flora SSSR*. Moscow-Leningrad, vol. 13, pp. 217–240.

Smetannikova, A.I. 1950a. K sravnitel'noi fiziologicheskoi kharakteristike nekotorykh vidov lyutserny (Comparative physiological characteristics of some alfalfa species). In: *Eksperimental'naya Botanika*. AN SSSR, Moscow-Leningrad, vol. 7, pp. 238–259.

Smetannikova, A.I. 1962. Soderzhanie vitamina C i karotina v list'yakh lyutserny raznykh vidov i reproduktsii (Vitamin C and carotene content in leaves of various alfalfa species and populations). *Trudy Botan. Instituta im. V.L. Komarova AN SSSR*, 4, 15, 84–100.

Smetannikova, A.I. 1965. Ekologo-fiziologicheskoe izuchenie lyutserny v novykh usloviyakh sushchesvovaniya (Ecophysiological study of alfalfa under new survival conditions). In: *Obshchie Zakonomernosti Rosta i Razvitiya Rastenii*. Vil'nyus, pp. 177–185.

Smetannikova, A.I. 1967. Lyutserna na Severo-Zapade SSSR (Alfalfa in the Northwest Soviet Union). Leningrad, 233 pp.

Smetannikova, A.I. 1967. Sravnitel'noe ekologo-fiziologicheskoe izuchenie lyutserny Tyan'shanskoi pri introduktsii (Comparative ecophysiological study of the Tian Shan alfalfa during its introduction).

In: *Ekologo-fiziologicheskie Osobennosti Introduktsiruemykh Rastenii*, pp. 3–22.

Stanford, E.H. 1957. Tetrasomic inheritance in alfalfa, *Agr. J.*, 49, 5, 589–592.

Stanford, E.H. 1959. The use of chromosome deficient plants in cytogenetic analyses of alfalfa, *Agr. J.*, 51, 8, 470–472.

Stanford E.H. 1959a. The zebra leaf character in alfalfa and its dosage-dominance relationship, *Agr. J.*, 51, 5, 274–277.

Stanford, E.H. and R.W. Cleveland. 1954. The inheritance of two-leaf abnormalities in alfalfa, *Agr. J.*, 46, 5, 203–206.

Stanford, E.H. and W.M. Clement. 1958. Cytology and crossing behavior of a haploid alfalfa plant, *Agr. J.*, 50, 10, 255–256.

Stanford, E.H., W.M. Clement and E.T. Bingham, Jr. 1972. Cytology and evaluation of the *Medicago sativa—falcata* complex. In: *Alfalfa Science and Technology*. Madison, Wisconsin, pp. 87–102.

Stankov, N.Z. 1964. Kornevaya sistema polevykh kul'tur (Root System of Field Crops). Moscow, 279 pp.

Staszewski, Z. 1970. Badania nad heterozja i formami meskojalowymi lucerny *Medicago sativa* L. 1. *M. media* Pers., *Hodowla Rosl. Aklimat. i Nasiennic*, 14, 6, 56–59.

Staszewski, Z. 1975. *Lucerny. Panstwowe wygawnictwo polnicze i lesne*. Warczawa, 355 pp.

Stebbins, G.L. 1947. Types of polyploids. Their classification and significance, *Advances in Genetics*, vol. 1, pp. 14–18.

Steinmetz, F.H. 1926. Winter hardiness in alfalfa varieties, *Technical Bull.*, no. 38, p. 151.

Stephen, W.P. and P.F. Torchio. 1961. Biological notes on the leaf-cutter bee, *Megachile (Eutricharaea) rotundata*, *Pan-Pacific Entom.*, vol. 37, pp. 136–141.

Stephen, W.P. and C.E. Osgood. 1965. The induction of emergence in the leaf-cutter bee *Megachile rotundata*, an important pollinator of alfalfa, *J. Econ. Entom.*, vol. 58, pp. 234–239.

Stewart, G. 1926. *Alfalfa-growing in the United States and Canada*. McMillan Co., New York, pp. 1–102.

Suleimanov, I.G. 1964. Strukturno-fizicheskie svoistva protoplasmy i ee komponentov v svyazi s problemoi morozoustoichivosti kul'turnykh rastenii (Structural and Physical Properties of Protoplasm and Its Components and Problem of Frost Resistance of Cultivated Plants). Kazanskii Gos. Un-t, 202 pp.

Sumnevich, G.P. 1932. O nekotorykh aziatskikh vidakh roda *Medicago* L. (Some Asiatic species of the genus *Medicago* L.). *Sistematicheskie Zametki Gerbariya Tomskogo Un-ta*, nos. 1–2, pp. 125–139.

Tarkovskii, M.I. 1964. Vvednie (Introduction). In: *Lyutserna*. Moscow, 329 pp.

Tarkovskii, M.I. 1972. Lyutserna (Alfalfa). In: *Sel'skokhozyaistvennaya Entsiklopediya*. Sov. Entsiklopediya, Moscow, vol. 3, pp. 820–825.

Tarkovskii, M.I. et al. 1974. Lyutserna (Alfalfa). Moscow, 240 pp.

Toomre, R.I. 1966. Dolgoletnie kul'turnye pastbishcha (Perennial Cultivated Pastures). Moscow, 400 pp.

Torssell, R. and S. Bingefors. 1961. Svalofs tuna lucernett forsta praktiskt resultat av mellansvensk lucernforadling, *Sver. Utsadesforen. Tidskr.*, no. 1, pp. 143–150.

Troitskii, N.A. 1928. O nekotorykh dikorastushchikh kavkazskikh lyutsernakh (Some wild Caucasian alfalfas). *Izv. Tiflis Politekhnich. In-ta*, vol. 2, pp. 25–32.

Troitskii, N.A. 1928a. K voprosu o roli gibridizatsii v protsesse vidoobrazovaniya (Role of hybridization in speciation). *Trudy po Prikl. Bot., Gen. i Sel.*, 19, 2, 213–232.

Troitskii, N.A. 1938. O roli gibridizatsii v protsesse vidoobrazovaniya (Role of hybridization in speciation). *Trudy po Prikl. Bot., Gen. i Sel.*, 24, 3, 128–136.

Tumanov, I.I. 1940. Fiziologicheskie osnovy zimostoiksti kul'turnykh rastenii (Physiological Basis of Winter Hardiness of Cultivated Plants). Moscow, 366 pp.

Tumanov, I.I. 1967. O fiziologicheskom mekhanizme morozostoikosti rastenii (Physiological mechanism of frost resistance of plants). *Fiziologiya Rasteniya*, 14, 3, 520–539.

Tysdal, H.M. 1933. Influence of light, temperature and soil moisture on the hardening process in alfalfa, *J. Agr. Res.*, 46, 6, 483–515.

Udovenko, G.V. 1970. Metodika diagnostiki ustoichivosti rastenii (Method for Diagnosing Plant Resistance). Leningrad, 74 pp.

Urban, J. 1873. Prodromus einer Monographie der Gattung *Medicago*. *Verhandl. des Botanischen Vereins der Provinz Brandenburg*. Berlin, vol. 15, pp. 74–82.

Ustimenko, A.S., P.V. Danil'chuk and A.T. Gvozdikovskaya. 1975. Kornevye sistemy i produktivnost' sel'skokhozyaistvennykh rastenii (Root Systems and Productivity of Agricultural Plants). Kiev, 368 pp.

Vasil'chenko, I.T. 1938. Novye dannye o dikoi sinei lyutserne v Tadzhikistane (New data on the wild blue alfalfa in Tadzhikistan). *Priroda*, nos. 7–8, pp. 127–129.

Vasil'chenko, I.T. 1938. Zapadnyi Tyan'-Shan' kak ochag raznoobraziya dikoi sinei lyutserny (Western Tien Shan as a center of diversity of the wild blue alfalfa). *Priroda*, nos. 11–12, p. 94.

Vasil'chenko, I.T. 1940. O estestvennoi gibridizatsii zheltoi i sinei lyutserny v Srednei Azii (Natural hybridization of the yellow and blue alfalfas in Central Asia). *Priroda*, no. 8, pp. 76–77.

Vasil'chenko, I.T. 1940a. Materialy k izucheniyu mnogoletnikh lyutsern Zapadnogo Tyan'-Shanya (Data from a study of perennial alfalfas in western Tien Shan). *Botanicheskii Zhurnal SSSR*, 25, 3, 244–251.

Vasil'chenko, I.T. 1946. Dikorastushchie mnogoletnie lyutserny SSSR kak material dlya selektsii i gibridizatsii (Wild perennial alfalfas of the Soviet Union as material for breeding and hybridization). In: *Sb. Nauchnykh Rabot BIN Za 1941-45 gg*. Leningrad, pp. 93–101.

Vasil'chenko, I.T. 1948. O proiskhozhdenii kul'turnoi lyutserny (On the origin of cultivated alfalfa). *Botanicheskii Zhurnal SSSR*, 33, 6, 591–604.

Vasil'chenko, I.T. 1949. Lyutserna—luchshee kormovoe rastenie (Alfalfa—the best fodder plant). *Trudy Botanicheskogo In-ta AN SSSR*, 1, 8, 9–240.

Vasil'chenko, I.T. 1950. Novye dlya kul'tury vidy lyutserny (New Alfalfa Species for Cultivation). Moscow, pp. 3–69.

Vasil'ev, I.M. 1953. Zimostoikost' rastenii (Winter Hardiness of Plants). Moscow, 191 pp.

Vavilov, N.I. 1926. Tsentry proiskhozhdeniya kul'turnykh rastenii (Centers of origin of cultivated plants). *Trudy po Prikl. Bot., Gen. i Sel.*, 16, 2, 3–248.

Vavilov, N.I. 1935. Botaniko-geograficheskie osnovy selektsii (Botanical and geographic basis of plant breeding). In: *Teoreticheskie Osnovy Selektsii*. Moscow-Leningrad, vol. 1, pp. 17–74.

Vavilov, N.I. 1935. Uchenie ob immunitete rastenii k infektsionnym zabolevaniyam (Concept of plant immunity to infectious diseases). In: *Teoreticheskie Osnovy Selektsii*. Moscow-Leningrad, vol. 1, pp. 893–990.

Vavilov, N.I. and D.D. Bukinich. 1929. Zemledel'cheskii Afganistan (Agrarian Afghanistan). *Trudy po Prikl. Bot., Gen. i Sel., Prilozhenie*, no. 33, 610 pp.

Willard, C.J., L.E. Thatcher, and J.S. Cutler. 1934. Alfalfa in Ohio, *Ohio Agric. Exper. Sta., Bull.* no. 540, 146 pp.

Wilsie, C.P. 1961. Alfalfa varieties versus crosses, blends, and hybrids, *Crops and Soils*, no. 4, pp. 555–600.

Winter, C.W. 1932. Vascular system of young plants of *Medicago sativa, The Bot. Gazette*. Chicago, 94, 1, 58.

Yupatov, A.A. 1954. Kormovye rasteniya pastbishch i senokosov Mongol'-skoi Narodnoi Respubliki (Fodder Plants of Pastures and Haylands of the Mongolian People's Republic). Moscow-Leningrad, 351 pp.

Yur'ev, V.Ya. 1958. Obshchaya selektsiya i semenovodstvo polevykh kul'-tur (General Selection and Seed Production of Field Crops). Moscow, 344 pp.

Zabashtanskii, S.A. 1957. Nakoplenie azota i fosfora v kornyakh lyutserny pri skashivanii ee v raznye fazy (Accumulation of nitrogen and phosphorus in the roots of alfalfa at different stages of cutting). *Dokl. AN Uzbekskoi SSR*, no. 8, pp. 46–55.

Zaitseva, A.A. 1955. Priemy vozdelyvaniya lyutserny na semena v Karagandinskoi oblasti (Measures for the cultivation of alfalfa for seed in Karaganda province). *Trudy In-ta Zemledeliya im. V.R. Vil'yamsa.* Alma-Ata, pp. 87–104.

Zhemchuzhnikov, E. and D. Sikstel'. 1935. Utochnenie skhem orosheniya pshenitsy i lyutserny s pomoshch'yu fiziologicheskikh metodov (Perfecting irrigation schemes for wheat and alfalfa through physiological methods). *Trudy po Prikl. Bot., Gen. i Sel.*, 4, 14, 65–102.

Zhukovskii, P.M. 1933. Zemledel'cheskaya Turtsiya (Agrarian Turkey). 907 pp.

Zhukovskii, P.M. 1965. Osnovnye gennye tsentry kul'turnykh rastenii i ikh dikikh sorodichei v predelakh territorii SSSR (Main gene centers of cultivated plants and their wild relatives in the Soviet Union). *Euphytica*, no. 14, pp. 75–79.

Zhukovskii, P.M. 1965a. Evolyutsiya kul'turnykh rastenii na osnove poliploidii (Evolution of cultivated plants by polyploidy). In: *Poliploidiya i Selektsiya.* Moscow-Leningrad, pp. 5–17.

Zhukovskii, P.M. 1968. Novye ochagi proiskhozhdeniya i gentsentry kul'turnykh rastenii i uzkoendemichnye mikrogentsentry rodstvennykh vidov (New loci of origin and gene centers of cultivated plants and narrow endemic microgene centers of related species). *Botan. Zhurnal SSSR*, 53, 4, 457–460.

Zhukovskii, P.M. 1970. Mirovoi genofond rastenii dlya selektsii (megagentsentry i endemichnye mikrogentsentry) [World Gene Pool of Plants for Breeding (Megagene Centers and Endemic Microgene Centers)]. 88 pp.

Zhukovskii, P.M. 1970a. Spontannaya i eksperimental'naya introgressiya u rastenii, ee znachenie v evolyutsii i selektsii (Natural and experimental introgression of plants, its importance in evolution and breeding). *Genetika*, 6, 4, 65–70.

Zhukovskii, P.M. 1970b. Spontannaya i eksperimental'naya introgressiya u rastenii, ee zhachenie v evolyutsii i dlya selektsii (Natural and experimental introgression of plants, its importance in evolution and breeding). *Botan. Zhurn. SSSR*, 55, 3, 364–368.

Zhukovskii, P.M. 1971. Mirovoi genofond rastenii dlya selektsii (mega- i mikrogentsentry) [World gene pool of plants for breeding (mega- and microgene centers)]. In: *Geneticheskie Osnovy Selektsii Rastenii.* Moscow, pp. 338–388.

318

Zhukovskii, P.M. 1971a. Kul'turnye rasteniya i ikh sorodichi (Cultivated Plants and Their Relatives). Leningrad, 752 pp.

Zoz, N.N. 1966. Khimicheskii Mutagenez u vysshikh rastenii (Chemical mutagenesis of higher plants). In: *Supermutageny*. Moscow, pp. 93–104.

Zykov, Yu.D. 1963. Ob izrastanii semennoi lyutserny i merakh po povysheniyu semennoi produktivnosti (Growing seed alfalfa and measures for increasing seed productivity). *Agrobiologiya*, no. 4, pp. 565–570.

Zykov, Yu.D. 1967. Semirechenskaya lyutserna (Semireche Alfalfa). Alma-Ata, 247 pp.